Econometric Methods

By the same author

Statistical Cost Analysis
(McGraw-Hill, New York, 1960)

Econometric Methods

J. Johnston

Professor of Econometrics
University of Manchester, England

McGraw-Hill Book Company

New York · San Francisco
Toronto · London

ECONOMETRIC METHODS

Library of Congress Catalog Card Number 62-17369

9-MP-98

32680

For A., R., and M.

Preface

The purpose of this book is to provide a fairly self-contained development and explanation of econometric methods for students who have already done about one year's work in statistical theory and method. It is divided into two parts. Part 1 contains a full exposition of the linear normal regression model. This serves as an essential basis for the theory of econometrics in Part 2. This latter part expounds the main statistical methods now available for the estimation of econometric models.

Students who have already done a year's work in mathematical statistics will be able to skip much of the first two chapters, which have been inserted as a link with the conventional courses in statistical methods taken by most students in the social sciences. Chapter 1 is a complete treatment of the two-variable linear model, including all the problems of estimation, hypothesis testing, and forecasting which arise in the context of this model. Most students will already be familiar with many of the topics treated in this chapter. An elementary knowledge of probability distributions, expected values, estimation, and hypothesis testing is assumed. Anyone who experiences difficulty with the material in Chap. 1 should refer to a good introductory book on statistics before proceeding any further.[1] As well as providing useful review material, Chap. 1 introduces all the basic inference problems, which will be considered in more complicated contexts throughout the rest of the book.

[1] For example, P. G. Hoel, *Introduction to Mathematical Statistics*, 2d ed., Wiley, New York, 1954. A. M. Mood, *Introduction to the Theory of Statistics*, McGraw-Hill, New York, 1950. D. A. S. Fraser, *Statistics: An Introduction*, Wiley, New York, 1958.

Chapter 2 deals with extensions of the two-variable linear model to embrace nonlinearities and also increases in the number of variables. One does not travel far along this road before the notational and other complexities call for a more powerful technique. Chapter 3 thus provides the essentials of matrix algebra, which is then used as the basic method of exposition throughout the rest of the book. Chapter 4 deals with the general linear model in k variables. This is the basic and final chapter in Part 1, and it contains a development of all the important results for this model. Chapters 1, 2, and 3 provide preparatory material which different readers will have to use more or less intensively before tackling Chap. 4. The material in Chap. 4 is an essential prerequisite for understanding the developments in econometric methods described in Part 2.

After a short introductory chapter, Part 2 contains a treatment of errors in variables in Chap. 6. This is a topic which sometimes receives scant attention in econometric work, but which is often of great practical importance. Chapter 7 gives a unified treatment of problems arising from autocorrelated disturbances, and various other problems which can arise in a single equation context such as multicollinearity, heteroscedasticity, lagged variables, and dummy variables are covered in Chap. 8. The final two chapters deal with simultaneous-equation problems, including identification problems, indirect least squares, two-stage least squares, limited-information methods, full-information, and three-stage least squares.

The emphasis throughout is on the rationale of the various methods. I have attempted to explain as fully as possible the assumptions underlying the various techniques and to give a fairly extensive development of the various results, in the hope that readers of varying backgrounds will be able to work through the material on their own and develop a real appreciation of the advantages and limitations of the various techniques in different practical applications. Numerical examples are given in the text, and theoretical and numerical exercises at the end of most chapters. I am grateful to various authorities for permission to use examples from examination papers of the Royal Statistical Society and the Universities of Cambridge, London, Manchester, and Oxford. I have given no treatment of computational problems since an ever-increasing number of research workers are now using various electronic computers with associated programs.

I am heavily indebted to certain individuals. The project would not have been undertaken at all had it not been for the encouragement and support that I received at a crucial stage from Prof. Guy H. Orcutt at the University of Wisconsin. J. Parry Lewis of the University of Manchester checked through the algebra, and he and R. J. Ball, also of Manchester, made many valuable suggestions. I am very grateful to them both. I am also greatly indebted to Prof. A. S. Goldberger of the University of Wisconsin for sending me his mimeographed lecture notes, which have materially improved my exposition at several points. Thanks also go to Profs. R. G. Lipsey and W. M. Gorman of London and Oxford, respectively, for valuable comments. Miss Pamela Drake checked the numerical examples, and L. T. Simister helped with the survey of empirical studies in Chap. 10. It is also a pleasure to acknowledge the patience and skill with which Mrs. Katherine Norrie and Miss Pauline O'Brien typed several versions of this manuscript. The final burden of proof correction was greatly eased by assistance from David Bugg.

J. Johnston

Contents

PART 1

The Linear Normal Regression Model

1

The Two-variable Linear Model

1-1. Relationships between Variables

The first basic idea to which the student of economics is introduced is that of relationships between economic variables. The quantity demanded of a commodity in a market is regarded as a function of its price, the costs of producing a product are assumed to be a function of the amount produced, consumption expenditure is taken as a function of income, and so forth. These are all examples of two-variable relations, but more realistic formulations require the specification of several variables in each relation. Thus quantity demanded may be regarded as a function of price, disposable income, and prices of related commodities; production costs will depend on rate of production, factor prices, and changes in production rate; and consumption expenditure may be specified as a function of income, liquid assets, and previous consumption levels. Economic theory consists of the study of various groups or sets of relations which are supposed to describe the functioning of a part or the whole of an economic system. The task of econometric work is to estimate these relationships *statistically*, and this empirical testing and measurement of economic relationships is an essential step in the acquisition of economic knowledge.

1-2. The Two-variable Linear Model

The first step in the measurement of economic relationships is the specification of which variables enter the various relations. To simplify matters as much as possible, we shall examine first of all the most elementary case, by making the twin assumptions that we are dealing only with a single relation and that it contains only two variables. Denoting the variables by Y and X, we may postulate

$$Y = f(X) \tag{1-1}$$

This step merely identifies the variable X, which is thought to influence the other variable Y.

The second step is to specify the form of the relation between Y and X. The theory underlying the development of (1-1) may suggest the precise functional form to use, or it may merely suggest certain side conditions on the intercept, slope, and curvature of the function. Such conditions may be satisfied by a variety of functions, and we then look to statistical analysis for some help in choosing between them.

The simplest relationship between two variables is a linear one, namely,

$$Y = \alpha + \beta X \tag{1-2}$$

where α and β are unknown parameters indicating the intercept and slope of the function. Other relationships between two variables include

$$Y = \alpha e^{\beta X} \qquad Y = \alpha X^{\beta} \qquad Y = \alpha + \beta \frac{1}{X}$$

The third relation is linear in the variables Y and $1/X$, and the first and second can be reduced to a linear form in transformed variables by taking logs of both sides to give

$$\log_e Y = \log_e \alpha + \beta X$$

and

$$\log_e Y = \log_e \alpha + \beta \log_e X$$

respectively. The first is linear in log Y and X, and the second is linear in the logs of both variables.

The bulk of conventional economic theory, whether expressed in diagrammatic or algebraic form, postulates exact functional relationships between variables. The most elementary acquaintance with economic data, however, indicates that points do not lie exactly on straight lines or other smooth functions. Thus, for measurement and testing purposes, formulations such as (1-1) and the various functional forms associated with it are inadequate. The extension employed is the introduction of a stochastic term into economic relationships.

Suppose, for example, that we are investigating the relationship between consumption expenditure and disposable income in a cross section of households for some given period in time. Letting Y denote consumption expenditure and X denote disposable income, completed budget data for, say, 10,000 households would provide 10,000 pairs of associated measurements X_i, Y_i ($i = 1, 2, \ldots, 10{,}000$). Let us suppose that we have already divided our households into various groups on the basis of household size and composition and are looking at the relationship between Y and X *within* a given group. We do not expect that all households within the group which have some given income X' will display an identical consumption expenditure Y'. Some will spend more than others, some will spend less, but we do expect a clustering of the expenditure figures around a value which is geared to the income value in question. These ideas may be expressed more formally in a new linear hypothesis

$$Y = \alpha + \beta X + u \tag{1-3}$$

where u denotes a variable which may take on positive or negative values. Thus, if we consider the subgroup of those households with a given income X', the central value of consumption expenditure for them will be $\alpha + \beta X'$, but actual consumption figures for individual households in the subgroup will be indicated by $\alpha + \beta X' + u_1$, $\alpha + \beta X' + u_2$, etc., where $u_1, u_2, \ldots$ indicate the amount by which the expenditures of particular households exceed or fall short of the central value $\alpha + \beta X'$.

There are three possible, though not mutually exclusive, ways of rationalizing the insertion of the u term in (1-3). First, we may say that the consumption expenditure of each and every household could be fully explained if we knew all the factors at work and had all the necessary data. Even among households of the same size and composition, there will be variations in the precise ages of the parents and children, in the number of years since marriage, in whether the husband is a golfer, drinker, poker player, or bird-watcher, in whether the wife is addicted to spring hats, Paris fashions, swimming pools, or foreign sports cars, in whether the household income has been increasing or decreasing, in whether the parents are themselves the children of thrifty, cautious folk or of carefree spendthrifts, and so forth. In explaining human behavior the list of relevant factors may be extended ad infinitum. Many of the factors, however, will not be quantifiable, and even if they are, it is not usually possible in practice to obtain data on them all. Even if one can do that, the number of factors is still almost certain to exceed the feasible number of observations, so that no statistical means exists for estimating their influence. Moreover, many variables may have very slight effects, so that even with substantial quantities of data, the statistical estimation of their influence will be difficult and uncertain. This case then amounts to saying that $Y = f(X_1, X_2, \ldots, X_n)$ where n is an impracticably large number, so that we choose instead to represent Y as an explicit function of just a small number of what are thought to be the more important X's and let the net effect of the excluded variables be represented by u. In the limiting case of a single, explicit variable we have

$$Y = f(X_1,u) \tag{1-4}$$

Since many factors may be at work and in a given household many may be pulling in opposite directions, we should expect small values of u to occur more frequently than large values. We are thus led to think of u as a variable with a probability distribution centered at zero and having a finite variance σ_u^2. This is why u is referred to as a stochastic disturbance (or error) term. In view of the many factors involved, an appeal to the Central Limit Theorem would further suggest a normal distribution for u.[1]

A second justification for the presence of a disturbance term in economic relations is to assume that, over and above the total effect of all relevant factors, there is a basic and unpredictable element of randomness in human responses which can be adequately characterized only by the inclusion of a random variable term. For purposes of practical statistics the distinction between these two rationalizations does not matter since, for reasons of both theory and data, we hardly ever claim to have included all distinguishable and relevant factors in any relationship, so that the insertion of a stochastic term is essential on the first count, and the second, if present, merely adds to its variance. Both these types of stochastic terms are sometimes referred to as disturbances, or errors, in the equation.

A third source of error lies in errors of observation or measurement. It may be that a variable Z is exactly related in a linear fashion to X by the relation $Z = \alpha + \beta X$, but errors of meas-

[1] See W. Feller, *An Introduction to Probability Theory and Its Applications*, 2d ed., Wiley, New York, 1957, vol. I, pp. 229, 238–241.

urement obscure the true value Z, and instead of Z we observe $Y = Z + u$ where u denotes the measurement error. We have then

$$Y = Z + u$$

that is,
$$Y = \alpha + \beta X + u$$

It is possible, of course, to have a measurement error superimposed on an equation error as in the case

$$Z = \alpha + \beta X + u \qquad \text{equation error}$$
$$Y = Z + v \qquad \text{measurement error}$$

therefore
$$Y = \alpha + \beta X + w$$

where $w = u + v$. It is probably unrealistic to consider measurement error as being present in only one variable, so we postpone a

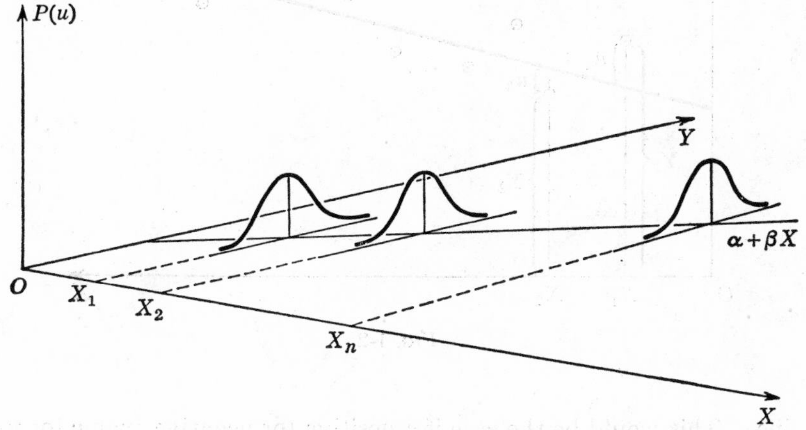

FIG. 1-1

complete treatment of measurement errors to Chap. 6 and concentrate in the intervening chapters on equation error.

The initial specification of the relationship must now include some assumptions about the probability distribution of the disturbance term. These must relate to mean, variance, and covariance. The simplest possible assumptions are to assume the mean to be zero, the variance to be constant and independent of X, and the various values of u to be drawn independently of one another. To continue our example, suppose we distinguish various levels of disposable income, which we shall enumerate for convenience from the smallest to the highest as $X_1, X_2, \ldots, X_n$. If a linear hypothesis is true and if the above assumptions about the disturbance term hold, the situation can be pictured as in Fig. 1-1. The distributions centered around the line $\alpha + \beta X$ are the assumed distribution for u. It might be more realistic in this particular example to assume that the variance of the disturbance term increases with X, but we postpone examination of this case until Chap. 8.

If we now select a sample of n households, one from each income level, the sample points can be represented on a scatter diagram, as in Fig. 1-2. If the u values have been drawn independently, the sample points will cluster more or less randomly around the straight

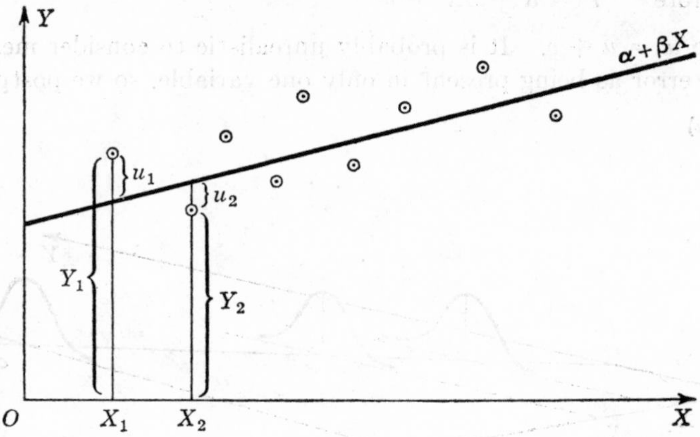

FIG. 1-2

line. This would be the case if a positive (or negative) value for u_1 did not in any way influence the $u_2, u_3, \ldots$ values. If, on the other hand, the people with lower incomes tended to be younger people in the early stages of married life and those with higher incomes older people with an eye on retirement, we should expect positive disturbances for lower values of X and negative disturbances for higher values. The nonrandom character of the disturbances would here be an indication that an important explanatory variable, age, had been omitted and that its inclusion in the disturbance term was preventing that term from displaying random behavior.

The practical situation then is that we have n pairs of sample observations on X, Y, which can be represented on a scatter diagram as in Fig. 1-2 above. The essential difference from that figure is that in practice the line $\alpha + \beta X$ is unknown. Instead we have a set of hypotheses

$$
\begin{aligned}
Y_i &= \alpha + \beta X_i + u_i & & i = 1, 2, \ldots, n \\
E(u_i) &= 0 & & \text{for all } i \\
E(u_i u_j) &= \begin{cases} 0 \\ \sigma_u^2 \end{cases} & & \begin{matrix} \text{for } i \neq j;\ i, j = 1, 2, \ldots, n \\ \text{for } i = j;\ i, j = 1, 2, \ldots, n \end{matrix}
\end{aligned}
\qquad (1\text{-}5)
$$

In (1-5), α, β, and σ_u^2 are unknown parameters. We wish to estimate these parameters statistically on the basis of our sample observations on X and Y, and we may also wish to test hypotheses about these parameters. For example, should we regard consumption as proportional to income ($\alpha = 0$)? Is the marginal propensity to consume, β, greater than one-half? Is a linear function an adequate representation of the data? Does the assumption of a constant variance for the disturbance term seem reasonable in the light of our sample data? These are typical problems of statistical inference, and our immediate task is to review what standard methods are available for dealing with them. As we shall see later, much of econometric theory is concerned with the development of new methods of dealing with statistical inference problems in the context of economic models, because standard methods are sometimes inapplicable, but a thorough grasp of the standard methods is an essential prerequisite for the understanding of more complicated techniques.

1-3. Least-squares Estimators

The statistical inference problem outlined above may be treated in a variety of ways according to the precise assumptions made. Let us first make the assumptions set out in (1-5) above. We denote the sample observations by

$$
\begin{matrix} X_1 & X_2 & \ldots & X_n \\ Y_1 & Y_2 & \ldots & Y_n \end{matrix}
$$

We can denote the arithmetic means by

$$
\bar{X} = \frac{1}{n} \sum_{i=1}^{n} X_i \qquad \text{and} \qquad \bar{Y} = \frac{1}{n} \sum_{i=1}^{n} Y_i
$$

On the scatter diagram in Fig. 1-3 insert perpendiculars to the axes at $\bar{X}$ and $\bar{Y}$ as shown. We wish to pass a line through the observations as our estimate of the true line $\alpha + \beta X$. Denote the estimated line by

$$
\hat{Y} = \hat{\alpha} + \hat{\beta} X \qquad (1\text{-}6)
$$

where $\hat{\alpha}$, $\hat{\beta}$ = estimates of two unknown parameters
$\hat{Y}$ = ordinate on line for any given value of X

To fit such a line we must develop formulas for $\hat{\alpha}$ and $\hat{\beta}$ in terms of the sample observations. We shall show how this is done by the principle of least squares and then examine the properties of the resultant estimators.

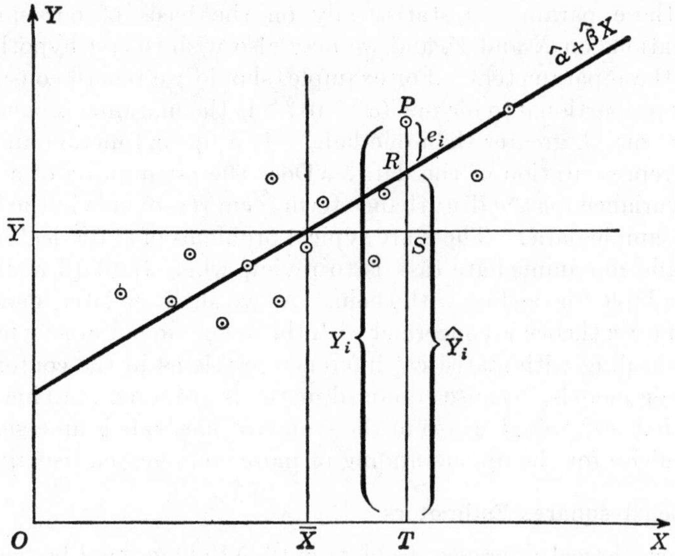

FIG. 1-3

Take any point P with coordinates, say, (X_i, Y_i) in the scatter. Drop a perpendicular from P to the X axis, intersecting our estimated line at R, the $\bar{Y}$ line at S, and the X axis at T. Then $OT = X_i$, $PT = Y_i$, and $RT = \hat{Y}_i$. Define the vertical difference between P and the estimated line by

$$e_i = Y_i - \hat{Y}_i = PR$$

These residuals, or deviations, from the estimated line will be positive or negative as the actual point lies above or below the line. If they are squared and summed, the resultant quantity must be nonnegative and will vary directly with the spread of the points from the line. Different pairs of values for $\hat{\alpha}$ and $\hat{\beta}$ will give different lines and hence different values for the sum of the squared residuals about the line. Thus we have

$$\sum_{i=1}^{n} e_i^2 = f(\hat{\alpha},\hat{\beta})$$

The principle of least squares is that the $\hat{\alpha}$, $\hat{\beta}$ values should be chosen so as to make Σe^2 as small as possible. A necessary condition is that the partial derivatives of the sum with respect to $\hat{\alpha}$ and $\hat{\beta}$ should both be zero. We thus have

$$\begin{aligned}\sum_{i=1}^{n} e_i^2 &= \sum_{i=1}^{n} (Y_i - \hat{Y}_i)^2 \\ &= \sum_{i=1}^{n} (Y_i - \hat{\alpha} - \hat{\beta}X_i)^2\end{aligned}$$

so that

$$\frac{\partial}{\partial\hat{\alpha}} \sum_{i=1}^{n} e_i^2 = -2 \sum_{i=1}^{n} (Y_i - \hat{\alpha} - \hat{\beta}X_i) = 0$$

$$\frac{\partial}{\partial\hat{\beta}} \sum_{i=1}^{n} e_i^2 = -2 \sum_{i=1}^{n} X_i(Y_i - \hat{\alpha} - \hat{\beta}X_i) = 0$$

Simplifying these two equations gives the standard form of the normal equations for a straight line:

$$\begin{aligned}\sum_{i=1}^{n} Y_i &= n\hat{\alpha} + \hat{\beta} \sum_{i=1}^{n} X_i \\ \sum_{i=1}^{n} X_iY_i &= \hat{\alpha} \sum_{i=1}^{n} X_i + \hat{\beta} \sum_{i=1}^{n} X_i^2\end{aligned} \tag{1-7}$$

When the indicated values from the sample observations are inserted, they give two simultaneous equations, which may be solved for $\hat{\alpha}$ and $\hat{\beta}$.

Alternatively, we see that if we divide through the first equation in (1-7) by n, we obtain

$$\bar{Y} = \hat{\alpha} + \hat{\beta}\bar{X} \tag{1-8}$$

that is, the least-squares estimates are such that the estimated line passes through the point of means $(\bar{X},\bar{Y})$. If we subtract (1-8) from (1-6), there results

$$\hat{Y} - \bar{Y} = \hat{\beta}(X - \bar{X})$$

Using the convention that lowercase letters denote deviations from means, so that

$$x_i = X_i - \bar{X} \qquad y_i = Y_i - \bar{Y} \qquad \hat{y}_i = \hat{Y}_i - \bar{Y}$$

we now have an alternative way of writing the equation of the least-squares line, namely,

$$\hat{y} = \hat{\beta}x \tag{1-9}$$

Referring to Fig. 1-3, the residual e_i may be indicated by

$$e_i = y_i - \hat{y}_i = y_i - \hat{\beta}x_i$$

so that the sum of squared residuals is

$$\sum_{i=1}^{n} e_i^2 = \sum_{i=1}^{n} (y_i - \hat{\beta}x_i)^2$$

Minimizing this last expression with respect to $\hat{\beta}$ gives

$$\hat{\beta} = \frac{\sum_{i=1}^{n} x_i y_i}{\sum_{i=1}^{n} x_i^2} \tag{1-10}$$

and $\hat{\alpha}$ is then obtained from the condition that the line passes through the point of means, namely,

$$\hat{\alpha} = \bar{Y} - \hat{\beta}\bar{X} \tag{1-11}$$

Equation (1-10) might also have been obtained merely by rewriting the second equation of (1-7) in deviation form and remembering that for any variable the sum of the deviations around the arithmetic mean is identically zero.

To illustrate the calculation of a least-squares relationship, consider the data in Table 1-1. The original data have been expressed in figures of approximately the same order of magnitude. It is important to choose units of measurement for the variables to achieve this result, especially in cases of three or more variables, in order to avoid having too few significant figures in some of the calculations.

From columns 2 and 3 we calculate the following quantities required for Eqs. (1-7):

$$n = 11 \qquad \Sigma X = 5{,}711 \qquad \Sigma Y = 2{,}396$$
$$\Sigma X^2 = 3{,}134{,}543 \qquad \Sigma XY = 1{,}296{,}836$$

Substitution in (1-7) gives

$$2{,}396 = 11\hat{\alpha} + 5{,}711\hat{\beta}$$
$$1{,}296{,}836 = 5{,}711\hat{\alpha} + 3{,}134{,}543\hat{\beta}$$

which solve to give

$$\hat{\alpha} = 55.85 \qquad \hat{\beta} = 0.3120$$

and the estimated relationship is written

$$\hat{Y} = 55.85 + 0.3120X$$

As an alternative method we compute the deviations from the arithmetic means in columns 4 and 5, and then from (1-10) and (1-11) obtain

$$\hat{\beta} = 52{,}876.36/169{,}495.64 = 0.3120$$
$$\hat{\alpha} = (217.818) - (0.31196)(519.182) = 55.85$$

as before. Notice that one should always retain more significant places in parameters that are reused in subsequent calculations than one may wish to use in writing the final estimate.

TABLE 1-1. ROAD CASUALTIES AND LICENSED VEHICLES IN THE UNITED KINGDOM

Year (1)	Road casualties (000) Y (2)	Licensed vehicles (0,000) X (3)	$y = Y - \bar{Y}$ (4)	$x = X - \bar{X}$ (5)
1947	166	352	−51.8	−167.2
1948	153	373	−64.8	−146.2
1949	177	411	−40.8	−108.2
1950	201	441	−16.8	−78.2
1951	216	462	−1.8	−57.2
1952	208	490	−9.8	−29.2
1953	227	529	9.2	9.8
1954	238	577	20.2	57.8
1955	268	641	50.2	121.8
1956	268	692	50.2	172.8
1957	274	743	56.2	223.8

SOURCE: Oxford P.P.E., 1959.

Next we establish the properties of these estimators.[1] We assume that the X_i values are fixed constants. This is equivalent to assum-

[1] Strictly speaking, estimator refers to a method, or formula, of estimation, and estimate to a particular numerical value yielded by that formula.

ing that in an experimental setup we can choose a set of X values and hold them constant in repeated samples. Alternatively, one may think of establishing the properties of $\hat{\alpha}$ and $\hat{\beta}$ *conditional* upon the given values of X and then, if for some applications it is more appropriate to consider X a random variable as well, to see how these properties hold up for this change of assumption about X.

Let us hold the X_i fixed and imagine repeated samples of size n being taken. The Y values will vary from sample to sample as a consequence of different drawings from the u distribution in each sample. Applying the formulas for $\hat{\alpha}$ and $\hat{\beta}$ to each set of sample observations would generate a series of $\hat{\alpha}$, $\hat{\beta}$ values. The distribution of these values is the joint sampling distribution of the least-squares estimators. Looking at the two marginal distributions for $\hat{\alpha}$ and $\hat{\beta}$, we are interested in the means and variances of these distributions and also in the comparison between these distributions and those of other possible estimators.

The first point to notice about the least-squares estimators is that they are *linear* functions of the actual observations on Y. From (1-10) we can write

$$\begin{aligned}\hat{\beta} &= \frac{\Sigma x_i y_i}{\Sigma x_i^2} \\ &= \frac{\Sigma x_i Y_i}{\Sigma x_i^2} - \frac{\bar{Y}\Sigma x_i}{\Sigma x_i^2} \\ &= \sum_{i=1}^{n} w_i Y_i \qquad \text{since } \sum_{i=1}^{n} x_i \equiv 0 \end{aligned} \tag{1-12}$$

where

$$w_i = \frac{x_i}{\sum_{i=1}^{n} x_i^2} \tag{1-13}$$

These w_i are fixed constants in repeated sampling, and it also follows directly that

$$\sum_{i=1}^{n} w_i = 0 \qquad \sum_{i=1}^{n} w_i^2 = \frac{1}{\sum_{i=1}^{n} x_i^2} \qquad \sum_{i=1}^{n} w_i x_i = \sum_{i=1}^{n} w_i X_i = 1 \tag{1-14}$$

By a similar algebraic manipulation of (1-11), $\hat{\alpha}$ may be expressed as a linear function of the Y_i, namely,

$$\hat{\alpha} = \sum_{i=1}^{n} \left(\frac{1}{n} - \bar{X} w_i\right) Y_i \tag{1-15}$$

To establish the means of the sampling distributions, we substitute for Y_i from (1-5), namely,

$$Y_i = \alpha + \beta X_i + u_i$$

Thus

$$\begin{aligned} \hat{\beta} &= \Sigma w_i Y_i \\ &= \Sigma w_i(\alpha + \beta X_i + u_i) \\ &= \beta + \sum_{i=1}^{n} w_i u_i \qquad \text{using (1-14)} \end{aligned} \tag{1-16}$$

Hence

$$\begin{aligned} E(\hat{\beta}) &= \beta + \sum_{i=1}^{n} w_i E(u_i) \\ &= \beta \end{aligned}$$

since $E(u_i) = 0$ for all i by assumption (1-5). The significance of the assumption of constant X values is seen in the above manipulations, in that the operation of taking expected values is applied to the u and Y values but not to X. Thus $\hat{\beta}$ is seen to be an unbiased linear estimator of β. Similarly, $\hat{\alpha}$ is an unbiased linear estimator of α. For

$$\begin{aligned} \hat{\alpha} &= \sum \left(\frac{1}{n} - \bar{X}w_i\right)(\alpha + \beta X_i + u_i) \\ &= \alpha - \alpha\bar{X}\sum w_i + \beta\bar{X} - \beta\bar{X}\sum w_i X_i + \sum\left(\frac{1}{n} - \bar{X}w_i\right)u_i \\ &= \alpha + \sum\left(\frac{1}{n} - \bar{X}w_i\right)u_i \qquad \text{using (1-14)} \end{aligned} \tag{1-17}$$

Hence

$$E(\hat{\alpha}) = \alpha$$

since $E(u_i) = 0$ for all i by assumption (1-5).

The variances of the estimates may be obtained from (1-16) and (1-17). We have, first, that

$$\begin{aligned} \hat{\beta} - \beta &= \sum_{i=1}^{n} w_i u_i \\ \text{var}(\hat{\beta}) &= E[(\hat{\beta} - \beta)^2] \\ &= E[(\Sigma w_i u_i)^2] \\ &= E(w_1^2 u_1^2 + \cdots + w_n^2 u_n^2 + 2w_1 w_2 u_1 u_2 \\ &\qquad + \cdots + 2w_{n-1} w_n u_{n-1} u_n) \\ &= \sigma_u^2 \sum_{i=1}^{n} w_i^2 \end{aligned}$$

since $E(u_i^2) = \sigma_u^2$ and $\underset{i \neq j}{E}(u_i u_j) = 0$ by assumption (1-5). Thus

$$\text{var}(\hat{\beta}) = \frac{\sigma_u^2}{\sum_{i=1}^{n} x_i^2} \qquad \text{from (1-14)} \tag{1-18}$$

Using (1-17), we derive in a similar fashion the variance of $\hat{\alpha}$.

$$\begin{aligned}
\text{var}(\hat{\alpha}) &= E[(\hat{\alpha} - \alpha)^2] \\
&= \sigma_u^2 \sum_{i=1}^{n} \left(\frac{1}{n} - \bar{X} w_i\right)^2 \\
&= \sigma_u^2 \left(\frac{1}{n} + \bar{X}^2 \sum w_i^2 - \frac{2\bar{X}}{n} \sum w_i\right) \\
&= \sigma_u^2 \left(\frac{1}{n} + \frac{\bar{X}^2}{\sum_{i=1}^{n} x_i^2}\right) \qquad \text{using (1-14)}
\end{aligned}$$

or rearranging slightly,

$$\text{var}(\hat{\alpha}) = \frac{\sum_{i=1}^{n} X_i^2}{n \sum_{i=1}^{n} x_i^2} \sigma_u^2 \tag{1-19}$$

Likewise, we may deduce that the covariance of the estimates is

$$\begin{aligned}
\text{cov}(\hat{\alpha}, \hat{\beta}) &= E[(\hat{\alpha} - \alpha)(\hat{\beta} - \beta)] \\
&= \frac{-\bar{X}}{\sum_{i=1}^{n} x_i^2} \sigma_u^2
\end{aligned} \tag{1-20}$$

Next we shall establish that these estimators are *best* linear unbiased, that is, that of the class of linear unbiased estimators, the least-squares estimators have the smallest variance. Define any arbitrary linear estimator of β as

$$\hat{\hat{\beta}} = \sum_{i=1}^{n} c_i Y_i$$

where

$$c_i = w_i + d_i \tag{1-21}$$

the w_i being defined in (1-13) and the d_i being arbitrary constants.

For $\hat{\hat{\beta}}$ to be an unbiased estimator of β, the d_i must fulfill certain conditions.

$$\begin{aligned} \hat{\hat{\beta}} &= \Sigma c_i(\alpha + \beta X_i + u_i) \\ &= \alpha \Sigma c_i + \beta \Sigma c_i X_i + \Sigma c_i u_i \end{aligned}$$

therefore
$$\begin{aligned} E(\hat{\hat{\beta}}) &= \alpha \Sigma c_i + \beta \Sigma c_i X_i \\ &= \beta \end{aligned}$$

if $\Sigma c_i = 0$ and $\Sigma c_i X_i = 1$. These two conditions, in conjunction with (1-21) and the properties of w in (1-14), give the required conditions on the d_i, namely,

$$\sum_{i=1}^{n} d_i = 0 \qquad \text{and} \qquad \sum_{i=1}^{n} d_i X_i = \sum d_i x_i = 0 \tag{1-22}$$

The variance of this arbitrary linear unbiased estimator is then

$$\begin{aligned} \text{var}\,(\hat{\hat{\beta}}) &= E\left[\left(\sum_{i=1}^{n} c_i u_i\right)^2\right] \\ &= \sigma_u^2 \sum_{i=1}^{n} c_i^2 \end{aligned}$$

but
$$\sum_{i=1}^{n} c_i^2 = \sum_{i=1}^{n} w_i^2 + \sum_{i=1}^{n} d_i^2 + 2\sum_{i=1}^{n} w_i d_i$$

$$\sum_{i=1}^{n} w_i d_i = \frac{\Sigma x_i d_i}{\Sigma x_i^2} = 0 \qquad \text{by (1-22)}$$

Thus
$$\text{var}\,(\hat{\hat{\beta}}) = \text{var}\,(\hat{\beta}) + \sigma_u^2 \sum_{i=1}^{n} d_i^2$$

Σd_i^2 is necessarily nonnegative and is zero only if each value of d is zero. Thus the least-squares estimator has the smallest variance of all linear unbiased estimates. A similar result may be demonstrated for var ($\hat{\alpha}$).

An alternative development is to obtain best linear unbiased estimators directly, and it can then be seen that they coincide with the least-squares estimators. This approach also illustrates a method which will find fruitful applications in later problems. Let us make the same assumptions (1-5) as before and define

$$\hat{\beta} = \sum_{i=1}^{n} c_i Y_i$$

where the problem is to choose the weights c_i to make $E(\hat{\beta}) = \beta$ and to make the variance of $\hat{\beta}$ as small as possible. From the definition of Y_i in (1-5),

$$\hat{\beta} = \alpha\Sigma c_i + \beta\Sigma c_i X_i + \Sigma c_i u_i$$
$$E(\hat{\beta}) = \alpha\Sigma c_i + \beta\Sigma c_i X_i$$

Thus $\hat{\beta}$ is an unbiased estimator of β if

$$\sum_{i=1}^{n} c_i = 0 \qquad \text{and} \qquad \sum_{i=1}^{n} c_i X_i = 1 \tag{1-23}$$

Using these conditions, the variance of $\hat{\beta}$ is

$$\text{var}\ (\hat{\beta}) = \sigma_u{}^2 \sum_{i=1}^{n} c_i{}^2$$

The problem now is to minimize var $(\hat{\beta})$ subject to the conditions (1-23). We define

$$\varphi = \sum_{i=1}^{n} c_i{}^2 - 2\lambda \sum_{i=1}^{n} c_i - 2\mu \left(\sum_{i=1}^{n} c_i X_i - 1 \right)$$

where λ and μ are Lagrangian multipliers. Differentiating φ partially with respect to c_i $(i = 1, \ldots, n)$, λ, and μ and equating to zero and rearranging gives the equations

$$c_i = \lambda + \mu X_i \qquad i = 1, \ldots, n \tag{1-24}$$
$$\Sigma c_i = 0 \tag{1-25}$$
$$\Sigma c_i X_i = 1 \tag{1-26}$$

Summing (1-24) over all values of i gives $\lambda = -\mu\bar{X}$, which on resubstitution in (1-24) yields

$$c_i = \mu(X_i - \bar{X}) = \mu x_i$$

Multiplying through this equation by X_i, summing over i, and using (1-26) gives

$$\mu\Sigma x_i X_i = \Sigma c_i X_i = 1$$

Hence
$$\mu = \frac{1}{\Sigma x_i X_i} = \frac{1}{\sum_{i=1}^{n} x_i{}^2}$$

Therefore
$$c_i = \frac{x_i}{\sum_{i=1}^{n} x_i{}^2} \qquad i = 1, \ldots, n \tag{1-27}$$

It is seen that the weights c_i are identical with the least-squares weights w_i, as defined in (1-13), so that the best linear unbiased estimator of β is $\Sigma x_i y_i / \Sigma x_i^2$ as before. A similar development to the above can also be obtained for $\hat{\alpha}$. This is a simple case of the famous Gauss-Markoff result on least squares.[1]

Summarizing the results so far, we have that if $Y_i = \alpha + \beta X_i + u_i$ $(i = 1, \ldots, n)$, where the u_i have zero expectation, constant variance σ_u^2, and zero covariances and the X_i are fixed constants, then the least-squares estimators

$$\hat{\beta} = \frac{\sum_{i=1}^{n} x_i y_i}{\sum_{i=1}^{n} x_i^2} = \frac{\sum_{i=1}^{n} x_i Y_i}{\sum_{i=1}^{n} x_i^2} = \frac{n \sum_{i=1}^{n} X_i Y_i - \left(\sum_{i=1}^{n} X_i\right)\left(\sum_{i=1}^{n} Y_i\right)}{n \sum_{i=1}^{n} X_i^2 - \left(\sum_{i=1}^{n} X_i\right)^2}$$

$$\hat{\alpha} = \bar{Y} - \hat{\beta}\bar{X}$$

are best linear unbiased estimators of α and β, and their variances are

$$\text{var}\,(\hat{\alpha}) = \frac{\sigma_u^2 \Sigma X_i^2}{n \Sigma x_i^2} \qquad \text{var}\,(\hat{\beta}) = \frac{\sigma_u^2}{\Sigma x_i^2}$$

It seems intuitively plausible to base an estimate of the variance of the disturbance term σ_u^2 on the squared residuals about the least-squares line. Referring to Fig. 1-3, we have

$$e_i = y_i - \hat{\beta} x_i$$

and if we average $Y_i = \alpha + \beta X_i + u_i$ over the n sample values, we obtain $\bar{Y} = \alpha + \beta \bar{X} + \bar{u}$, so that

$$y_i = \beta x_i + (u_i - \bar{u})$$

Hence

$$e_i = -(\hat{\beta} - \beta) x_i + (u_i - \bar{u})$$

Therefore

$$\sum_{i=1}^{n} e_i^2 = (\hat{\beta} - \beta)^2 \sum_{i=1}^{n} x_i^2 + \sum_{i=1}^{n} (u_i - \bar{u})^2 - 2(\hat{\beta} - \beta) \sum_{i=1}^{n} x_i (u_i - \bar{u})$$

[1] F. N. David and J. Neyman, "Extension of the Markoff Theorem on Least Squares," *Statist. Research Mems.*, vol. 2, pp. 105–116, 1938.

Taking expected values of each term on the right-hand side gives

$$E[(\hat{\beta} - \beta)^2 \Sigma x_i^2] = \sigma_u^2 \qquad \text{using (1-18)}$$

$$E\left[\sum_{i=1}^{n} (u_i - \bar{u})^2\right] = E\left[\sum_{i=1}^{n} u_i^2 - \frac{1}{n}\left(\sum_{i=1}^{n} u_i\right)^2\right]$$
$$= (n-1)\sigma_u^2$$

$$E[(\hat{\beta} - \beta)\Sigma x_i(u_i - \bar{u})] = E\left[\frac{\Sigma u_i x_i}{\Sigma x_i^2}(\Sigma u_i x_i - \bar{u}\Sigma x_i)\right] \qquad \text{using (1-16)}$$
$$= E\left[\frac{(\Sigma u_i x_i)^2}{\Sigma x_i^2}\right] \qquad \text{since } \Sigma x_i = 0$$
$$= \sigma_u^2$$

Hence
$$E\left(\sum_{i=1}^{n} e_i^2\right) = \sigma_u^2 + (n-1)\sigma_u^2 - 2\sigma_u^2$$
$$= (n-2)\sigma_u^2$$

Thus if we define

$$\hat{\sigma}_u^2 = \frac{\sum_{i=1}^{n} e_i^2}{n-2} \tag{1-28}$$

$\hat{\sigma}_u^2$ is an unbiased estimator of σ_u^2.

So far we have made no assumptions about the probability distribution of the u_i beyond those of zero mean, constant variance, and zero covariances. If we postulate a normal distribution, then we can obtain maximum-likelihood estimators. Assumptions (1-5) combined with normality give the probability of obtaining the observed u's as

$$p(u_1 \quad u_2 \quad \cdots \quad u_n) = \frac{1}{(\sigma_u^2\, 2\pi)^{n/2}} \exp\left(-\frac{1}{2\sigma_u^2}\sum_{i=1}^{n} u_i^2\right) du_1 \cdots du_n$$

Since $Y_i = \alpha + \beta X_i + u_i$ $(i = 1, \ldots, n)$ gives a linear transformation of u_i into Y_i and the Jacobian of the transformation is unity, the likelihood function for the sample is

$$L = \frac{1}{(\sigma_u^2\, 2\pi)^{n/2}} \exp\left[-\frac{1}{2\sigma_u^2}\sum_{i=1}^{n} (Y_i - \alpha - \beta X_i)^2\right]$$

and

$$\log L = -\frac{n}{2}\log 2\pi - \frac{n}{2}\log \sigma_u^2 - \frac{1}{2\sigma_u^2}\sum_{i=1}^{n} (Y_i - \alpha - \beta X_i)^2$$

Differentiating partially with respect to α, β, and σ_u^2 gives

$$\frac{\partial(\log L)}{\partial\alpha} = \frac{1}{\sigma_u^2}\sum(Y_i - \alpha - \beta X_i)$$

$$\frac{\partial(\log L)}{\partial\beta} = \frac{1}{\sigma_u^2}\sum X_i(Y_i - \alpha - \beta x_i)$$

$$\frac{\partial(\log L)}{\partial\sigma_u^2} = -\frac{n}{2\sigma_u^2} + \frac{1}{2\sigma_u^4}\sum(Y_i - \alpha - \beta x_i)^2$$

On equating to zero and simplifying, the first two equations reduce to the least-squares equations already obtained.

$$\Sigma Y_i = n\tilde{\alpha} + \tilde{\beta}\Sigma X_i$$
$$\Sigma X_i Y_i = \tilde{\alpha}\Sigma X_i + \tilde{\beta}\Sigma X_i^2$$

where we use the tilde over a parameter to indicate a maximum-likelihood estimate of that parameter. The third equation then gives the maximum-likelihood estimate of the variance of the disturbance term as

$$\tilde{\sigma}_u^2 = \frac{1}{n}\sum_{i=1}^{n}(Y_i - \tilde{\alpha} - \tilde{\beta}X_i)^2 \tag{1-29}$$

Since $\tilde{\alpha}$ and $\tilde{\beta}$ are identical with the least-squares estimators, it follows from (1-16) and (1-17) that they are linear functions of the u_i, which have a multivariate normal distribution. Thus $\tilde{\alpha}$ and $\tilde{\beta}$ themselves are normally distributed.[1] The means are α and β, since we have already shown these estimators to be unbiased, and the variances and covariance are given in formulas (1-18) to (1-20) above, so that the bivariate distribution of $\tilde{\alpha}$ and $\tilde{\beta}$ is determined. The variances and covariance, however, involve the unknown variance of the disturbance term σ_u^2. In order to test hypotheses about α and β and compute interval estimates, we need one further result. This is that $n\tilde{\sigma}_u^2/\sigma_u^2$ has a χ^2 distribution with $n - 2$ degrees of freedom and that this statistic is distributed independently of $\tilde{\alpha}$ and $\tilde{\beta}$.[2]

Let us recall the definition of the t distribution, that if z has a standard normal distribution $N(0,1)$ and v^2 has an independent χ^2

[1] See R. L. Anderson and T. A. Bancroft, *Statistical Theory in Research*, McGraw-Hill, New York, 1952, pp. 63–64.

[2] See A. M. Mood, *Introduction to the Theory of Statistics*, McGraw-Hill, New York, 1950, pp. 294–295. This result will be proved for the general case of k variables in Chap. 4.

distribution with r degrees of freedom, the quantity

$$t = \frac{z\sqrt{r}}{v}$$

has *Student's t* distribution with r degrees of freedom.[1] The equation of the t distribution is

$$f(t) = c\left(1 + \frac{t^2}{r}\right)^{-(r+1)/2}$$

where c is an appropriate constant. This is symmetrical about a zero mean, and it approaches $N(0,1)$ as r tends to infinity.

For tests on $\hat{\alpha}$ we have[2]

$$\hat{\alpha} \text{ is } N\left(\alpha, \frac{\sigma_u{}^2 \Sigma X^2}{n\Sigma x^2}\right)$$

Hence $$z = \frac{(\hat{\alpha} - \alpha)\sqrt{n}\sqrt{\Sigma x^2}}{\sigma_u \sqrt{\Sigma X^2}} \text{ is } N(0,1)$$

Further, $$v^2 = \frac{\sum_{i=1}^{n} e_i{}^2}{\sigma_u{}^2} = \frac{(n-2)\hat{\sigma}_u{}^2}{\sigma_u{}^2}$$

has an independent χ^2 distribution with $n - 2$ degrees of freedom. Hence

$$t = \frac{(\hat{\alpha} - \alpha)\sqrt{n\Sigma x^2}}{\hat{\sigma}_u \sqrt{\Sigma X^2}} \tag{1-30}$$

[1] See P. G. Hoel, *Introduction to Mathematical Statistics*, 2d ed., Wiley, New York, 1954, pp. 222–226, or Mood, *op. cit.*, p. 206.

[2] We are using two separate results here which are very important. (1) If x is a random variable with mean $E(x) = \mu$ and y is defined as $x - k$, where k is a constant, then the mean of y is the mean of x less k.

$$E(y) = E(x - k) = \mu - k$$

(2) If x is a random variable with mean μ and variance $\sigma^2 = E[(x - \mu)^2]$, and y is defined as kx, where k is a constant, then the variance of y is k^2 times the variance of x.

$$E\{[y - E(y)]^2\} = E[(kx - k\mu)^2] = k^2E[(x - \mu)^2] = k^2\sigma^2$$

has the t distribution with $n - 2$ degrees of freedom. In formula (1-30), $\hat{\sigma}_u$ is the estimated disturbance standard deviation, as defined in (1-28). It can be seen that the unknown true disturbance variance σ_u^2 has disappeared on the formation of the t quantity and we have a test function which depends solely on the sample observations and the hypothetical value of α.

To perform a two-tailed test of the hypothesis that $\alpha = \alpha_0$, we should substitute α_0 in (1-30) and see whether the resultant t value falls within an appropriate critical region determined from the t distribution with $n - 2$ degrees of freedom. To obtain a 95 per cent confidence-interval estimate for α, we should proceed as follows:

$$\Pr\,(-t_{0.025} < t < t_{0.025}) = 0.95$$

where $t_{0.025}$ is the value of t such that

$$0.025 = \int_{t_{0.025}}^{\infty} f(t)\, dt$$

Substituting for t from (1-30) gives

$$\Pr\left[-t_{0.025} < \frac{(\hat{\alpha} - \alpha)\sqrt{n\Sigma x^2}}{\hat{\sigma}_u\sqrt{\Sigma X^2}} < t_{0.025}\right] = 0.95$$

The inequality statements inside the brackets may be rearranged to isolate α on one side of the inequality sign, and the probability statement rewritten as

$$\Pr\left(\hat{\alpha} - t_{0.025}\frac{\hat{\sigma}_u\sqrt{\Sigma X^2}}{\sqrt{n\Sigma x^2}} < \alpha < \hat{\alpha} + t_{0.025}\frac{\hat{\sigma}_u\sqrt{\Sigma X^2}}{\sqrt{n\Sigma x^2}}\right) = 0.95 \qquad (1\text{-}31)$$

so that the 95 per cent confidence limits for α are

$$\hat{\alpha} \pm t_{0.025}\frac{\hat{\sigma}_u\sqrt{\Sigma X^2}}{\sqrt{n\Sigma x^2}} \qquad (1\text{-}32)$$

In general, the $100(1 - \epsilon)$ per cent confidence limits are

$$\hat{\alpha} \pm t_{\epsilon/2}\frac{\hat{\sigma}_u\sqrt{\Sigma X^2}}{\sqrt{n\Sigma x^2}} \qquad (1\text{-}33)$$

In a similar fashion, to carry out tests on β, we have

$$\hat{\beta} \text{ is } N\left(\beta, \frac{\sigma_u^2}{\Sigma x^2}\right)$$

Hence
$$z = \frac{(\hat{\beta} - \beta)\sqrt{\Sigma x^2}}{\sigma_u} \text{ is } N(0,1)$$

$$v^2 = \frac{(n-2)\hat{\sigma}_u^2}{\sigma_u^2}$$

is an independent χ^2 distribution with $n - 2$ degrees of freedom. Hence

$$t = \frac{(\hat{\beta} - \beta)\sqrt{\Sigma x^2}}{\hat{\sigma}_u} \tag{1-34}$$

has the t distribution with $n - 2$ degrees of freedom. It follows that a $100(1 - \epsilon)$ per cent confidence interval for β is given by

$$\hat{\beta} \pm t_{\epsilon/2} \frac{\hat{\sigma}_u}{\sqrt{\Sigma x^2}} \tag{1-35}$$

These are tests on α and β separately. Joint tests can be obtained from the following result. The quadratic form of the joint distribution of $\hat{\alpha}$ and $\hat{\beta}$,

$$Q = \frac{1}{\sigma_u^2}[n(\hat{\alpha} - \alpha)^2 + 2n\bar{X}(\hat{\alpha} - \alpha)(\hat{\beta} - \beta) + \Sigma X_i^2(\hat{\beta} - \beta)^2]$$

has a χ^2 distribution with 2 degrees of freedom.[1] The quantity $(n - 2)\hat{\sigma}_u^2/\sigma_u^2$ has an independent χ^2 distribution with $n - 2$ degrees of freedom. Recalling the definition of the F distribution, it then follows that

$$F = \frac{Q/2}{\hat{\sigma}_u^2/\sigma_u^2} \tag{1-36}$$

has the F distribution with 2 and $n - 2$ degrees of freedom.[2] In (1-36) the unknown σ_u^2 will cancel out, leaving only the unknown parameters α and β. If we use the inequality

$$\Pr(F < F_\epsilon) = 1 - \epsilon$$

[1] See Mood, *op. cit.*, p. 295.

[2] *Ibid.*, pp. 204, 296.

to read off the appropriate F_ϵ from the table of the F distribution and substitute this value for F in (1-36), we obtain a $100(1 - \epsilon)$ per cent elliptical confidence region for α and β in the α, β plane. To test a joint hypothesis at the 100ϵ per cent level of significance that $\alpha = \alpha_0$ and $\beta = \beta_0$, we should substitute these values for α and β in (1-36) and observe whether or not the resultant F value exceeded F_ϵ, indicating rejection of the hypothesis.

Tests on σ_u^2 may be obtained by use of the χ^2 distribution. The probability statement

$$\Pr\left[\chi^2_{0.975} < \frac{(n-2)\hat{\sigma}_u^2}{\sigma_u^2} < \chi^2_{0.025}\right] = 0.95$$

gives 95 per cent confidence limits for σ_u^2 as

$$\frac{(n-2)\hat{\sigma}_u^2}{\chi^2_{0.025}} \quad \text{and} \quad \frac{(n-2)\hat{\sigma}_u^2}{\chi^2_{0.975}}$$

and the same result may be used to test hypotheses about σ_u^2.

All the tests and estimation procedures derived so far in this chapter rest on the assumption that $X_1, X_2, \ldots, X_n$ are constants. It is important to understand the economic and statistical significance of this assumption and to see what would happen to our test procedure if it were relaxed. Statistically, the meaning of the assumption is that, if one computes, say, a 95 per cent confidence interval for β, one is saying that if one were to take repeated samples of size n, with the X_i fixed, and compute an interval for each sample from (1-35), then approximately 95 per cent of these intervals would include the true value of β. Economically, this assumption is sometimes interpreted as a condition that the econometrician in obtaining his data must be able to hold one variable constant at predetermined levels, and that the usual statistical inferences do not hold if the data have not been obtained in this fashion. Since experimental control over variables is usually impossible in economics, the outlook seems bleak and most of this statistical theory irrelevant, but fortunately the state of affairs is not quite as black as this.

There are, in fact, two possible lines of approach. One is to say that no matter how the X, Y data have been obtained, if the assumptions about the *conditional* distribution of Y_i, given X_i, made in (1-5) are valid, then our probability statements about confidence intervals and powers of tests are still valid, but they are statements of *conditional* probabilities for the given X values. These conditional statements, valid as they are, may not, however, seem very interesting or relevant for the economic or social situation under study. The alternative is to assume that the X_i are also random variables and to examine what meaning or usefulness now attaches to our procedures.

Assume that the X_i are independent random variables with probability distribution $g(X_i)$, $i = 1, \ldots, n$, and assume also that the conditional distributions of the Y_i, given X_i, are normal and independent with expectations given by $E(Y_i|X_i) = \alpha + \beta X_i$ and with constant variance denoted by σ_u^2. The likelihood function for the sample observations is then

$$L = g(X_1)g(X_2) \cdots g(X_n) \frac{1}{(2\pi\sigma_u^2)^{n/2}} \exp\left[-\frac{1}{2\sigma_u^2}\sum_{i=1}^{n}(Y_i - \alpha - \beta X_i)^2\right] \qquad (1\text{-}37)$$

On the assumption that the distribution $g(X_i)$ does *not* involve the parameters α, β, σ_u^2, the maximum-likelihood estimators of these parameters from (1-37) are easily shown to be

$$\tilde{\beta} = \frac{\Sigma x_i y_i}{\Sigma x_i^2}$$

$$\tilde{\alpha} = \bar{Y} - \tilde{\beta}\bar{X}$$

$$\tilde{\sigma}_u^2 = \frac{1}{n}\sum(Y_i - \tilde{\alpha} - \tilde{\beta}X_i)^2$$

which are exactly the same as those obtained on page 21 above for the case of fixed X_i. These may be shown to have the same means as before by the use of the following important lemma.

Lemma: If $f(X,Y)$ is the joint distribution of two random variables X and Y and if $h(X,Y)$ is any function such that $E[h(X,Y)]$ exists, then

$$E[h(X,Y)] = E_X\{E_{Y|X}[h(X,Y)]\}$$

where $E_{Y|X}$ = expected value in *conditional* distribution of Y, given X

E_X = expected value in *marginal* distribution of X

Proof: Let $f(X,Y) = k(Y|X)g(X)$.

$$\begin{aligned} E[h(X,Y)] &= \int_{-\infty}^{\infty}\int_{-\infty}^{\infty} h(X,Y)f(X,Y)\,dY\,dX \\ &= \int_{-\infty}^{\infty}\int_{-\infty}^{\infty} h(X,Y)k(Y|X)g(X)\,dY\,dX \\ &= \int_{-\infty}^{\infty}\left[\int_{-\infty}^{\infty} h(X,Y)k(Y|X)\,dY\right] g(X)\,dX \end{aligned}$$

The term in brackets is $E_{Y|X}[h(X,Y)]$, which is a function of X only. Thus

$$\begin{aligned} E[h(X,Y)] &= \int_{-\infty}^{\infty} E_{Y|X}[h(X,Y)]g(X)\,dX \\ &= E_X\{E_{Y|X}[h(X,Y)]\} \end{aligned}$$

We have already shown in (1-12) and (1-13) that

$$\tilde{\beta} = \hat{\beta} = \Sigma w_i Y_i$$

where $w_i = x_i/\Sigma x_i^2$, and in (1-16) that the expected value of $\tilde{\beta}$, for given X, is β, that is, that

$$E_{Y|X}(\tilde{\beta}) = \beta$$

For the case of X and Y both being random variables, we have

$$\begin{aligned} E(\tilde{\beta}) &= E_X[E_{Y|X}(\tilde{\beta})] \\ &= E_X(\beta) \\ &= \beta \end{aligned}$$

since the distribution of the X values does not involve β. Similarly, it may be shown that $E(\tilde{\alpha}) = \alpha$ and $E(\tilde{\sigma}_u^2) = (n-2)\sigma_u^2/n$. An important special case of the likelihood function (1-37) is where the marginal distribution $g(X_i)$ is itself normal. The joint distribution of X_i, Y_i is then bivariate normal, and our result, of course, still holds that the maximum-likelihood estimators are identical with those for the case of fixed X_i and also with the least-squares estimators. The meaning of the above results about the estimators $\tilde{\alpha}$ and $\tilde{\beta}$ still being unbiased is that if we now envisage repeated sampling of *both* X_i and Y_i from the bivariate distribution of X_i, Y_i, the repeated application of the formulas for $\tilde{\alpha}$ and $\tilde{\beta}$ will yield unbiased estimators of α and β.

Turning now to probability statements such as (1-31) and the associated confidence intervals for α and β, we recall that these involve *Student's t* distribution on the assumption of fixed X_i. The type of probability statement is

$$\Pr(-t_{\epsilon/2} < t < t_{\epsilon/2}) = 1 - \epsilon$$

where t is some function of the observations on X and Y. Denote the conditional distribution of this t variable for given X_i by $f(t|X_1, \ldots, X_n)$ and let the density function of the X_i be $g(X_1, X_2, \ldots, X_n)$. The joint density for $t, X_1, X_2, \ldots, X_n$ is then given by

$$h(t, X_1, \ldots, X_n) = f(t|X_1, \ldots, X_n)g(X_1, \ldots, X_n)$$

Our probability statement is

$$\begin{aligned} 1 - \epsilon &= \Pr(-t_{\epsilon/2} < t < t_{\epsilon/2}) \\ &= \int_{-t_{\epsilon/2}}^{t_{\epsilon/2}} (t|X_1, \ldots, X_n)\,dt \\ &= \int_{-\infty}^{\infty} \cdots \int_{-\infty}^{\infty} \int_{-t_{\epsilon/2}}^{t_{\epsilon/2}} f(t|X_1, \ldots, X_n)g(X_1, \ldots, X_n)\,dt \\ &\qquad dX_1 \ldots dX_n \end{aligned}$$

since the integral of $g(X_1, \ldots, X_n)$ over the range of the X_i values is unity. Thus

$$1 - \epsilon = \int_{-\infty}^{\infty} \cdots \int_{-\infty}^{\infty} \int_{-t_{\epsilon/2}}^{t_{\epsilon/2}} h(t, X_1, \ldots, X_n)\,dt\; dX_1 \ldots dX_n \qquad (1\text{-}38)$$

Thus our original probability statement is still true when the X_i are random variables. We can therefore compute confidence intervals by formulas (1-33) and (1-35) exactly as before, but the interpretation of the confidence coefficient is now that if we take repeated samples where the X_i as well as the Y_i may change from sample to sample, approximately $100(1 - \epsilon)$ per cent of our confidence intervals will contain the true value.

The probabilities of type I error for our initial tests on α and β also depend on these same t distributions. By a similar argument to the above it can be seen that these probabilities remain unaltered when the X_i are taken to be random variables. Thus our original procedures turn out to be still valid and important when our original assumptions are extended to make the X_i random variables. It is important, however, to emphasize that this extended validity of the initial results depends upon the X, Y distribution being such that the conditional distribution of Y, given X, still fulfills the assumptions made in (1-5) above.

1-4. The Correlation Coefficient

Elementary treatments of the relationship between two variables usually emphasize the correlation coefficient as well as the principle

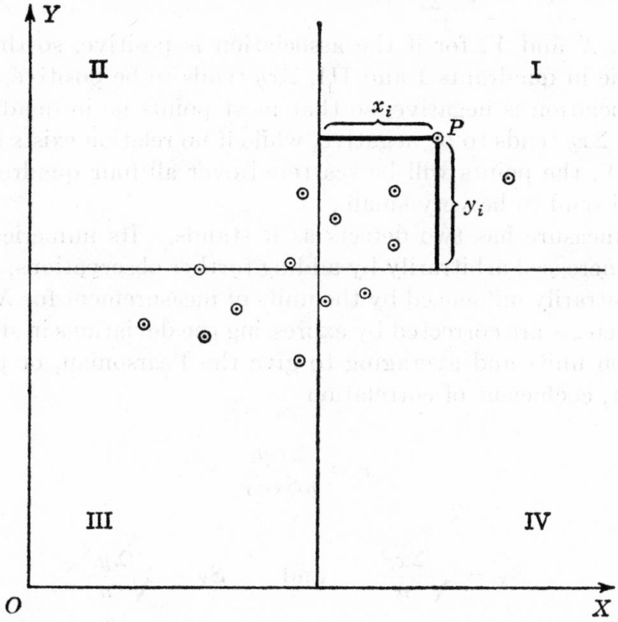

FIG. 1-4

of least squares. We have developed the application of least squares and also of maximum-likelihood estimators in the context of specific assumptions about the generation of the X, Y values and the nature of the disturbance term. We now proceed to show the link between correlation analysis and our treatment above and also to develop the analysis of variance for the two-variable case.

Assume a sample of X_i, Y_i observations ($i = 1, \ldots, n$) which are represented on a scatter diagram as in Fig. 1-4. Divide the diagram into four quadrants by erecting perpendiculars to the axes at $\bar{X}$ and $\bar{Y}$. For any point P with coordinates (X_i, Y_i), define the deviations $x_i = X_i - \bar{X}$ and $y_i = Y_i - \bar{Y}$. It is clear from inspection of the diagram that

For all points in quadrant I the product x_iy_i is positive
For all points in quadrant II the product x_iy_i is negative
For all points in quadrant III the product x_iy_i is positive
For all points in quadrant IV the product x_iy_i is negative

Hence the quantity $\sum_{i=1}^{n} x_iy_i$ serves as a measure of association between X and Y, for if the association is positive, so that most points lie in quadrants I and III, Σxy tends to be positive, while if the association is negative, so that most points lie in quadrants II and IV, Σxy tends to be negative, while if no relation exists between X and Y, the points will be scattered over all four quadrants and Σxy will tend to be very small.

The measure has two defects as it stands. Its numerical value can be increased arbitrarily by adding further observations, and it is also arbitrarily influenced by the units of measurement for X and Y. These defects are corrected by expressing the deviations in standard-deviation units and averaging to give the Pearsonian, or product-moment, coefficient of correlation

$$r = \frac{\Sigma x_iy_i}{nS_XS_Y} \tag{1-39}$$

where

$$S_X = \sqrt{\frac{\Sigma x_i^2}{n}} \qquad \text{and} \qquad S_Y = \sqrt{\frac{\Sigma y_i^2}{n}}$$

Alternative forms for r such as

$$r = \frac{\Sigma xy}{\sqrt{(\Sigma x^2)(\Sigma y^2)}} = \frac{n\Sigma XY - (\Sigma X)(\Sigma Y)}{\sqrt{n\Sigma X^2 - (\Sigma X)^2}\,\sqrt{n\Sigma Y^2 - (\Sigma Y)^2}} \tag{1-40}$$

are easily developed from the basic definition in (1-39).

If we fit a least-squares line $\hat{Y} = \hat{\alpha} + \hat{\beta}X$ to the observations by (1-7) above, then we have some interesting relations. First,

$$\hat{\beta} = \frac{\Sigma xy}{\Sigma x^2} \qquad \text{(1-10)}$$

$$= r\frac{S_Y}{S_X} \qquad \text{using (1-40)} \tag{1-41}$$

Second, from the definition of the least-squares line,

$$y_i = \hat{y}_i + e_i$$

Thus $\Sigma y_i^2 = \Sigma \hat{y}_i^2 + \Sigma e_i^2 + 2\Sigma \hat{y}_i e_i$

But
$$\begin{aligned} \Sigma \hat{y}_i e_i &= \hat{\beta}\Sigma e_i x_i && \text{using (1-9)} \\ &= \hat{\beta}\Sigma x_i(y_i - \hat{\beta}x_i) \\ &= 0 && \text{using (1-10)} \end{aligned}$$

Thus
$$\Sigma y_i^2 = \Sigma \hat{y}_i^2 + \Sigma e_i^2 \qquad (1\text{-}42)$$

In words, the total variation of the Y values about their sample mean can be partitioned into two parts. The first is the variation of the $\hat{Y}$ values about their mean $\bar{\hat{Y}}$.[1] This is often referred to as the sum of squares "due to," or "explained by," the linear influence of X. The second component is the *residual*, or "unexplained," variation of the Y values about the least-squares line. As we shall see below, (1-42) is the basis of the analysis-of-variance treatment of the two-variable case.

Taking the ratio of the explained to the total sum of squares, we have

$$\begin{aligned} \frac{\Sigma \hat{y}_i^2}{\Sigma y_i^2} &= \frac{\Sigma(\hat{\beta}x_i)^2}{\Sigma y_i^2} \\ &= \hat{\beta}^2 \frac{\Sigma x_i^2}{\Sigma y_i^2} \\ &= r^2 \qquad \text{using (1-41)} \end{aligned} \qquad (1\text{-}43)$$

Thus the square of the correlation coefficient, sometimes called the coefficient of determination, is equal to the proportion of the Y variance explained by the linear influence of X. An r value of 0.9, therefore, indicates that the least-squares regression of Y on X accounts for 81 per cent of the variance in Y.

Combining (1-42) and (1-43), we may write

$$r^2 = 1 - \frac{\Sigma e_i^2}{\Sigma y_i^2} \qquad (1\text{-}44)$$

from which it is clear that the maximum value of r^2 must be unity, and this can occur only when $\Sigma e_i^2 = 0$, that is, when each and

[1] Notice that $\bar{\hat{Y}} = \bar{Y}$; that is, the mean of the values on the least-squares line is equal to the mean of the actual Y values, for

$$\hat{Y} = \hat{\alpha} + \hat{\beta}X$$
$$\bar{\hat{Y}} = \hat{\alpha} + \hat{\beta}\bar{X} = (\bar{Y} - \hat{\beta}\bar{X}) + \hat{\beta}\bar{X} = \bar{Y}$$

every e_i is zero, so that the points on the scatter diagram lie on a straight line. Thus the limits of r are ± 1, the sign being determined by the sign of the product-moment term Σxy.

1-5. The Analysis of Variance

The analysis of variance may be developed as follows. We have shown that

$$\frac{\hat{\beta} - \beta}{\sigma_u / \sqrt{\Sigma x^2}} \quad \text{is} \quad N(0,1)$$

Hence $(\hat{\beta} - \beta)^2/(\sigma_u^2/\Sigma x^2)$ has the χ^2 distribution with 1 degree of freedom.[1] $\Sigma e^2/\sigma_u^2$ has an independent χ^2 distribution with $n - 2$ degrees of freedom. Hence

$$F = \frac{(\hat{\beta} - \beta)^2 \Sigma x^2}{\Sigma e^2/(n-2)}$$

has the F distribution with $(1, n - 2)$ degrees of freedom. If $\beta = 0$, then our F ratio reduces to

$$F = \frac{Q_1}{Q_2/(n-2)} \tag{1-45}$$

where $Q_1 = \hat{\beta}^2 \Sigma x^2$
$= \Sigma \hat{y}_i^2$ using the development of (1-43)
$=$ "explained" sum of squares

and $Q_2 = \Sigma e^2 =$ "unexplained" sum of squares

Hence the hypothesis of no relationship between Y and X $(\beta = 0)$ may be tested by computing the F value defined in (1-45) and rejecting the hypothesis at the 100ϵ level of significance if $F > F_\epsilon$.

TABLE 1-2

Source of variation	Sum of squares	Degrees of freedom	Mean square
X	$Q_1 = \Sigma \hat{y}_i^2$	1	$\Sigma \hat{y}_i^2$
Residual	$Q_2 = \Sigma e_i^2$	$n - 2$	$\Sigma e_i^2/(n-2)$
Total	$\Sigma y^2 = Q_1 + Q_2$	$n - 1$	

This calculation is usually set out in an analysis-of-variance table as in Table 1-2. The explained sum of squares may be computed variously as

$$Q_1 = \hat{\beta}^2 \Sigma x^2 = r^2 \Sigma y^2 = \hat{\beta} \Sigma xy$$

[1] Using the basic theorem that if x is normally distributed with zero mean and unit variance, the sum of the squares of n random sample values of x has a χ^2 distribution with n degrees of freedom. See Hoel, *op. cit.*, pp. 216–217.

The unexplained sum of squares is obtained simply as

$$Q_2 = \Sigma y^2 - Q_1$$

and the appropriate F value is the ratio of the two mean squares in the final column of the table.

Exactly the same test is performed when one tests the significance of a sample correlation coefficient. This test is performed by computing

$$t = \frac{r\sqrt{n-2}}{\sqrt{1-r^2}}$$

and inferring a significant correlation between X and Y if $|t| > t_\epsilon$, where t_ϵ is an appropriate value from the t distribution with $n - 2$ degrees of freedom.[1]

$$\begin{aligned} t &= \frac{r\sqrt{n-2}}{\sqrt{1-r^2}} \\ &= \frac{\hat{\beta} S_X \sqrt{n-2}}{S_Y\sqrt{1-r^2}} \qquad \text{using (1-41)} \\ &= \frac{\hat{\beta}\sqrt{\Sigma x^2}}{\sqrt{\Sigma y^2(1-r^2)/(n-2)}} \\ &= \frac{\hat{\beta}\sqrt{\Sigma x^2}}{\hat{\sigma}_u} \end{aligned}$$

since

$$\begin{aligned} \hat{\sigma}_u^2 &= \frac{\Sigma e^2}{n-2} \qquad \text{defined in (1-28)} \\ &= \frac{\Sigma y^2(1-r^2)}{n-2} \qquad \text{using (1-44)} \end{aligned}$$

If one looks at (1-34), this is exactly the t quantity that would test the hypothesis $\beta = 0$. Squaring this quantity gives $t^2 = \hat{\beta}^2\Sigma x^2/\hat{\sigma}_u^2$, which is identical with the analysis-of-variance test described above, since the square of a t variable with γ degrees of freedom is an F variable with $(1,\gamma)$ degrees of freedom. Thus correlation, regression, and variance tests are all equivalent ways of testing the basic hypothesis of no linear relationship between Y and X.

To continue the numerical example on road casualties and licensed vehicles from Table 1-1:

$$\Sigma xy = 52{,}876.36 \qquad \Sigma x^2 = 169{,}495.64$$
$$\hat{\beta} = 0.31196 \qquad \Sigma y^2 = 17{,}619.64$$

[1] See Mood, *op. cit.*, p. 314.

Hence the explained sum of squares is

$$Q_1 = \hat{\beta}\Sigma xy = (0.31196)(52{,}876.36) = 16{,}495.31$$

and the unexplained sum of squares is

$$Q_2 = \Sigma y^2 - Q_1 = 17{,}619.64 - 16{,}495.31 = 1{,}124.33$$

The analysis of variance is shown in Table 1-3.

TABLE 1-3

Source of variation	Sum of squares	Degrees of freedom	Mean square
X	16,495.31	1	16,495.31
Residual	1,124.33	9	124.93
Total	17,619.64	10	

$F = 16{,}495.31/124.93 = 132.0$ with (1,9) degrees of freedom. For these degrees of freedom $F_{0.01} = 10.56$, so that the data decisively reject the hypothesis of no relation between the two variables.

To obtain, say, a 95 per cent confidence interval for β, we substitute in (1-35)

$$\hat{\beta} \pm \frac{t_{\epsilon/2}\hat{\sigma}_u}{\sqrt{\Sigma x^2}}$$

where

$$\hat{\sigma}_u = \sqrt{\frac{Q_2}{n-2}} = \sqrt{\frac{1{,}124.33}{9}} = 11.18$$

For 9 degrees of freedom, $t_{0.025} = 2.262$. Hence the 95 per cent interval is

$$0.3120 \pm \frac{(2.262)(11.18)}{(411.7)}$$

that is,

$$0.2506 \text{ to } 0.3734$$

1-6. Prediction

Suppose we continue our two-variable model and pose the problem of predicting the *mean* value of Y corresponding to some given value of X, say, X_0, which may or may not lie within the range of the sample observations X_1 to X_n. Our prediction may take the form of a point or interval prediction. To take a point prediction first, suppose we define the predictor as an arbitrary linear function of the Y_i ($i = 1, \ldots, n$), say,

$$\hat{Y}_0 = \sum_{i=1}^{n} c_i Y_i \tag{1-46}$$

where the weights c_i are to be chosen so as to make $\hat{Y}_0$ a best linear unbiased predictor.

Since we are still assuming

$$Y_i = \alpha + \beta X_i + u_i$$

we have

$$E(Y_0|X_0) = \alpha + \beta X_0 \tag{1-47}$$

and

$$\hat{Y}_0 = \alpha \sum_{i=1}^{n} c_i + \beta \sum_{i=1}^{n} c_i X_i + \sum_{i=1}^{n} c_i u_i$$

so that

$$E(\hat{Y}_0|X_0) = \alpha \sum_{i=1}^{n} c_i + \beta \sum_{i=1}^{n} c_i X_i$$

Hence $\hat{Y}_0$ will be an unbiased linear predictor of $E(Y_0|X_0)$ if and only if

$$\sum_{i=1}^{n} c_i = 1 \qquad \text{and} \qquad \sum_{i=1}^{n} c_i X_i = X_0 \tag{1-48}$$

The variance of $\hat{Y}_0$ is given by

$$\begin{aligned} E\{[\hat{Y}_0 - E(\hat{Y}_0|X_0)]^2\} &= E[(\Sigma c_i u_i)^2] \\ &= \sigma_u^2 \sum_{i=1}^{n} c_i^2 \end{aligned}$$

We thus define the function

$$\varphi = \Sigma c_i^2 - 2\lambda(\Sigma c_i - 1) - 2\mu(\Sigma c_i X_i - X_0)$$

which, on taking partial derivatives, gives

$$\frac{\partial \varphi}{\partial c_i} = 2c_i - 2\lambda - 2\mu X_i = 0 \qquad i = 1, \ldots, n$$

$$\frac{\partial \varphi}{\partial \lambda} = 2(\Sigma c_i - 1) = 0$$

$$\frac{\partial \varphi}{\partial \mu} = 2(\Sigma c_i X_i - X_0) = 0$$

From the first two of these equations we obtain

$$\Sigma c_i = n\lambda + \mu \Sigma X_i = 1$$

giving

$$\lambda = \frac{1}{n} - \mu \bar{X}$$

which, on substitution in the first equation again, gives

$$c_i = \frac{1}{n} + \mu x_i$$

Multiplying this by X_i, summing over i, and using the third equation gives

$$\Sigma c_i X_i = \bar{X} + \mu \Sigma x_i X_i = X_0$$

which gives

$$\mu = \frac{X_0 - \bar{X}}{\Sigma x_i X_i} = \frac{X_0 - \bar{X}}{\Sigma x_i^2}$$

since $\quad X_i = x_i + \bar{X} \quad$ and $\quad \sum_{i=1}^{n} x_i = 0$

Hence

$$c_i = \frac{1}{n} + \frac{(X_0 - \bar{X})x_i}{\Sigma x_i^2}$$

Substitution in (1-46) gives the best linear unbiased estimator as

$$\begin{aligned} \hat{Y}_0 &= \sum \left[\frac{1}{n} + \frac{(X_0 - \bar{X})x_i}{\Sigma x_i^2} \right] Y_i \\ &= \sum \left[\frac{1}{n} - \bar{X}\frac{x_i}{\Sigma x_i^2} + X_0 \frac{x_i}{\Sigma x_i^2} \right] Y_i \\ &= (\bar{Y} - \hat{\beta}\bar{X}) + \hat{\beta} X_0 \qquad \text{using (1-10) and (1-11)} \\ &= \hat{\alpha} + \hat{\beta} X_0 \end{aligned}$$

Thus the best unbiased linear estimator of $\alpha + \beta X_0$ is $\hat{\alpha} + \hat{\beta} X_0$, where $\hat{\alpha}$ and $\hat{\beta}$ are the familiar least-squares estimators.

It follows immediately that the variance of $\hat{Y}_0$ is

$$\begin{aligned} E\{[\hat{Y}_0 - E(\hat{Y}_0 | X_0)]^2\} &= E\{[(\hat{\alpha} - \alpha) + (\hat{\beta} - \beta)X_0]^2\} \\ &= \text{var}(\hat{\alpha}) + X_0^2 \text{ var}(\hat{\beta}) + 2X_0 \text{ cov}(\hat{\alpha}, \hat{\beta}) \\ &= \sigma_u^2 \left[\frac{1}{n} + \frac{(X_0 - \bar{X})^2}{\sum_{i=1}^{n} x_i^2} \right] \qquad \text{using (1-18) to (1-20)} \qquad (1\text{-}49) \end{aligned}$$

so that the variance of the prediction increases the further the X_0 value lies from the mean of the sample values employed to compute $\hat{\alpha}$ and $\hat{\beta}$. Since $\hat{Y}_0$ is a linear function of $\hat{\alpha}$ and $\hat{\beta}$, which have a bivariate normal distribution, it will have a normal distribution with mean $\alpha + \beta X_0$ and variance as given by (1-49). Since $(n-2)\hat{\sigma}_u^2/\sigma_u^2$ has an independent χ^2 distribution with $n-2$ degrees of freedom, the quantity

$$t = \frac{\hat{Y}_0 - E(Y_0|X_0)}{\hat{\sigma}_u \sqrt{\dfrac{1}{n} + \dfrac{(X_0 - \bar{X})^2}{\Sigma x_i^2}}}$$

has the t distribution with $n - 2$ degrees of freedom. Thus a $100(1 - \epsilon)$ confidence interval for $E(Y_0|X_0)$ is

$$(\hat{\alpha} + \hat{\beta}X_0) \pm t_{\epsilon/2}\hat{\sigma}_u \sqrt{\frac{1}{n} + \frac{(X_0 - \bar{X})^2}{\Sigma x_i^2}} \qquad (1\text{-}50)$$

The above development has concentrated upon obtaining a confidence interval for the *mean* value of Y associated with a given X value, X_0. Sometimes we may be more interested in obtaining a confidence interval for the individual Y_0 value associated with X_0, or alternatively, the problem may occur in a slightly different form, with a new pair of observations (X_0, Y_0) being obtained and the question arising of whether they belong to the same linear structure.

To deal with these problems we proceed as follows. If the same linear relationship holds, then

$$Y_0 = \alpha + \beta X_0 + u_0$$
$$\hat{Y}_0 = \hat{\alpha} + \hat{\beta} X_0$$

Therefore $\qquad Y_0 - \hat{Y}_0 = u_0 - (\hat{\alpha} - \alpha) - (\hat{\beta} - \beta)X_0 \qquad (1\text{-}51)$

Taking expected values of both sides gives $E(Y_0 - \hat{Y}_0) = 0$, so that $\hat{Y}_0$ is an unbiased predictor of Y_0, just as it is of the mean value of Y_0. Squaring (1-51) and taking expected values,

$$E(Y_0 - \hat{Y}_0)^2 = E(u_0^2) + E\{[(\hat{\alpha} - \alpha) + (\hat{\beta} - \beta)X_0]^2\}$$

since u_0 is independent of the $u_1 \ldots u_n$ values influencing $\hat{\alpha}$ and $\hat{\beta}$. Thus

$$E(Y_0 - \hat{Y}_0)^2 = \sigma_u^2\left[1 + \frac{1}{n} + \frac{(X_0 - \bar{X})^2}{\sum_{i=1}^{n} x_i^2}\right] \quad \text{using (1-49)} \qquad (1\text{-}52)$$

By the usual shift to the t distribution,

$$t = \frac{Y_0 - \hat{Y}_0}{\hat{\sigma}_u \sqrt{1 + \frac{1}{n} + \frac{(X_0 - \bar{X})^2}{\sum_{i=1}^{n} x_i^2}}} \tag{1-53}$$

has t distribution with $n - 2$ degrees of freedom, and a $100(1 - \epsilon)$ per cent confidence interval for Y_0 is

$$(\hat{\alpha} + \hat{\beta}X_0) \pm t_{\epsilon/2}\hat{\sigma}_u \sqrt{1 + \frac{1}{n} + \frac{(X_0 - \bar{X})^2}{\sum_{i=1}^{n} x_i^2}} \tag{1-54}$$

To continue the previous numerical example, suppose the number of licensed vehicles rises to 10 million. What prediction should we make for road casualties on the basis of the estimated linear relationship for the decade 1947–1957? It should perhaps be emphasized that in a real situation one would not make a simple prediction from the statistical relationship unless a thorough examination of relevant factors such as road and travel developments, the nature and type of additional vehicles, and the uses to which they were to be put seemed to indicate the complex of accident-producing forces to be substantially unchanged.

Ten million vehicles gives $X_0 = 1{,}000$. Substitution in

$$\hat{Y} = 55.85 + 0.3120X$$

gives

$$\hat{Y}_0 = 367.85$$

that is, 367,850, as the expected number of road casualties. Applying (1-50), a 95 per cent confidence interval for this expected figure would be

$$367.85 \pm (2.262)(11.18)\sqrt{\frac{1}{11} + \frac{(1{,}000 - 519.18)^2}{169{,}495.64}}$$

i.e., 367.85 ± 30.50, or 337,350 to 398,350 road casualties.

Suppose much sterner penalties are introduced for dangerous driving and in the following year there are 8 million licensed vehicles and 270,000 road casualties. Does this indicate a significant change in the relationship, or might these figures easily come from the same relationship as before?

$$X_0 = 800 \qquad Y_0 = 270$$
$$\hat{Y}_0 = 305.45$$
$$\hat{\sigma}_u \sqrt{1 + \frac{1}{n} + \frac{(X_0 - \bar{X})^2}{\Sigma x^2}} = 11.18 \sqrt{1 + \frac{1}{11} + \frac{(280.82)^2}{169{,}495.64}}$$
$$= 13.95$$

Substituting in (1-53),

$$t = \frac{-35.45}{13.95} = -2.54$$

Since we are testing here for a reduction in road casualties, it is appropriate to use a one-tailed test. The 5 per cent value of t for 9 degrees of freedom is -1.833, and the 1 per cent value is -2.764. The computed value is suggestive of a reduction, being significant at the 5 per cent, but not at the 1 per cent, level.

References

The elementary statistical theory used in this chapter is fully described in

1. A. M. Mood: *Introduction to the Theory of Statistics,* McGraw-Hill, New York, 1950,

or in

2. P. G. Hoel: *Introduction to Mathematical Statistics,* 2d ed., Wiley, New York, 1954.

A very lucid and compact survey of the same material is also available in

3. R. L. Anderson and T. A. Bancroft: *Statistical Theory in Research,* McGraw-Hill, New York, 1952, chaps. 1–12.

The *algebra* of correlation and regression analysis is well set out in

4. J. G. Smith and A. J. Duncan: *Fundamentals of the Theory of Statistics,* vol. I, *Elementary Statistics and Applications,* McGraw-Hill, New York, 1945.
5. G. U. Yule and M. G. Kendall: *An Introduction to the Theory of Statistics,* 14th ed., Griffin, London, 1950.

An excellent short treatment of estimation theory for the two-variable linear case is given in Anderson and Bancroft, Ref. 3, chap. 13.

Exercises

1-1. The two normal equations for a least-squares line are

$$\Sigma Y = n\hat{\alpha} + \hat{\beta}\Sigma X$$
$$\Sigma XY = \hat{\alpha}\Sigma X + \hat{\beta}\Sigma X^2$$

Show by direct substitution from the first into the second that these are equivalent to

$$\hat{\beta} = \frac{\Sigma xy}{\Sigma x^2}$$
$$\hat{\alpha} = \bar{Y} - \hat{\beta}\bar{X}$$

where $x = X - \bar{X}$ and $y = Y - \bar{Y}$

1-2. The least-squares estimate of α in $Y = \alpha + \beta X + u$ is $\hat{\alpha} = \Sigma(1/n - \bar{X}w_i)Y_i$ where $w_i = x_i/\Sigma x_i^2$ with

$$\text{var}(\hat{\alpha}) = \sigma_u^2(1/n + \bar{X}^2/\sum_{i=1}^{n} x_i^2)$$

Show that no other linear unbiased estimate of α can be constructed with a smaller variance.

1-3. Let $\hat{\alpha} = \sum_{i=1}^{n} c_iY_i$, where $Y_i = \alpha + \beta X_i + u_i$. Using Lagrangian multipliers, find the weights c_i $(i = 1, \ldots, n)$ which will make $\hat{\alpha}$ a best linear unbiased estimate of α and show that

$$c_i = \frac{1}{n} - \frac{\bar{X}x_i}{\sum_{i=1}^{n} x_i^2}$$

1-4. Show that if z_i are independent quantities from the same population, with variance σ^2, then the sampling variance of

$$b = \sum_{i=1}^{n} a_iz_i$$

is $\sigma^2 \sum_{i=1}^{n} a_i^2$. Observations Y_i are related to fixed quantities X_i and the quantities z_i above by the relations $Y_i = \alpha + \beta X_i + z_i$ $(i = 1, \ldots, n)$. If the values of X_i are

X_1	X_2	X_3	X_4	X_5	X_6
1	2	3	4	5	6

an alternative estimate of β is

$$\tfrac{1}{8}(Y_6 + Y_5 - Y_2 - Y_1)$$

Deduce the sampling variance of this estimate and compare it with the sampling variance of the least-squares estimate. (Oxford, Diploma, 1958)

1-5. Personal disposable income in the United States is expected to reach 350 billion (in constant 1954 dollars) in a few years' time. What figure would you predict for personal consumption at that time on the basis of experience in recent years, as given in the accompanying table? Explain briefly the method of prediction you have employed, and give the reasons for your choice.

INCOME AND CONSUMPTION IN THE UNITED STATES, 1948–1957
(Billions, constant 1954 dollars)

Year	Personal consumption	Personal disposable income
1948	199	212
1949	204	214
1950	216	231
1951	218	237
1952	224	244
1953	235	255
1954	238	257
1955	256	273
1956	264	284
1957	270	290

(Manchester, 1960)

1-6. From a sample of 200 pairs of observations the following quantities were calculated:

$$\Sigma X = 11.34 \qquad \Sigma Y = 20.72 \qquad \Sigma X^2 = 12.16$$
$$\Sigma Y^2 = 84.96 \qquad \Sigma XY = 22.13$$

Estimate the two regression lines and the variance of the estimated regression coefficient of Y on X. (R.S.S. Certificate, 1956)

(*Note:* The exposition in Chap. 1 concentrated upon the estimation of $\hat{\alpha}$ and $\hat{\beta}$ in $\hat{Y} = \hat{\alpha} + \hat{\beta}X$. One may similarly minimize the sum of the squared residuals measured in the X direction by fitting the line $\hat{X} = \hat{\gamma} + \hat{\delta}Y$, where $\hat{\gamma}$ and $\hat{\delta}$ are obtained from the formulas for $\hat{\alpha}$ and $\hat{\beta}$ by interchanging X and Y.)

1-7. Show that if r is the correlation coefficient between n pairs of values (X_i, Y_i), then the correlation coefficient between the n pairs $(aX_i + b, cY_i + d)$, where a, b, c, d are constants, is also r. (R.S.S. Certificate, 1956)

1-8. Fat percentage (X) and solids-nonfat percentage (Y) are measured on milk samples of a number of dairy cows in two herds. A summary of the data is set out below. Calculate the linear regression equations of Y on X for each herd, and test whether the two lines differ in slope.

Herd A. Number of cows = 16.

$\Sigma X = 51.13 \qquad \Sigma Y = 117.25 \qquad \Sigma x^2 = 1.27 \qquad \Sigma y^2 = 4.78 \qquad \Sigma xy = 1.84$

Herd B. Number of cows = 10.

$\Sigma X = 37.20 \qquad \Sigma Y = 78.75 \qquad \Sigma x^2 = 1.03 \qquad \Sigma y^2 = 2.48 \qquad \Sigma xy = 1.10$

(R.S.S. Certificate, 1956)

[*Note:* If $\hat{\beta}_1$ is $N(\beta_1, \sigma_1^2/\Sigma x_1^2)$ and $\hat{\beta}_2$ is $N(\beta_2, \sigma_2^2/\Sigma x_2^2)$, where $\hat{\beta}_1$ and $\hat{\beta}_2$ are independent, then $\hat{\beta}_1 - \hat{\beta}_2$ is $N(\beta_1 - \beta_2, \sigma_1^2/\Sigma x_1^2 + \sigma_2^2/\Sigma x_2^2)$. If σ_1^2 and σ_2^2 are unknown, then a shift to the t distribution can be made if we assume $\sigma_1^2 = \sigma_2^2 = \sigma^2$ and pool the sum of squared residuals from each regression so that $(\Sigma e_1^2 + \Sigma e_2^2)/\sigma^2$ has a χ^2 distribution with $n_1 + n_2 - 4$ degrees of freedom.]

1-9. If $u = ax + by$ and $v = bx - ay$, where x and y are in deviation form, and if the correlation coefficient between x and y is r but u and v are uncorrelated, show that

$$S_u S_v = (a^2 + b^2) S_x S_y \sqrt{1 - r^2}$$

where S indicates a sample standard deviation. (L.S.E., 1948)

1-10. For certain data, $\hat{y} = 1.2x$ and $\hat{x} = 0.6y$ are the regression lines expressed in deviation form. Compute r_{xy} and S_x/S_y. If $y = x + u$, compute r_{xu}, r_{yu}, and S_u/S_y. (R.S.S. Certificate, 1948)

1-11. The table below gives the means and standard deviations of two variables X and Y and the correlation between them for each of two samples.

Sample	No. in sample	$\bar{X}$	$\bar{Y}$	S_x	S_y	r_{xy}
1	600	5	12	2	3	0.6
2	400	7	10	3	4	0.7

Calculate the correlation between X and Y for the composite sample consisting of the two samples taken together. Comment on the fact that this correlation is lower than either of the two original values. (R.S.S. Certificate, 1955)

1-12

Wage Income in the United Kingdom

Year	1947	1948	1949	1950	1951	1952	1953
Wages, millions of £	3,710	4,160	4,385	4,596	5,110	5,430	5,770

Let Y = wages in millions of pounds and X = year, measured in years from 1900, and let a and b be constants to be found and v a value to make the equation $Y = a + bX + v$ exact for every year. Determine a and b in such a way that $\Sigma v = 0 = \Sigma vX$. In which year did wages fall most below the straight-line trend, and how much was the deficit? Estimate wages in 1954 and discuss the advisability of making such an estimate. (R.S.S. Diploma, 1955)

1-13. Calculate the coefficient of correlation between the two following series:

	1935	1936	1937	1938	1939	1940	1941	1942	1943	1944	1945	1946
Deaths of children under 1 year (000)	60	62	61	55	53	60	63	53	52	48	49	43
Consumption of beer, bbl	23	23	25	25	26	26	29	30	30	32	33	31

Eliminate the trend from *one* of the series graphically or otherwise and recalculate the correlation. Comment on the difference between the two values.

(R.S.S. Certificate, 1954)

1-14. Y is known to be distributed normally about some linear function of X with variance independent of X. Using the following pairs of observations of X and Y, plot two curves showing the 95 per cent confidence limits for $\bar{Y}$, the mean value of Y in a further sample of 10 pairs of values, for values of $\bar{X}$, the mean of X in that sample, between 80 and 120.

TABLE OF VALUES OF X AND Y IN THE FIRST SAMPLE

X	98	64	122	106	84	110	126	102	90	118
Y	55	48	63	79	55	65	99	79	75	105

(Oxford, Diploma, 1956)

[*Note:* This example cannot be done by using (1-50) but requires a further theoretical development from that result. See, for example, Franklin A. Graybill, *An Introduction to Linear Statistical Models,* McGraw-Hill, New York, 1961, vol. I, pp. 122–124.]

1-15. A sample of 20 observations corresponding to the regression model

$$Y = \alpha + \beta X + \epsilon$$

where ϵ is normal with zero mean and unknown variance σ^2, gave the following data:

$$\Sigma Y = 21.9 \qquad \Sigma(Y - \bar{Y})^2 = 86.9 \qquad \Sigma(X - X)(Y - \bar{Y}) = 106.4$$
$$\Sigma X = 186.2 \qquad \Sigma(X - \bar{X})^2 = 215.4$$

Estimate α amd β and calculate estimates of variance of your estimates. Estimate the (conditional) mean value of Y corresponding to a value of X fixed at $X = 10$ and find a 95 per cent confidence interval for this (conditional) mean.

(L.S.E., 1958)

2

Extensions of the Two-variable Linear Model

The theory of Chap. 1 has been wholly concerned with linear relationships between two variables. Obvious extensions are now required, first to cover the case of nonlinear relationships between two variables, and then more generally to treat relationships between *more than* two variables.

2-1. Two-variable Nonlinear Relationships

Economic theory may suggest that the relationship between a certain pair of variables can be adequately represented only by a nonlinear form. Or, in the absence of any firm theoretical indications, an inspection of the scatter diagram may indicate the inappropriateness of attempting to fit a linear relationship. In such a case the two possibilities are to attempt to fit an appropriate nonlinear relationship directly to the data or else to seek an initial transformation of the data such that the relationship between the transformed data appears approximately linear and the techniques of Chap. 1 may be applied.

The most commonly used transformations are the logarithmic and the reciprocal, and a judicious choice of these can encompass a wide variety of nonlinear relationships. The difficulty is that making transformations to keep the calculations in a simple linear framework may lead to a violation of some of the basic assumptions underlying the linear techniques of Chap. 1. One has to guard against this by making those tests, described in Chaps. 7 and 8, which are available to check on some of the basic underlying assumptions. On the other hand, there are sometimes cases where transformations substantially improve the validity of certain basic assumptions; examples are given in Chaps. 7 and 8, in the treatments of autocorrelation and heteroscedasticity.

To illustrate the use of transformations, suppose we have a variable Z, growing at approximately a constant rate of $100g$ per cent per unit of time t. We then have the following table.

t	Z
0	$Z_0 = A$
1	$Z_1 = A(1+g)$
2	$Z_2 = A(1+g)^2$
3	$Z_3 = A(1+g)^3$
.	.
.	.
.	.

Since this is only an approximate relation, let us postulate a disturbance term v. If we assume here that the effect of a disturbance is, say, proportional to the trend value of Z, we may write

$$Z_t = AB^t v_t \tag{2-1}$$

where

$$B = 1 + g \tag{2-2}$$

Taking logs of both sides of (2-1) gives

$$\log Z_t = \log A + (\log B)t + \log v_t \tag{2-3}$$

and if we define

$$\begin{aligned} Y_t &= \log Z_t \\ X_t &= t \\ \alpha &= \log A \\ \beta &= \log B \\ u_t &= \log v_t \end{aligned} \tag{2-4}$$

(2-3) may be rewritten as

$$Y_t = \alpha + \beta X_t + u_t \tag{2-5}$$

The assumption of a multiplicative disturbance in (2-1) conveniently yields an additive disturbance in the transformed relation (2-5). One often has no strong a priori information on the appropriate assumptions, and in such a case one starts with the simplest possible assumptions and attempts, as far as possible, to check from the data on the validity of the assumptions made.

The coefficients α and β in (2-5) may be estimated by applying least squares to Y and X. By use of the transformations defined in (2-4) we can then estimate A and B of (2-1) and from B obtain an estimate of g, the rate of growth. An example is given in Table 2-1.

Example

TABLE 2-1. BITUMINOUS COAL OUTPUT IN THE UNITED STATES, 1841–1910

Decade	Average annual output (1,000 net tons) Z	$Y = \log_{10} Z$	$X = t$
1841–1850	1,837	3.2641	−3
1851–1860	4,868	3.6873	−2
1861–1870	12,411	4.0937	−1
1871–1880	32,617	4.5135	0
1881–1890	82,770	4.9179	1
1891–1900	148,457	5.1718	2
1901–1910	322,958	5.5092	3

Inspection of the two least-squares equations in (1-7) shows that they could be further simplified if the X variable had zero sample mean. Since X stands for time in this example, we can easily achieve this result by taking the origin of time at the middle of the 1871–1880 decade and then inserting ± 1, ± 2, ± 3 in column 4 of Table 2-1, using 10 years as our unit of measurement for the variable X. The least-squares equations then become

$$\hat{\alpha} = \bar{Y}$$

$$\hat{\beta} = \frac{\Sigma X_i Y_i}{\Sigma X_i^2}$$

which give

$$\hat{\alpha} = 31.1575/7 = 4.4511$$

$$\hat{\beta} = 10.5285/28 = 0.3760$$

Taking antilogs, we have

$$\hat{A} = 28{,}260 \quad \text{and} \quad \hat{B} = 2.377$$

Thus

$$\hat{g} = \hat{B} - 1 = 1.377$$

This gives a rate of increase of 137.7 per cent per decade. The corresponding annual rate of increase is given by g', where

$$(1 + g')^{10} = 2.377$$

yielding

$$g' = 0.09$$

that is, a 9 per cent annual increase. The problem might also have been worked by taking X in units of a year so that the X values read $-30, -20, -10$, etc. This would give $\hat{\beta} = 105.285/2{,}800 = 0.0376$, with an antilog of 1.09 and an annual growth rate of 9 per cent as before. The coefficient of determination for (2-5) is 0.994, which indicates that the assumption of constant growth in (2-1) seems very reasonable for this series.

It is useful to have an idea of the various nonlinearities that can be transformed by using logarithms and reciprocals. The accompanying figures illustrate some of the main cases, where α and β are positive parameters and logs are always taken to base e. We also confine the illustrations to the positive X,Y quadrant.

Semilog Transformation. $Y = \alpha + \beta \log X$; $X = AB^Y$.

$$\frac{dY}{dX} = \frac{\beta}{X}$$

so that the slope decreases steadily as X increases. When $Y = 0$,

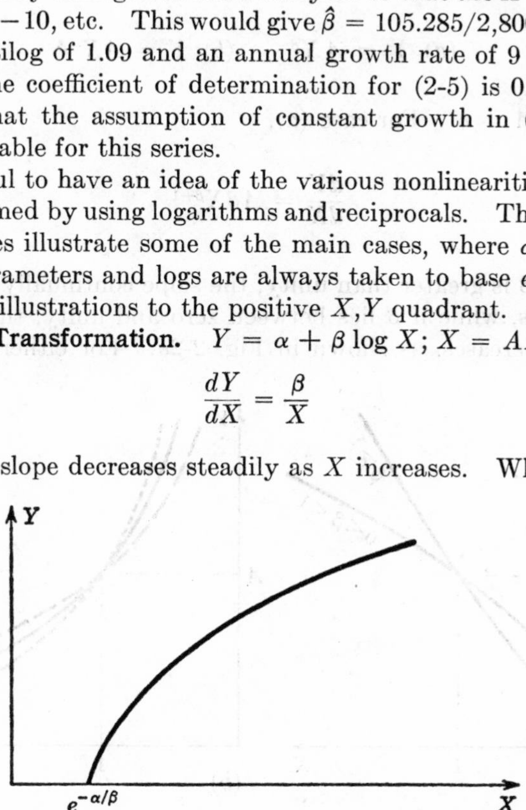

FIG. 2-1

$\log X = -\alpha/\beta$, so that the point of intersection on the X axis is at $e^{-\alpha/\beta}$. The inverse of this function is $X = e^{-\alpha/\beta}e^{Y/\beta}$, which may be written

$$X = AB^Y$$

where $A = e^{-\alpha/\beta}$
$B = e^{1/\beta}$

This is the steady-growth function employed in the previous example.

Double-log Transformation

$$(a)\ \log Y = \alpha + \beta \log X \qquad (b)\ \log Y = \alpha - \beta \log X$$

These functions may also be written

$$(a)\ Y = AX^{\beta} \qquad (b)\ Y = AX^{-\beta}$$

where $\log A = \alpha$. For case (*a*),

$$\frac{dY}{dX} = A\beta X^{\beta-1}$$

so that, if β is greater than unity, the slope continually increases as X increases, while if β lies between zero and unity, the slope continually decreases, as shown in Fig. 2-2*a*. For either value of β,

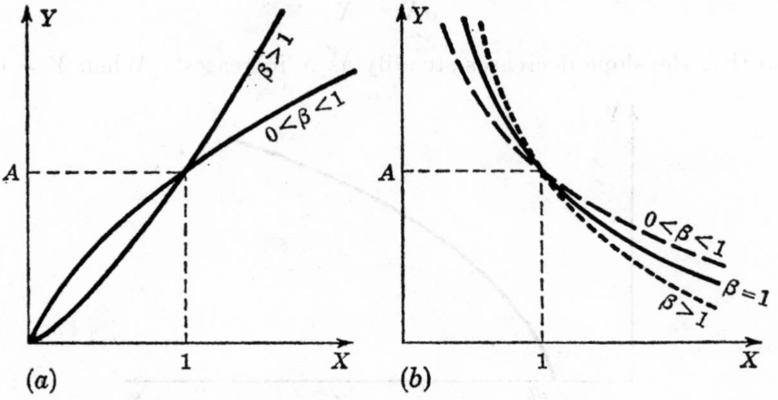

FIG. 2-2

Y tends to infinity as X tends to infinity. For case (*b*), a value of unity for β produces a rectangular hyperbola, that is, the locus of a point such that the product of its coordinates XY is a constant. The double-log transformation is commonly employed by econometricians because it corresponds to the assumption of a *constant elasticity* between Y and X and the simple application of linear methods to the logarithms of the variables produces directly an estimate of that elasticity.[1]

Reciprocal Transformation

$$(a)\ Y = \alpha + \frac{\beta}{X} \qquad (b)\ Y = \alpha - \frac{\beta}{X}$$

Taking case (*a*) first of all, $dY/dX = -\beta/X^2$, so that the slope is everywhere negative and decreases in absolute value as X increases. As $X \to 0$, $Y \to \infty$, and as $X \to \infty$, $Y \to \alpha$. With a similar analysis for case (*b*) we have Fig. 2-3. The reciprocal transformation is

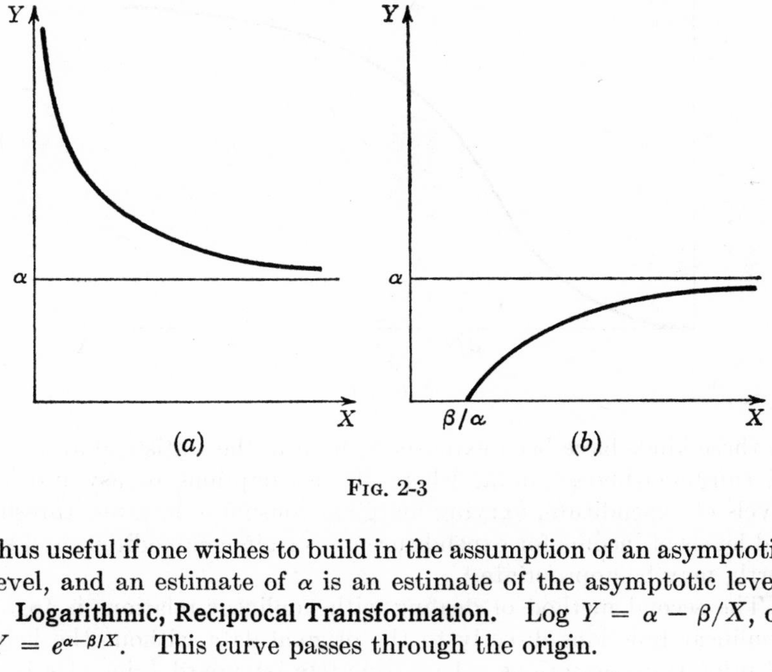

FIG. 2-3

thus useful if one wishes to build in the assumption of an asymptotic level, and an estimate of α is an estimate of the asymptotic level.

Logarithmic, Reciprocal Transformation. Log $Y = \alpha - \beta/X$, or $Y = e^{\alpha - \beta/X}$. This curve passes through the origin.

$$\frac{dY}{dX} = e^{\alpha-\beta/X}\left(\frac{\beta}{X^2}\right)$$

[1] The elasticity of Y with respect to X is defined as $\frac{X}{Y}\frac{dY}{dX}$. For case (*a*) this gives $(X/AX^\beta)A\beta X^{\beta-1} = \beta$. For extensive illustrations of double-log applications in statistical demand analysis, see J. R. N. Stone, *The Measurement of Consumers' Expenditure and Behaviour in the United Kingdom, 1920–1938*, Cambridge, London, 1954.

Thus the slope is positive for positive X.

$$\frac{d^2Y}{dX^2} = e^{\alpha-\beta/X}\left(\frac{\beta^2}{X^4} - \frac{2\beta}{X^3}\right)$$

Hence there is a point of inflection where $X = \beta/2$. To the left of this point the slope increases with X; to the right of it the slope diminishes. As $X \to \infty$, $Y \to e^{\alpha}$. Thus we have Fig. 2-4. Curves

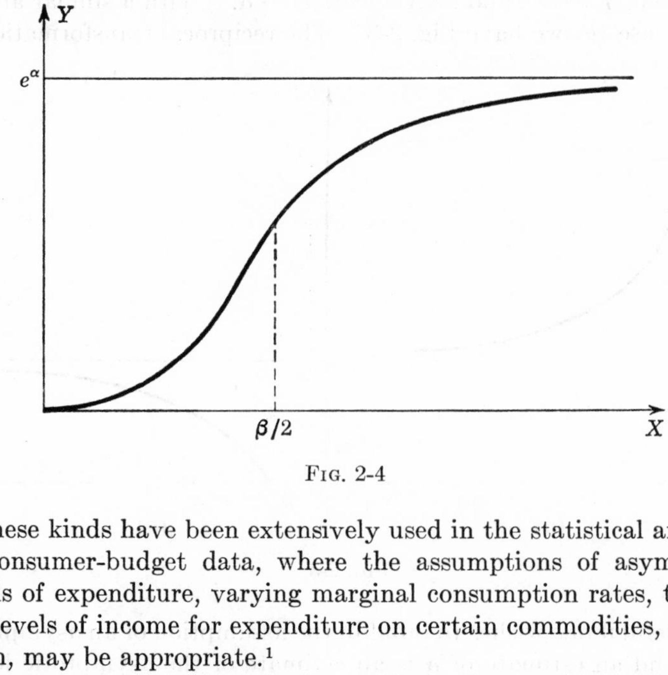

FIG. 2-4

of these kinds have been extensively used in the statistical analysis of consumer-budget data, where the assumptions of asymptotic levels of expenditure, varying marginal consumption rates, threshold levels of income for expenditure on certain commodities, and so forth, may be appropriate.[1]

The second method of dealing with nonlinear relations is to fit nonlinear functions directly to the original data without the help of prior transformations. Unfortunately, standard principles like least squares or maximum likelihood often yield extremely complicated, or even insoluble, estimating equations, even for very simple nonlinear forms. For example, applying least squares to

$$Y = AB^X + u$$

[1] For detailed illustrations and examples the reader should consult S. J. Prais and H. S. Houthakker, *The Analysis of Family Budgets*, Cambridge, London, 1955.

would give

$$\Sigma Y_i B^{X_i} = A \Sigma B^{2X_i}$$
$$A \Sigma Y_i X_i B^{X_i - 1} = A^2 \Sigma X_i B^{2X_i - 1}$$

which would have to be solved for A and B.

One case where such difficulties do not arise is where Y is approximated by means of a simple polynomial in X. Two points can, of course, always be fitted *exactly* by a straight line (polynomial of the first degree), three points by a second-degree function, and n points by a polynomial of degree $n - 1$. One seeks, however, for a polynomial of as low a degree as possible. Suppose one attempts to represent Y by

$$Y_i = a + bX_i + cX_i^2 \tag{2-6}$$

The residual sum of squares is then

$$\sum_{i=1}^{n} (Y_i - a - bX_i - cX_i^2)^2$$

Applying the least-squares principle then gives the following set of normal equations to be solved for the unknowns a, b, and c.

$$\begin{aligned} \Sigma Y_i &= na + b\Sigma X_i + c\Sigma X_i^2 \\ \Sigma X_i Y_i &= a\Sigma X_i + b\Sigma X_i^2 + c\Sigma X_i^3 \\ \Sigma X_i^2 Y_i &= a\Sigma X_i^2 + b\Sigma X_i^3 + c\Sigma X_i^4 \end{aligned} \tag{2-7}$$

The fit obtained by such a nonlinear function may be measured by a coefficient analogous to the coefficient of determination r^2 of

TABLE 2-2

Time t, min (1)	X (2)	Temperature T, °C (3)	Y (4)	X^2	X^4
5	−5	99.2	2	25	625
10	−4	99.7	7	16	256
15	−3	99.9	9	9	81
20	−2	100.2	12	4	16
25	−1	100.3	13	1	1
30	0	100.4	14	0	0
35	1	100.4	14	1	1
40	2	100.3	13	4	16
45	3	100.0	10	9	81
50	4	99.8	8	16	256
55	5	99.4	4	25	625

SOURCE: R.S.S. Certificate, 1955.

Chap. 1. One can measure the residual variance of the Y_i about the fitted function and then define the coefficient as 1 minus the ratio of the residual variance to the total variance in Y. The above approach may also be easily extended to polynomials of higher degree, but there is no need to elaborate this case further as it is really a special case of functions of three or more variables, to which we now turn.

To illustrate the fitting of parabolas, consider the observations shown in Table 2-2 on page 51 of temperature made at intervals of 5 minutes during a chemical experiment.

To simplify the calculations we have defined

$$X = \frac{t - 30}{5}$$

$$Y = (T - 99.0) \times 10$$

Equations (2-7) then give

$$\begin{aligned} 106 &= 11a + 110c \\ 20 &= 110b \\ 688 &= 110a + 1{,}958c \end{aligned}$$

These give the parabolic regression of Y on X as

$$\hat{Y} = 13.9721 + 0.1818X - 0.4336X^2$$

Substituting for X and Y from the above relations gives

$$\hat{T} = 98.727 + 0.1077t - 0.001734t^2$$

To find the time at which maximum temperature occurs,

$$\frac{d\hat{T}}{dt} = 0.1077 - 0.003{,}468t = 0$$

giving $$t = 31.06 \text{ min}$$

2-2. Relations between Three Variables

Suppose we have three associated variables, which we shall denote by Y, X_2, and X_3. For example, Y might represent the quantity of a commodity purchased by a household, X_2 the price of the commodity to that household, and X_3 the household income. A sample of n households would give related observations, which we can denote in general by

Y	X_2	X_3
Y_1	X_{21}	X_{31}
Y_2	X_{22}	X_{32}
.	.	.
.	.	.
.	.	.
Y_i	X_{2i}	X_{3i}
.	.	.
.	.	.
.	.	.
Y_n	X_{2n}	X_{3n}

where X_{ki} denotes the value of the variable X_k for the ith household. A linear hypothesis might then be written

$$Y_i = \beta_1 + \beta_2 X_{2i} + \beta_3 X_{3i} + u_i \qquad i = 1, \ldots, n \tag{2-8}$$

and the problem formulated as that of estimating the βs and the variance of the disturbance term. Relation (2-8) might also be written as

$$Y_i = \sum_{j=1}^{3} \beta_j X_{ji} + u_i$$

where $X_{1i} = 1$ for all i; that is, Y can be regarded as a linear function of X's, the sample values of the first X variable always being a set of units.

The full treatment of the general model for k variables will be given in Chap. 4. Our present objective is to give the reader a firm grasp and understanding of the basic concepts required in the analysis of a relationship between three variables so that extension to the general case is facilitated. For this purpose we concentrate upon the algebra of the analysis, and the connection between the various statistical measures will be simplified if we use a slightly different notation for our estimators than that developed in Chap. 1.

Let the least-squares estimate of the relationship (2-8) be denoted by

$$\hat{Y}_i = a_{1.23} + b_{12.3} X_{2i} + b_{13.2} X_{3i} \tag{2-9}$$

where we also define

$$e_i = Y_i - \hat{Y}_i \tag{2-10}$$

Relation (2-9) is referred to as the equation of the regression of Y on X_2 and X_3. It represents a plane in three-dimensional space: $a_{1\cdot 23}$ is the intercept made by the plane on the Y axis and is an estimate of the parameter β_1 in (2-8); $b_{12\cdot 3}$ denotes the amount by which a unit change in X_2 is expected to affect Y and is an estimate of β_2, while $b_{13\cdot 2}$ is the amount by which a unit change in X_3 is expected to affect Y and is an estimate of β_3. The advantage of the subscript notation in (2-9) is that it clearly indicates the number of variables in the analysis. The figure 1 in the subscripts refers to the variable Y, the figure 2 to X_2, and 3 to X_3. The subscript 1·23 on a indicates that this is the intercept in the regression of Y on X_2 and X_3 since the figure 1 comes before the point and the figures 2 and 3 after it. In the subscripts to the b coefficients, the first figure indicates the variable on the left-hand side of the equation, the second indicates the variable to which this b coefficient is attached, and figures after the point indicate which other variables have also been taken into account in the estimation of the relationship.

There are three sets of sample statistics that may be employed in describing the relationship between three (or more) variables. The first set consists of the regression coefficients $a_{1\cdot 23}$, $b_{12\cdot 3}$, and $b_{13\cdot 2}$. These are a simple extension of the regression coefficients in the two-variable case, the only difference being that in the computation of these estimates several explanatory variables have been taken into consideration.

In the two-variable case the coefficient of correlation r was defined in (1-44) as

$$r^2 = 1 - \frac{\Sigma e_i^2}{\Sigma y_i^2}$$

that is, the fit of a straight line to the two-variable scatter was measured in terms of the ratio of the sum of squared deviations of Y about the line to the total sum of squared deviations of Y about the mean. In the three-variable case we define the *coefficient of multiple correlation* $R_{1\cdot 23}$ analogously in terms of the residual variation about the regression *plane;* i.e.,

$$R^2_{1\cdot 23} = 1 - \frac{\Sigma e_i^2}{\Sigma y_i^2} = 1 - \frac{S^2_{1\cdot 23}}{S_1^2} \tag{2-11}$$

where

$$S^2_{1\cdot 23} = \frac{1}{n}\sum (Y_i - \hat{Y}_i)^2 = \frac{1}{n}\sum (Y_i - a_{1\cdot 23} - b_{12\cdot 3}X_{2i} - b_{13\cdot 2}X_{3i})^2 \tag{2-12}$$

and

$$S_1^2 = \frac{1}{n}\sum y_i^2 \tag{2-13}$$

A new concept is that of the partial correlation coefficient. For example, we may ask whether an observed correlation between Y and X_2 is merely due to the fact that each is influenced by X_3 or whether there is a net association between Y and X_2, over and above the association due to the common influence of X_3. Thus in computing a partial correlation between Y and X_2, one attempts to remove the influence of X_3 from each and see what correlation exists between the "unexplained" residuals that remain. This is the statistical equivalent of the economic theorist's technique of impounding certain variables in a *ceteris paribus* clause. These partial correlation coefficients are denoted as follows:

$r_{12 \cdot 3}$ = partial correlation between Y and X_2, when X_3 is held constant

$r_{13 \cdot 2}$ = partial correlation between Y and X_3, when X_2 is held constant

$r_{23 \cdot 1}$ = partial correlation between X_2 and X_3, when Y is held constant

As we shall see, these partial correlation coefficients are intimately related to the regression coefficients in (2-9). Using the same subscript notation, we can indicate the simple correlation coefficients.

$$r_{12} = \frac{\Sigma(yx_2)}{\sqrt{(\Sigma y^2)(\Sigma x_2^2)}} = \text{simple correlation between } Y \text{ and } X_2$$

$$r_{13} = \frac{\Sigma(yx_3)}{\sqrt{(\Sigma y^2)(\Sigma x_3^2)}} = \text{simple correlation between } Y \text{ and } X_3$$

$$r_{23} = \frac{\Sigma(x_2x_3)}{\sqrt{(\Sigma x_2^2)(\Sigma x_3^2)}} = \text{simple correlation between } X_2 \text{ and } X_3$$

Similarly, we may indicate simple regression coefficients in the two-variable case, for example, $b_{12} = \Sigma yx_2/\Sigma x_2^2$ = coefficient of X_2 in the regression of Y on X_2.

We have, in fact, a hierarchy of coefficients. Examples of zero-order coefficients are r_{12}, r_{23}, S_1, etc. These coefficients have no *secondary* subscripts, that is, no subscripts after the point. Examples of first-order coefficients are $r_{13 \cdot 2}$ and $S_{1 \cdot 2}$, where

$$S_{1 \cdot 2} = \sqrt{\frac{1}{n} \sum (y - b_{12}x_2)^2}$$

the standard deviation of the Y values measured about the regression line of Y on X_2. An example of a second-order coefficient is $S_{1 \cdot 23}$, defined in (2-12). Coefficients of a given order can, in general, be expressed in terms of coefficients of the next lower order, and for three or four variables this often provides the simplest computational approach. For larger numbers of variables and extensive computations the general formulas developed in Chap. 4 are more useful.

2-3. Fitting the Regression Plane

Using (2-9) and (2-10), the sum of squared residuals about the plane is

$$\sum_{i=1}^{n} e_i^2 = \sum_{i=1}^{n} (Y_i - a_{1.23} - b_{12.3}X_{2i} - b_{13.2}X_{3i})^2$$

Taking the partial derivative with respect to $a_{1.23}$ and equating to zero gives

$$\Sigma Y_i = na_{1.23} + b_{12.3}\Sigma X_{2i} + b_{13.2}\Sigma X_{3i}$$

i.e.,

$$\bar{Y} = a_{1.23} + b_{12.3}\bar{X}_2 + b_{13.2}\bar{X}_3 \tag{2-14}$$

Thus the least-squares plane passes through the point of means. Subtracting (2-14) from (2-9) we can rewrite the regression equation in deviation form,

$$\hat{y}_i = b_{12.3}x_{2i} + b_{13.2}x_{3i} \tag{2-15}$$

and express the sum of squared residuals as

$$\Sigma e_i^2 = \Sigma(y_i - b_{12.3}x_{2i} - b_{13.2}x_{3i})^2 \tag{2-16}$$

Minimizing with respect to $b_{12.3}$ and $b_{13.2}$ gives the two normal equations

$$\begin{aligned} b_{12.3}\Sigma x_2^2 + b_{13.2}\Sigma x_2x_3 &= \Sigma yx_2 \\ b_{12.3}\Sigma x_2x_3 + b_{13.2}\Sigma x_3^2 &= \Sigma yx_3 \end{aligned} \tag{2-17}$$

Solving these for $b_{12.3}$ and $b_{13.2}$ and substituting the results in (2-14) gives $a_{1.23}$ as

$$a_{1.23} = \bar{Y} - b_{12.3}\bar{X}_2 - b_{13.2}\bar{X}_3$$

Alternatively, (2-17) may be solved algebraically to give

$$b_{12.3} = \frac{(\Sigma yx_2)(\Sigma x_3^2) - (\Sigma yx_3)(\Sigma x_2x_3)}{(\Sigma x_2^2)(\Sigma x_3^2) - (\Sigma x_2x_3)^2}$$

which may be reduced to the following expression in terms of zero-order coefficients:

$$b_{12\cdot3} = \frac{r_{12} - r_{13}r_{23}}{1 - r_{23}^2}\frac{S_1}{S_2} \tag{2-18}$$

Similarly,

$$b_{13\cdot2} = \frac{r_{13} - r_{12}r_{23}}{1 - r_{23}^2}\frac{S_1}{S_3} \tag{2-19}$$

2-4. The Coefficient of Multiple Correlation

This is defined in (2-11) above, but for practical computation it is more convenient to obtain a simpler expression for the residual variance $S^2_{1\cdot23}$.

$$\begin{aligned} nS^2_{1\cdot23} &= \Sigma e_i^2 \\ &= \Sigma e_i(y_i - b_{12\cdot3}x_{2i} - b_{13\cdot2}x_{3i}) \qquad \text{using (2-10) and (2-15)} \\ &= \Sigma e_i y_i - b_{12\cdot3}\Sigma e_i x_{2i} - b_{13\cdot2}\Sigma e_i x_{3i} \end{aligned}$$

but from (2-16),

$$\frac{\partial(\Sigma e_i^2)}{\partial b_{12\cdot3}} = -2\Sigma e_i x_{2i} = 0 \tag{2-20}$$

and

$$\frac{\partial(\Sigma e_i^2)}{\partial b_{13\cdot2}} = -2\Sigma e_i x_{3i} = 0 \tag{2-21}$$

since both these partial derivatives are equated to zero in obtaining $b_{12\cdot3}$ and $b_{13\cdot2}$. Thus

$$\begin{aligned} \Sigma e_i^2 &= \Sigma e_i y_i \\ &= \Sigma y_i(y_i - b_{12\cdot3}x_{2i} - b_{13\cdot2}x_{3i}) \qquad \text{using (2-10) and (2-15)} \\ &= \Sigma y_i^2 - b_{12\cdot3}\Sigma y_i x_{2i} - b_{13\cdot2}\Sigma y_i x_{3i} \end{aligned} \tag{2-22}$$

Thus, since $R^2_{1\cdot23} = 1 - \Sigma e_i^2/\Sigma y_i^2$, we have

$$R^2_{1\cdot23} = \frac{b_{12\cdot3}\Sigma y_i x_{2i} + b_{13\cdot2}\Sigma y_i x_{3i}}{\Sigma y_i^2} \tag{2-23}$$

Substituting from (2-18) and (2-19), we may derive an alternative expression for $R^2_{1\cdot23}$ in terms of simple correlation coefficients, namely,

$$R^2_{1\cdot23} = \frac{r_{12}^2 + r_{13}^2 - 2r_{12}r_{13}r_{23}}{1 - r_{23}^2} \tag{2-24}$$

From (2-20) and (2-21) we see that the residual term is uncorrelated with each explanatory variable X_2 and X_3. Hence the residual term is uncorrelated with the regression values $\hat{Y}_i$, for

$$\begin{aligned}\Sigma e_i\hat{y}_i &= b_{12.3}\Sigma e_i x_{2i} + b_{13.2}\Sigma e_i x_{3i}\\ &= 0\end{aligned}$$

Thus, since $y_i = \hat{y}_i + e_i$, we can write

$$\Sigma y_i^2 = \Sigma \hat{y}_i^2 + \Sigma e_i^2$$

which is an exact parallel of the result obtained in (1-42) for the two-variable case, that the total variation in Y can be partitioned into two components, the "explained" variation due to the linear influence of X_2 and X_3 and the residual variation. From (2-23) it then follows that the explained variation may be computed from

$$\Sigma \hat{y}_i^2 = b_{12.3}\Sigma y_i x_{2i} + b_{13.2}\Sigma y_i x_{3i} \tag{2-25}$$

and $R^2_{1.23}$, called the coefficient of multiple determination, has the familiar interpretation of the proportion of the Y variance accounted for by the linear influence of X_2 and X_3.

Another illuminating way of looking at $R_{1.23}$ is that it is the simple correlation coefficient between the actual values Y_i and the regression values $\hat{Y}_i$, given by (2-9). To see this we write

$$\begin{aligned}r_{Y\hat{Y}}^2 &= \frac{(\Sigma y_i\hat{y}_i)^2}{(\Sigma y_i^2)(\Sigma \hat{y}_i^2)}\\ &= \frac{(\Sigma \hat{y}_i^2)^2}{(\Sigma y_i^2)(\Sigma \hat{y}_i^2)}\end{aligned}$$

since $\quad \Sigma y_i\hat{y}_i = \Sigma(\hat{y}_i + e_i)\hat{y}_i = \Sigma \hat{y}_i^2 \quad$ for $\Sigma \hat{y}_i e_i = 0$

Thus

$$\begin{aligned}r_{Y\hat{Y}}^2 &= \frac{\Sigma \hat{y}_i^2}{\Sigma y_i^2}\\ &= R^2_{1.23}\end{aligned}$$

A similar interpretation also applies to the two-variable case; i.e., the correlation between Y and X is simply the correlation between Y and the linear regression values $\hat{Y}$.

2-5. Partial Correlation Coefficients

To calculate, say, $r_{12.3}$, we first of all eliminate the linear influence of X_3 from Y and from X_2. To do this we take the linear regression of Y on X_3, giving

$$Y_i = a_{1.3} + b_{13}X_{3i} + u_i$$

which may be written in deviation form as

$$y_i = b_{13}x_{3i} + u_i$$

The unexplained residuals in Y_i from this regression are given by

$$u_i = Y_i - a_{1\cdot 3} - b_{13}X_{3i} = y_i - b_{13}x_{3i}$$

Similarly, the unexplained residuals in X_2 after the removal of the linear influence of X_3 may be defined by

$$v_i = X_{2i} - a_{2\cdot 3} - b_{23}X_{3i} = x_{2i} - b_{23}x_{3i}$$

The partial correlation coefficient between Y and X_2, with X_3 held constant, is then defined as the simple correlation coefficient between u_i and v_i; that is,

$$r_{12\cdot 3} = \frac{\Sigma u_i v_i}{\sqrt{\Sigma u_i^2}\sqrt{\Sigma v_i^2}}$$

where we notice that u and v, being themselves residuals from least-squares regressions, have zero means. Thus

$$r_{12\cdot 3} = \frac{\Sigma(y_i - b_{13}x_{3i})(x_{2i} - b_{23}x_{3i})}{\sqrt{\Sigma y_i^2(1 - r_{13}^2)}\sqrt{\Sigma x_{2i}^2(1 - r_{23}^2)}}$$

applying (1-44) to each regression. Thus

$$r_{12\cdot 3} = \frac{\sum y_i x_{2i} - r_{13}\dfrac{S_1}{S_3}\sum x_{2i}x_{3i} - r_{23}\dfrac{S_2}{S_3}\sum y_i x_{3i} + r_{13}r_{23}\dfrac{S_1S_2}{S_3^2}\sum x_{3i}^2}{\sqrt{\Sigma y_i^2}\sqrt{\Sigma x_{2i}^2}\sqrt{1 - r_{13}^2}\sqrt{1 - r_{23}^2}}$$

applying (1-41). Hence

$$r_{12\cdot 3} = \frac{nS_1S_2(r_{12} - r_{13}r_{23})}{nS_1S_2\sqrt{1 - r_{13}^2}\sqrt{1 - r_{23}^2}}$$

Thus

$$r_{12\cdot 3} = \frac{r_{12} - r_{13}r_{23}}{\sqrt{1 - r_{13}^2}\sqrt{1 - r_{23}^2}} \tag{2-26}$$

Similarly,

$$r_{13\cdot 2} = \frac{r_{13} - r_{12}r_{23}}{\sqrt{1 - r_{12}^2}\sqrt{1 - r_{23}^2}} \tag{2-27}$$

and

$$r_{23\cdot 1} = \frac{r_{23} - r_{12}r_{13}}{\sqrt{1 - r_{12}^2}\sqrt{1 - r_{13}^2}} \tag{2-28}$$

Comparing (2-18) and (2-26), we see that

$$b_{12\cdot 3} = \frac{r_{12} - r_{13}r_{23}}{1 - r_{23}^2}\frac{S_1}{S_2}$$

$$= \frac{r_{12} - r_{13}r_{23}}{\sqrt{1 - r_{13}^2}\sqrt{1 - r_{23}^2}}\frac{S_1\sqrt{1 - r_{13}^2}}{S_2\sqrt{1 - r_{23}^2}}$$

that is, $$b_{12\cdot 3} = r_{12\cdot 3}\frac{S_{1\cdot 3}}{S_{2\cdot 3}} \tag{2-29}$$

Similarly, $$b_{13\cdot 2} = r_{13\cdot 2}\frac{S_{1\cdot 2}}{S_{3\cdot 2}} \tag{2-30}$$

These last two formulas are the first-order equivalent of the zero-order relationship obtained in (1-41) for the two-variable case, namely,

$$b_{12} = r_{12}\frac{S_1}{S_2}$$

They show that the least-squares coefficients of the regression plane are, in fact, the simple regression coefficients between the pairs of residuals which are obtained by eliminating from each variable the linear influence of the third variable.

Finally, we may derive a further revealing way of looking at the partial correlation coefficients. It may be shown that[1]

$$S_{1\cdot 23}^2 = S_{1\cdot 2}^2(1 - r_{13\cdot 2}^2) = S_1^2(1 - r_{12}^2)(1 - r_{13\cdot 2}^2) \tag{2-31}$$

$$S_{1\cdot 23}^2 = S_{1\cdot 3}^2(1 - r_{12\cdot 3}^2) = S_1^2(1 - r_{13}^2)(1 - r_{12\cdot 3}^2) \tag{2-32}$$

Using (2-32) we can write

$$r_{12\cdot 3}^2 = \frac{S_{1\cdot 3}^2 - S_{1\cdot 23}^2}{S_{1\cdot 3}^2}$$

$$= \frac{S_1^2(1 - r_{13}^2) - S_1^2(1 - R_{1\cdot 23}^2)}{S_1^2(1 - r_{13}^2)}$$

$$= \frac{R_{1\cdot 23}^2 - r_{13}^2}{1 - r_{13}^2} \tag{2-33}$$

Now

$$S_1^2(1 - r_{13}^2) = \text{variation in } Y \text{ unexplained by } X_3$$

$$S_1^2 r_{13}^2 = \text{variation in } Y \text{ explained by } X_3$$

$$S_1^2 R_{1\cdot 23}^2 = \text{variation in } Y \text{ explained by } X_2 \text{ and } X_3$$

$$S_1^2(R_{1\cdot 23}^2 - r_{13}^2) = \text{increase in explained variation in } Y \text{ due to } X_2$$

[1] For example, using (2-24), $S_{1\cdot 23}^2$ may be expressed in terms of zero-order coefficients as $S_1^2(1 - r_{12}^2 - r_{13}^2 - r_{23}^2 + 2r_{12}r_{13}r_{23})/(1 - r_{23}^2)$, and the expressions of the right-hand sides of (2-31) and (2-32) may easily be seen to reduce to the same quantity.

so that $r_{12\cdot3}^2$ measures the proportion of the Y variation unaccounted for by X_3 that has been explained by the addition of X_2.

Similarly, from (2-31) we can derive

$$r_{13\cdot2}^2 = \frac{R_{1\cdot23}^2 - r_{12}^2}{1 - r_{12}^2} \tag{2-34}$$

that is, $r_{13\cdot2}^2$ measures the proportion of the Y variation unaccounted for by X_2 that is explained by the addition of X_3.

2-6. Summary of Calculations for the Three-variable Case

1. First calculate the means $\bar{Y}$, $\bar{X}_2$, and $\bar{X}_3$, the zero-order standard deviations S_1, S_2, and S_3, and the zero-order correlations r_{12}, r_{13}, and r_{23}.
2. From the statistics in step 1 compute

$$r_{12\cdot3} = \frac{r_{12} - r_{13}r_{23}}{\sqrt{1 - r_{13}^2}\sqrt{1 - r_{23}^2}} \qquad r_{13\cdot2} = \frac{r_{13} - r_{12}r_{23}}{\sqrt{1 - r_{12}^2}\sqrt{1 - r_{23}^2}}$$

and

$$S_{1\cdot2} = S_1\sqrt{1 - r_{12}^2}$$
$$S_{1\cdot3} = S_1\sqrt{1 - r_{13}^2}$$
$$S_{2\cdot3} = S_2\sqrt{1 - r_{23}^2}$$
$$S_{3\cdot2} = S_3\sqrt{1 - r_{32}^2}$$

3. From the quantities in step 2 calculate the regression coefficients

$$b_{12\cdot3} = r_{12\cdot3}\frac{S_{1\cdot3}}{S_{2\cdot3}} \qquad b_{13\cdot2} = r_{13\cdot2}\frac{S_{1\cdot2}}{S_{3\cdot2}}$$

and

$$a_{1\cdot23} = \bar{Y} - b_{12\cdot3}\bar{X}_2 - b_{13\cdot2}\bar{X}_3$$

4. Finally, $R_{1\cdot23}^2$ may be computed from

$$R_{1\cdot23}^2 = \frac{b_{12\cdot3}\Sigma yx_2 + b_{13\cdot2}\Sigma yx_3}{\Sigma y^2}$$

or

$$S_{1\cdot23}^2 = S_{1\cdot2}^2(1 - r_{13\cdot2}^2) = S_{1\cdot3}^2(1 - r_{12\cdot3}^2)$$

and

$$R_{1\cdot23}^2 = 1 - \frac{S_{1\cdot23}^2}{S_1^2}$$

One may similarly build up to the four-variable case with coefficients of second and third order, which may in turn be expressed in terms of coefficients of lower order, but this approach becomes excessively tedious and cumbersome. The formulas also mushroom exponentially in number and complexity. We have, moreover, said nothing about the inference problems for the case of three and more variables. All these problems can be treated more efficiently if we make use of matrix algebra to cut through the jungle of subscripts and summation signs. This is done in Chap. 4. Chapter 3 presents a summary of the necessary matrix algebra, for those not already familiar with it.

References

For practical illustrations of the use of logarithmic and inverse transformations, see

1. S. J. Prais and H. S. Houthakker: *The Analysis of Family Budgets*, Cambridge, London, 1955.

For the algebra of three and more variables consult

2. J. G. Smith and J. A. Duncan: *Fundamentals of the Theory of Statistics*, vol. I, *Elementary Statistics and Applications*, McGraw-Hill, New York, 1945, or
3. G. U. Yule and M. G. Kendall: *An Introduction to the Theory of Statistics*, 14th ed., Griffin, London, 1950.

Exercises

2-1. Given five observations u_{-2}, u_{-1}, u_0, u_1, u_2 at equally spaced points of time $t = -2, -1, 0, 1, 2$, show how to fit a parabola to the observations by least squares and show that the value given by the parabola at time $t = 0$ is

$$\tfrac{1}{35}(-3u_{-2} + 12u_{-1} + 17u_0 + 12u_1 - 3u_2)$$

(R.S.S. Certificate, 1955)

2-2. The "firmness" of cheese depends upon the time allowed for a certain process in the manufacture. In an experiment on this topic, 18 cheeses were taken and at each of several times firmness was determined on samples from three of the cheeses. The results (on an arbitrary scale) are given below:

Time, hr	½	1	1½	2	3	4
Firmness	102 105 115	110 120 115	126 128 119	132 143 139	160 149 147	164 166 172

Estimate the parameters in a linear regression of firmness on time. Give standard errors of the estimates and test the adequacy of a linear regression to describe the results. (R.S.S. Certificate, 1955)
(*Note:* For the description of a test of linearity, see Yule and Kendall, Ref. 3, pp. 519–520.)

2-3. Discuss briefly the advantages and disadvantages of the relation

$$v_i = \alpha + \beta \log v_0$$

as a representation of an Engel curve, where v_i is expenditure per person on commodity i and v_0 is income per person. Fit such a curve to the following data, and from your results estimate the income elasticity at an income of £5 per week.

	Pounds per week							
v_i	0.8	1.2	1.5	1.8	2.2	2.3	2.6	3.1
v_0	1.7	2.7	3.6	4.6	5.7	6.7	8.1	12.0

(Manchester, 1956)

[*Note:* The elasticity of y with respect to x is defined as $\frac{x}{y}\frac{dy}{dx}$. But notice that the use of $d(\log y)/dx = 1/x$ implies that logs have been taken to base e. If logs to base 10 are used in the calculations, an adjustment must be made before a correct estimate of the elasticity is obtained.]

2-4

RESPONSE RATES AT VARIOUS LEVELS OF RATABLE VALUE

Range of ratable value	*A*	*B*	*C*	*D*	*E*	*F*	*G*	*H*	*I*	*J*
Assumed central value, £/annum (X)	3	7	12	17	25	35	45	55	70	120
Response rate, per cent (Y)	86	79	76	69	65	62	52	51	51	48

The data relate to a survey recently conducted in England. Estimate the constants in the regression equation

$$\frac{100}{100 - Y} = a + \frac{b}{X}$$

(Oxford, Diploma, 1955)

2-5. In the following equation,

$$Y = a + bX + ct$$

the coefficients a, b, and c are estimated by least squares from n annual observations of X and Y; t is time measured in years. Show that the estimate of b is the same as that obtained from a simple regression of Y on X after a linear time trend has been removed from X.

(Cambridge, Economic Tripos, Part II, 1960)

2-6. X_1, X_2, and X_3 are three correlated variables, where $S_1 = 1$, $S_2 = 1.3$, $S_3 = 1.9$, and $r_{12} = 0.370$, $r_{13} = -0.641$, and $r_{23} = -0.736$. Compute $r_{13 \cdot 2}$. If $X_4 = X_1 + X_2$, obtain r_{42}, r_{43}, and $r_{43 \cdot 2}$. Verify that the two partial coefficients are equal and explain this result. (L.S.E., 1952)

2-7. A steel bar 18 inches long is subjected to a carefully regulated hardening process. The hardness is determined at the extremities of the bar and at nine positions between the ends. The following results are obtained:

Distance from end of bar d, in.	0	1.8	3.6	5.4	7.2	9.0	10.8	12.6	14.4	16.2	18.0
Vickers hardness number, h	250	276	298	335	374	414	454	503	558	604	671

It is required to determine a mathematical function to graduate the change in hardness along the bar. Two forms of function are suggested:

(i) $$h = A + Bd + Cd^2$$

(ii) $$h = \alpha e^{\beta d}$$

Which of these formulas appears to give the better representation of the changes in hardness along the bar? (R.S.S. Certificate, 1951)

3

Elements of Matrix Algebra

It is clear from Chap. 1 that it would be excessively tedious and complicated to build up to the general case of k variables in a stepwise fashion. Fortunately, by the use of matrix algebra we can obtain a compact and powerful way of treating the general case, and we shall see that all the results of Chaps. 1 and 2 may be obtained from a few very simple matrix formulas. The rest of this chapter presents the elements of matrix algebra necessary for following the treatment in the remainder of the book.

We may write the linear relation in k variables as

$$Y = \beta_1 + \beta_2 X_2 + \cdots + \beta_k X_k + u$$

If we have n observations, they give the following set of equations:

$$\begin{aligned} Y_1 &= \beta_1 + \beta_2 X_{21} + \cdots + \beta_k X_{k1} + u_1 \\ Y_2 &= \beta_1 + \beta_2 X_{22} + \cdots + \beta_k X_{k2} + u_2 \\ &\cdot \\ &\cdot \\ &\cdot \\ Y_n &= \beta_1 + \beta_2 X_{2n} + \cdots + \beta_k X_{kn} + u_n \end{aligned} \tag{3-1}$$

When systems of equations like (3-1) occur frequently, it is convenient to have a neater and more powerful notation for handling them. The method we adopt allows us to write this system of equations as

$$\mathbf{Y} = \mathbf{X}\boldsymbol{\beta} + \mathbf{u} \tag{3-2}$$

where the boldface letters indicate appropriately specified vectors or matrices.

3-1. Matrices

A matrix is defined as a rectangular array of elements arranged in rows or columns as in

$$\mathbf{A} = \begin{bmatrix} a_{11} & a_{12} & \cdots & a_{1n} \\ a_{21} & a_{22} & \cdots & a_{2n} \\ \cdot & & & \cdot \\ \cdot & & & \cdot \\ \cdot & & & \cdot \\ a_{m1} & a_{m2} & \cdots & a_{mn} \end{bmatrix}$$

If it has mn elements arranged in m rows and n columns, it is said to be of order m by n, which is often written $m \times n$.

The element in the ith row and jth column is represented by a_{ij}. The matrix may be indicated even more concisely by

$$\mathbf{A} = [a_{ij}]$$

Alternatives to the use of brackets for enclosing the elements of a matrix are parentheses or pairs of parallel vertical lines.

A matrix of order $1 \times n$ contains only a single row of elements and is commonly referred to as a *row vector*, for example,

$$\mathbf{b} = [b_1 \quad b_2 \quad \cdots \quad b_n]$$

while a matrix of order $m \times 1$ is a *column vector*,

$$\mathbf{c} = \begin{bmatrix} c_1 \\ c_2 \\ \cdot \\ \cdot \\ \cdot \\ c_m \end{bmatrix}$$

To economize space, column vectors will be written in horizontal position but enclosed in braces, thus:

$$\mathbf{c} = \{c_1 \quad c_2 \quad \cdots \quad c_m\}$$

We now require a set of rules and definitions for operating with matrices.

Equality of Two Matrices. Two matrices **A** and **B** are said to be equal when they are of the same order and $a_{ij} = b_{ij}$ for all i, j; that is, the matrices are equal, element by element.

Addition of Two Matrices. If **A** and **B** are of the same order, then we define **A** + **B** to be a new matrix **C** in which

$$c_{ij} = a_{ij} + b_{ij}$$

that is, we add corresponding elements of **A** and **B** to obtain the elements of **C** = **A** + **B**. For example, if

$$\mathbf{A} = \begin{bmatrix} 2 & 0 \\ -5 & 6 \end{bmatrix} \quad \text{and} \quad \mathbf{B} = \begin{bmatrix} -3 & 6 \\ 4 & 1 \end{bmatrix}$$

then

$$\mathbf{C} = \mathbf{A} + \mathbf{B} = \begin{bmatrix} -1 & 6 \\ -1 & 7 \end{bmatrix}$$

Scalar Multiplication. If λ is a scalar, then we define scalar multiplication such that

$$\lambda\mathbf{A} = [\lambda a_{ij}]$$

that is, each element of **A** is multiplied by λ. For example, if

$$\mathbf{A} = \begin{bmatrix} 2 & 0 \\ -5 & 6 \end{bmatrix} \quad \text{and} \quad \lambda = -5$$

then

$$\lambda\mathbf{A} = \begin{bmatrix} -10 & 0 \\ 25 & -30 \end{bmatrix}$$

It follows from the rules for addition and scalar multiplication that

$$\mathbf{A} - \mathbf{B} = [a_{ij} - b_{ij}]$$

Matrix Multiplication. If **A** is of order $m \times n$ and **B** is of order $n \times p$, then the product **AB** is defined to be a matrix of order $m \times p$ whose ijth element is

$$c_{ij} = \sum_{k=1}^{n} a_{ik}b_{kj}$$

that is, the ijth element in the product matrix is found by multiplying the elements of the ith row of the first matrix by the corresponding elements of the jth column of the second matrix and summing over all terms. For this to be possible it is clear that the number of elements in a *row* of the first matrix has to be equal to the number of elements in a *column* of the second matrix, that is, that the number of *columns* in the first should equal the numbers of *rows* in the second. The matrices are then said to be *conformable* with respect to multiplication.

It is also of crucial importance to note the order of the matrices in multiplication.

In **AB** we refer to **A** being postmultiplied by **B** or to **A** premultiplying **B**. **BA** is usually different from **AB** and may not exist. The two products **AB** and **BA** will exist only if the matrices are of order $m \times n$ and $n \times m$. In this case the first product will be of order $m \times m$, and the second $n \times n$.

Example

$$\mathbf{A} = \begin{bmatrix} a_{11} & a_{12} & a_{13} \\ a_{21} & a_{22} & a_{23} \end{bmatrix} \qquad \mathbf{B} = \begin{bmatrix} b_{11} & b_{12} \\ b_{21} & b_{22} \\ b_{31} & b_{32} \end{bmatrix}$$

Then **AB** is a 2×2 matrix:

$$\mathbf{AB} = \begin{bmatrix} a_{11}b_{11} + a_{12}b_{21} + a_{13}b_{31} & a_{11}b_{12} + a_{12}b_{22} + a_{13}b_{32} \\ a_{21}b_{11} + a_{22}b_{21} + a_{23}b_{31} & a_{21}b_{12} + a_{22}b_{22} + a_{23}b_{32} \end{bmatrix}$$

while **BA** is a 3×3 matrix:

$$\mathbf{BA} = \begin{bmatrix} b_{11}a_{11} + b_{12}a_{21} & b_{11}a_{12} + b_{12}a_{22} & b_{11}a_{13} + b_{12}a_{23} \\ b_{21}a_{11} + b_{22}a_{21} & b_{21}a_{12} + b_{22}a_{22} & b_{21}a_{13} + b_{22}b_{23} \\ b_{31}a_{11} + b_{32}a_{21} & b_{31}a_{12} + b_{32}a_{22} & b_{31}a_{13} + b_{32}a_{23} \end{bmatrix}$$

We must be careful not to assume that the laws of ordinary scalar algebra necessarily hold for matrix algebra. Most do, but some do not. The following are the more important laws which we shall need for subsequent operations with matrices.

I. $\mathbf{A} + \mathbf{B} = \mathbf{B} + \mathbf{A}$; that is, the commutative law of addition holds. **A** and **B** must, of course, be of the same order, and the result follows directly from the definition of the addition of matrices.

Example

$$\begin{bmatrix} 2 & 3 \\ -5 & 0 \end{bmatrix} + \begin{bmatrix} 0 & -1 \\ -2 & 6 \end{bmatrix} = \begin{bmatrix} 0 & -1 \\ -2 & 6 \end{bmatrix} + \begin{bmatrix} 2 & 3 \\ -5 & 0 \end{bmatrix} = \begin{bmatrix} 2 & 2 \\ -7 & 6 \end{bmatrix}$$

II. $\mathbf{AB} \neq \mathbf{BA}$ except for rather special square matrices; i.e., the commutative law of multiplication does not, in general, hold. If the matrices are of order $m \times n$ and $n \times m$, then both products will exist, but they will be of different orders and hence cannot be equal. If both are square matrices of the same order, then both products will exist and will be of the same order but not necessarily equal, as the following examples show.

Examples

$$\mathbf{A} = \begin{bmatrix} 2 & 1 \\ 1 & 1 \end{bmatrix} \qquad \mathbf{B} = \begin{bmatrix} 3 & 0 \\ 1 & 2 \end{bmatrix}$$

$$\mathbf{AB} = \begin{bmatrix} 7 & 2 \\ 4 & 2 \end{bmatrix} \qquad \mathbf{BA} = \begin{bmatrix} 6 & 3 \\ 4 & 3 \end{bmatrix}$$

whereas if

$$\mathbf{A} = \begin{bmatrix} 2 & 1 \\ 1 & 1 \end{bmatrix} \qquad \mathbf{B} = \begin{bmatrix} 1 & -1 \\ -1 & 2 \end{bmatrix}$$

then

$$\mathbf{AB} = \begin{bmatrix} 1 & 0 \\ 0 & 1 \end{bmatrix} = \mathbf{BA}$$

III. $(\mathbf{A} + \mathbf{B}) + \mathbf{C} = \mathbf{A} + (\mathbf{B} + \mathbf{C})$; that is, the associative law of addition holds. Since addition of matrices is simply achieved by the addition of corresponding elements and since it does not matter in which order elements are added together, the associative law holds.

IV. $(\mathbf{AB})\mathbf{C} = \mathbf{A}(\mathbf{BC})$; that is, the associative law of multiplication holds. We can first form **AB** and then postmultiply by **C**, or first form **BC** and premultiply by **A**. For suppose

$$\begin{aligned} \mathbf{A} &= [a_{ir}] \text{ of order } m \times n \\ \mathbf{B} &= [b_{rs}] \text{ of order } n \times p \\ \mathbf{C} &= [c_{sj}] \text{ of order } p \times q \end{aligned}$$

then **AB** is a matrix of order $m \times p$ whose isth element is $\sum_{r=1}^{n} a_{ir}b_{rs}$. The matrix **ABC** formed by postmultiplying **AB** by **C** is a matrix of order $m \times q$, whose ijth element is

$$\sum_{s=1}^{p} \left(\sum_{r=1}^{n} a_{ir}b_{rs} \right) c_{sj} = \sum_{s=1}^{p} \sum_{r=1}^{n} a_{ir}b_{rs}c_{sj}$$

Similarly, the rjth element in (**BC**) is $\sum_{s=1}^{p} b_{rs}c_{sj}$, and the ijth element in **A**(**BC**) is

$$\sum_{r=1}^{n} a_{ir} \left(\sum_{s=1}^{p} b_{rs}c_{sj} \right) = \sum_{s=1}^{p} \sum_{r=1}^{p} a_{ir}b_{rs}c_{sj} = ij\text{th element in } (\mathbf{AB})\mathbf{C}$$

V. $\mathbf{A}(\mathbf{B} + \mathbf{C}) = \mathbf{AB} + \mathbf{AC}$, and $(\mathbf{B} + \mathbf{C})\mathbf{A} = \mathbf{BA} + \mathbf{CA}$; that is, the distributive law holds. For

$$\begin{aligned} ij\text{th element in } \mathbf{A}(\mathbf{B} + \mathbf{C}) &= \sum_k a_{ik}(b_{kj} + c_{kj}) \\ &= \sum_k a_{ik}b_{kj} + \sum_k a_{ik}c_{kj} \\ &= ij\text{th element in } \mathbf{AB} + ij\text{th element in } \mathbf{AC} \end{aligned}$$

VI. $\lambda(\mathbf{A} + \mathbf{B}) = \lambda\mathbf{A} + \lambda\mathbf{B}$, and $(\lambda + \mu)\mathbf{A} = \lambda\mathbf{A} + \mu\mathbf{A}$; that is, the distributive law of scalar multiplication holds.

These six results are important for the manipulation of matrices, and the student should get a firm grasp of them by working out arbitrary numerical examples.

Unit, or Identity, Matrix. This is defined as

$$\mathbf{I}_n = \begin{bmatrix} 1 & 0 & \cdots & 0 \\ 0 & 1 & \cdots & 0 \\ \cdot & & & \cdot \\ \cdot & & & \cdot \\ \cdot & & & \cdot \\ 0 & 0 & \cdots & 1 \end{bmatrix}$$

a square matrix of order $n \times n$ with units in the principal diagonal and zeros everywhere else.

It is easy to verify that premultiplying or postmultiplying any matrix $\mathbf{A}$ by the unit matrix of appropriate order leaves $\mathbf{A}$ unchanged; that is,

$$\mathbf{IA} = \mathbf{AI} = \mathbf{A}$$

Scalar Matrix. A scalar matrix has a common scalar element in the principal diagonal and zeros everywhere else; e.g.,

$$\lambda\mathbf{I} = \begin{bmatrix} \lambda & 0 & \cdots & 0 \\ 0 & \lambda & \cdots & 0 \\ \cdot & & & \cdot \\ \cdot & & & \cdot \\ \cdot & & & \cdot \\ 0 & 0 & \cdots & \lambda \end{bmatrix}$$

For this reason we can always replace a scalar by a scalar matrix and choose the order of that matrix to suit our convenience. Scalar multiplication (already defined) is thus equivalent to matrix multiplication and may be thought of as pre- or postmultiplication, since

$$\lambda\mathbf{A} = (\lambda\mathbf{I})\mathbf{A} = \mathbf{A}(\lambda\mathbf{I}) = \mathbf{A}\lambda$$

For example,

$$\lambda\mathbf{A} = \lambda\mathbf{IA} = \begin{bmatrix} \lambda & 0 & 0 \\ 0 & \lambda & 0 \\ 0 & 0 & \lambda \end{bmatrix} \begin{bmatrix} a_{11} & a_{12} & a_{13} \\ a_{21} & a_{22} & a_{23} \\ a_{31} & a_{32} & a_{33} \end{bmatrix} = \begin{bmatrix} \lambda a_{11} & \lambda a_{12} & \lambda a_{13} \\ \lambda a_{21} & \lambda a_{22} & \lambda a_{23} \\ \lambda a_{31} & \lambda a_{32} & \lambda a_{33} \end{bmatrix}$$
$$= \mathbf{A}\lambda\mathbf{I} = \mathbf{A}\lambda$$

We thus see that the unit matrix may be inserted or suppressed at will in matrix expressions without altering their value.

Diagonal Matrix. A diagonal matrix has scalar elements, not necessarily equal, in the principal diagonal and zeros in the off-diagonal positions; i.e.,

$$\mathbf{A} = [a_{ij}] \qquad i,j = 1, 2, \ldots, n$$
$$a_{ij} = 0, \; i \neq j$$

that is,
$$\mathbf{A} = \begin{bmatrix} a_{11} & 0 & \cdots & 0 \\ 0 & a_{22} & \cdots & 0 \\ \cdot & & & \cdot \\ \cdot & & & \cdot \\ \cdot & & & \cdot \\ 0 & 0 & \cdots & a_{nn} \end{bmatrix}$$

A scalar matrix is thus a special form of diagonal matrix.

Transposition. In scalar algebra division follows simply as the inverse of multiplication. In matrix algebra it is less simple, and before we can usefully consider the problem, we have to introduce an operation on the matrix **A** that has no equivalent in scalar algebra.

The transpose of **A** is defined to be the matrix obtained from **A** by interchanging rows and columns; that is, the first row of **A** becomes the first column of the transpose, the second row of **A** becomes the second column of the transpose, and in general the jith element in the transpose is the ijth element of the original matrix. We indicate the transposed matrix by **A**′; for example,

$$\mathbf{A} = \begin{bmatrix} a_{11} & a_{12} & a_{13} \\ a_{21} & a_{22} & a_{23} \end{bmatrix}$$

$$\mathbf{A}' = \begin{bmatrix} a_{11} & a_{21} \\ a_{12} & a_{22} \\ a_{13} & a_{23} \end{bmatrix}$$

If $\mathbf{A}' = \mathbf{A}$, then $\mathbf{A}$ is said to be a *symmetric* matrix; it must obviously be a square matrix such that

$$a_{ij} = a_{ji}$$

Let $\mathbf{A}$ be as defined above; e.g.,

$$\mathbf{A} = \begin{bmatrix} a_{11} & a_{12} & a_{13} \\ a_{21} & a_{22} & a_{23} \end{bmatrix}$$

then

$$\mathbf{AA}' = \begin{bmatrix} a_{11}^2 + a_{12}^2 + a_{13}^2 & a_{11}a_{21} + a_{12}a_{22} + a_{13}a_{23} \\ a_{21}a_{11} + a_{22}a_{12} + a_{23}a_{13} & a_{21}^2 + a_{22}^2 + a_{23}^2 \end{bmatrix}$$

and

$$\mathbf{A}'\mathbf{A} = \begin{bmatrix} a_{11}^2 + a_{21}^2 & a_{11}a_{12} + a_{21}a_{22} & a_{11}a_{13} + a_{21}a_{23} \\ a_{12}a_{11} + a_{22}a_{21} & a_{12}^2 + a_{22}^2 & a_{12}a_{13} + a_{22}a_{23} \\ a_{13}a_{11} + a_{23}a_{21} & a_{13}a_{12} + a_{23}a_{22} & a_{13}^2 + a_{23}^2 \end{bmatrix}$$

Notice that both $\mathbf{AA}'$ and $\mathbf{A}'\mathbf{A}$ are symmetric. Since $\mathbf{A}$ is not square, these products are of different orders, but their *traces* are equal, the trace of a square matrix being defined as the sum of the elements in the principal diagonal. The trace of $\mathbf{AA}'$, denoted by tr $(\mathbf{AA}')$, is in fact the sum of the squares of the elements of $\mathbf{A}$.

Notice that if $\mathbf{x}$ is a column vector of n elements, $\mathbf{x}'$ is then a row vector of n elements and

$$\mathbf{x}'\mathbf{x} = \sum_{i=1}^{n} x_i^2$$

and

$$\mathbf{xx}' = \begin{bmatrix} x_1^2 & x_1x_2 & \cdots & x_1x_n \\ x_2x_1 & x_2^2 & \cdots & x_2x_n \\ \cdot & & & \cdot \\ \cdot & & & \cdot \\ \cdot & & & \cdot \\ x_nx_1 & x_nx_2 & \cdots & x_n^2 \end{bmatrix}$$

Theorems about Transposed Matrices

$$(\mathbf{A}')' = \mathbf{A} \qquad (3\text{-}3)$$

$$(\mathbf{A} + \mathbf{B})' = \mathbf{A}' + \mathbf{B}' \qquad (3\text{-}4)$$

$$(\mathbf{AB})' = \mathbf{B}'\mathbf{A}' \qquad (3\text{-}5)$$

The first two are obvious from the definition of transposition. To prove (3-5), we note that

$$\begin{aligned} ji\text{th element in } \mathbf{B'A'} &= j\text{th row of } \mathbf{B'} \text{ into } i\text{th column of } \mathbf{A'} \\ &= j\text{th column of } \mathbf{B} \text{ into } i\text{th row of } \mathbf{A} \\ &= ij\text{th element in } \mathbf{AB} \end{aligned}$$

It also follows that

$$(\mathbf{ABC})' = \mathbf{C'B'A'} \tag{3-6}$$

for $$(\mathbf{ABC})' = [(\mathbf{AB})\mathbf{C}]' = \mathbf{C'}(\mathbf{AB})' = \mathbf{C'B'A'}$$

The following examples illustrate some simple operations with matrices and also serve to introduce some algebraic expressions, which will be of subsequent use.

Example i. The set of simultaneous equations

$$\begin{aligned} a_{11}x_1 + a_{12}x_2 + \cdots + a_{1n}x_n &= h_1 \\ a_{21}x_1 + a_{22}x_2 + \cdots + a_{2n}x_n &= h_2 \\ &\vdots \\ a_{n1}x_1 + a_{n2}x_2 + \cdots + a_{nn}x_n &= h_n \end{aligned}$$

may be written

$$\mathbf{Ax} = \mathbf{h}$$

where $\mathbf{A}$ = matrix of a_{ij} coefficients of order $n \times n$
$\mathbf{x}$ = column vector of n elements $\{x_1 \quad x_2 \quad \cdots \quad x_n\}$
$\mathbf{h}$ = column vector of n elements $\{h_1 \quad h_2 \quad \cdots \quad h_n\}$

The product of the matrix $\mathbf{A}$ and the vector $\mathbf{x}$ gives a column vector of n elements, which is then equated, element by element, with the $\mathbf{h}$ vector. The first element in the vector $\mathbf{Ax}$ is $a_{11}x_1 + a_{12}x_2 + \cdots + a_{1n}x_n$, which is equated to h_1, and similarly for the other elements, giving n simultaneous equations in all.

Example ii. Sum of squares

$$\begin{aligned} e_1^2 + e_2^2 + \cdots + e_n^2 &= \sum_{i=1}^{n} e_i^2 \\ &= \mathbf{e'e} \end{aligned}$$

where $$\mathbf{e} = \{e_1 \quad e_2 \quad \cdots \quad e_n\}$$

Example iii. A weighted sum of squares

$$a_{11}x_1^2 + a_{22}x_2^2 + \cdots + a_{nn}x_n^2 = \mathbf{x'Ax}$$

where $\mathbf{A}$ = a diagonal matrix of order $n \times n$
$\mathbf{x}$ = a column vector of n elements

This result may be seen by a straightforward application of the multiplication rule. As an illustration of the 3×3 case,

$$\mathbf{x}'\mathbf{A}\mathbf{x} = [x_1 \quad x_2 \quad x_3] \begin{bmatrix} a_{11} & 0 & 0 \\ 0 & a_{22} & 0 \\ 0 & 0 & a_{33} \end{bmatrix} \begin{bmatrix} x_1 \\ x_2 \\ x_3 \end{bmatrix}$$
$$= [x_1 \quad x_2 \quad x_3] \begin{bmatrix} a_{11}x_1 \\ a_{22}x_2 \\ a_{33}x_3 \end{bmatrix}$$
$$= a_{11}x_1^2 + a_{22}x_2^2 + a_{33}x_3^2$$

Example iv. Quadratic forms. $\mathbf{x}'\mathbf{A}\mathbf{x}$. A very important function in statistics is obtained when we consider the general expression $\mathbf{x}'\mathbf{A}\mathbf{x}$, without the restriction that $\mathbf{A}$ is a diagonal matrix, but postulating simply that $\mathbf{A}$ is *symmetric.* For the 2×2 case, we obtain, on multiplying out,

$$\mathbf{x}'\mathbf{A}\mathbf{x} = a_{11}x_1^2 + 2a_{12}x_1x_2 + a_{22}x_2^2$$

and for the 3×3 case,

$$\begin{aligned}\mathbf{x}'\mathbf{A}\mathbf{x} = a_{11}x_1^2 &+ 2a_{12}x_1x_2 + 2a_{13}x_1x_3 \\ &+ \quad a_{22}x_2^2 + 2a_{23}x_2x_3 \\ &\qquad\qquad + a_{33}x_3^2\end{aligned}$$

The restriction that the matrix $\mathbf{A}$ of the quadratic form be symmetric is not a serious one, since if we have a nonsymmetric matrix $\mathbf{A}^*$, a typical cross-product term would be $(a^*_{ij} + a^*_{ji})x_ix_j$. If we now define

$$a_{ij} = a_{ji} = \frac{a^*_{ij} + a^*_{ji}}{2}$$

this term becomes $2a_{ij}x_ix_j$ and the associated matrix is a symmetric one.

The general quadratic form may be written

$$\begin{aligned}\mathbf{x}'\mathbf{A}\mathbf{x} = a_{11}x_1^2 &+ 2a_{12}x_1x_2 + \cdots + 2a_{1n}x_1x_n \\ &+ \quad a_{22}x_2^2 \quad + \cdots + 2a_{2n}x_2x_n \\ &\qquad\qquad + \cdots \\ &\qquad\qquad\quad \cdot \\ &\qquad\qquad\qquad \cdot \\ &\qquad\qquad\qquad\quad \cdot \\ &\qquad\qquad\qquad\qquad + a_{nn}x_n^2\end{aligned}$$

where $\mathbf{A}$ is a symmetric matrix of order $n \times n$ and $\mathbf{x}$ is a column vector of n elements.

As an illustration, if we are given the quadratic form

$$x_1^2 + 3x_2^2 - 5x_3^2 + 2x_1x_2 - 8x_2x_3$$

we can by inspection write

$$\mathbf{x} = \begin{bmatrix} x_1 \\ x_2 \\ x_3 \end{bmatrix} \quad \text{and} \quad \mathbf{A} = \begin{bmatrix} 1 & 1 & 0 \\ 1 & 3 & -4 \\ 0 & -4 & -5 \end{bmatrix}$$

since the coefficients of the terms in x_i^2 appear on the principal diagonal of **A** and the symmetric off-diagonal terms are one-half the coefficients of the x_ix_j terms.

The Inverse Matrix. The matrix form $\mathbf{Ax} = \mathbf{h}$ of the set of equations in Example i suggests that if it were possible and meaningful to divide each side of the equation by **A**, by analogy with division in scalar algebra, we should obtain as a solution

$$\mathbf{x} = \mathbf{A}^{-1}\mathbf{h}$$

If $\mathbf{A}^{-1}$ is an $n \times n$ matrix with elements which are functions of the elements of **A**, then the right-hand side of the above equation becomes a column vector of n elements, which we equate, element by element, with the unknown x_i, and so obtain a solution to the original set of equations.

In order to establish the nature of the matrix $\mathbf{A}^{-1}$, we need a few results on determinants.

3-2. Determinants

Associated with any square matrix **A** there is a *scalar* quantity, called the determinant of **A**, which is indicated by det **A** or by the special symbol $|\mathbf{A}|$. This quantity is obtained by summing various products of the elements of **A**. For example, the determinant of a 2×2 matrix is defined to be

$$\begin{vmatrix} a_{11} & a_{12} \\ a_{21} & a_{22} \end{vmatrix} = a_{11}a_{22} - a_{12}a_{21}$$

and of a 3×3 matrix

$$\begin{vmatrix} a_{11} & a_{12} & a_{13} \\ a_{21} & a_{22} & a_{23} \\ a_{31} & a_{32} & a_{33} \end{vmatrix} = a_{11}a_{22}a_{33} - a_{12}a_{21}a_{33} + a_{12}a_{23}a_{31} - a_{13}a_{22}a_{31} + a_{13}a_{21}a_{32} - a_{11}a_{23}a_{32}$$

We notice various features of the above determinants.

1. Each term on the right-hand side is the product of the same number of elements as the order of **A**, namely, two elements for a

2×2 matrix and three elements for a 3×3 matrix. In general, we then expect n elements in each term.

2. In each term there is one and only one element from each row and one and only one element from each column of **A**. Thus no element appears twice in the same term.

3. The number of terms in the expansions are $2 = 2!$ and $6 = 3!$, respectively, and all terms are different. In general, we expect $n!$ different terms.

4. In the subscripts attaching to the elements in each term the elements have been written so that *within* each term the first subscripts are in natural order, that is, 1, 2, 3, etc. The second subscripts, however, are various permutations of the natural order. Since there are $n!$ permutations of n distinct objects, this gives the $n!$ different terms as noted in item 3 above.

5. Half the terms have positive signs, and half have negative signs. The sign depends upon the second subscripts. An *inversion* of natural order is said to occur when of two integers the larger precedes the smaller. The number of inversions in a permutation of n integers is the number of pairs of elements, not necessarily adjacent, in which a larger integer precedes a smaller one. A permutation is *even* when the number of inversions is even and *odd* when the number of inversions is odd. Even permutations carry a positive sign, and odd permutations a negative sign. For example, the second term in the expansion of the third-order determinant has second subscripts in the order 2 1 3, which contains only one inversion, 2 before 1, and is therefore odd and has a negative sign. The next term has second subscripts in the order 2 3 1, which contains two inversions since 2 comes before 1 and 3 comes before 1: it is therefore even and carries a plus sign.

These five points lead to the general definition of the determinant of an nth-order matrix **A** as

$$|\mathbf{A}| = \Sigma \pm a_{1i}a_{2j} \cdots a_{nr}$$

the sum being taken over all permutations of the second subscripts, with a positive sign attached to even permutations and a negative one to odd permutations.

Properties of Determinants

$$|\mathbf{A}'| = |\mathbf{A}| \tag{3-7}$$

i.e., the determinant of the transposed matrix is equal to the determinant of the original matrix. To prove this result let $\mathbf{B} = \mathbf{A}'$. We require to find the determinant of **B** in terms of the determinant of **A**. The proof is illustrated by considering a matrix of order 3×3. In this the term $b_{13}b_{21}b_{32}$ in the expansion of **B** consists of the product of the three elements a_{31}, a_{12}, and a_{23}. Its sign in the determinant of **B** is given by the number of inversions in 3 1 2 (second subscripts of the b expression) and is thus positive. The sign of $a_{31}a_{12}a_{23}$ in the determinant of **A** can be found when these three terms are rearranged with the first subscript in natural order. This rearrangement, however, will give exactly the same

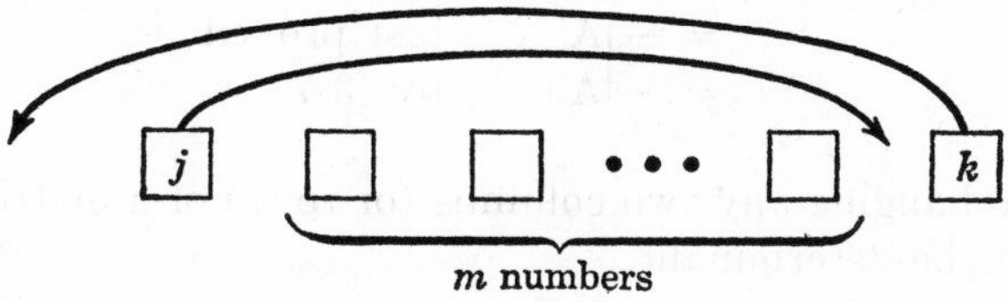

FIG. 3-1

number of inversions in the second subscripts as it removes from the first subscripts. For example, as the first element is moved into third position, two inversions are removed from the first subscripts as the integer 3 now comes after 1 and 2, but two inversions are created in the second subscript as the integer 1 moves to the right of 2 and 3. Thus $a_{31}a_{12}a_{23}$ will have the same sign in the expansion of the determinant of **A** as in the expansion of the determinant of **B**. This will apply to any term, and so the result is proved.

Interchanging any two columns (or rows) of **A** *changes the sign of the determinant of* **A** (3-8)

To prove this we notice that the interchange of any two elements in a permutation must always change the class of the permutation from odd to even, or vice versa. Suppose, for example, that we are interchanging j and k, which are separated by m numbers as in Fig. 3-1. To achieve the interchange, k must move over $m + 1$ numbers and j must pass over m numbers. Any time one number passes over another, an inversion is either introduced or removed. Thus the interchange of any two numbers j and k separated by m numbers causes $2m + 1$ inversion changes, and since this must be an odd number, the class of the permutation changes.

Interchanging any two columns of **A** thus means that the first subscripts in all terms in $|\mathbf{A}|$ are unchanged but the sign of each term changes, so that the sign of $|\mathbf{A}|$ changes.

Let **B** denote the matrix obtained from **A** by interchanging columns j and k. We have thus shown that

$$|\mathbf{B}| = -|\mathbf{A}|$$

Then $\mathbf{B}'$ is the matrix obtained from $\mathbf{A}'$ by interchanging *rows* j and k.

We then have

$$\begin{aligned} |\mathbf{B}'| &= |\mathbf{B}| && \text{by (3-7)} \\ &= -|\mathbf{A}| && \text{just proved} \\ &= -|\mathbf{A}'| && \text{by (3-7)} \end{aligned}$$

Thus interchanging any two columns (or rows) of a matrix changes the sign of the determinant.

The determinant of a matrix with two rows (or columns) identical is zero (3-9)

This follows directly from (3-8), for the interchange of two rows (or columns) gives a new determinant equal to $-|\mathbf{A}|$. Yet if the two rows are identical, their interchange must have $|\mathbf{A}|$ unaltered. Thus

$$|\mathbf{A}| = -|\mathbf{A}|$$

that is,

$$|\mathbf{A}| = 0$$

If every element of a row (or column) of **A** *is multiplied by a scalar* λ *to give a new matrix* **B**, *then*

$$|\mathbf{B}| = \lambda|\mathbf{A}| \qquad (3\text{-}10)$$

If every element of **A** *is multiplied by* λ, *then*

$$|\lambda\mathbf{A}| = \lambda^n|\mathbf{A}| \qquad (3\text{-}11)$$

These two results follow directly from the fact that each term in the expansion of a determinant contains one element and one element only from each row (or column) of the matrix.

If we consider

$$|\mathbf{A}| = \Sigma \pm a_{1\alpha}a_{2\beta} \cdots a_{n\nu}$$

and collect all the terms in the expansion containing a_{11}, the coefficient of the element a_{11} is

$$\Sigma \pm a_{2\beta}a_{3\gamma} \cdots a_{n\nu} \tag{3-12}$$

where the summation takes place over all $(n - 1)!$ permutations of the integers $2, 3, \ldots, n$. Since the row and column suffixes 1, 1 in a_{11} are in correct natural order, they make no contribution to the sign of any term in (3-12). This sign is therefore given by the permutation $(\beta, \gamma, \ldots, \nu)$ of the natural order $(2, 3, \ldots, n)$. In fact,

$$\Sigma \pm a_{2\beta}a_{3\gamma} \cdots a_{n\nu}$$

is the determinant of order $n - 1$.

$$\begin{vmatrix} a_{22} & \cdots & a_{2n} \\ \cdot & & \cdot \\ \cdot & & \cdot \\ \cdot & & \cdot \\ a_{n2} & \cdots & a_{nn} \end{vmatrix}$$

is the matrix obtained from **A** by deleting its first row and first column.

Minor. Such a determinant is called a minor. Denote it by $\mathbf{A}_{11}$. In general,

$$|\mathbf{A}_{ij}| = \begin{vmatrix} a_{11} & a_{12} & \cdots & a_{1,j-1} & a_{1,j+1} & \cdots & a_{1n} \\ \cdot & & & & & & \cdot \\ \cdot & & & & & & \cdot \\ \cdot & & & & & & \cdot \\ a_{i-1,1} & a_{i-1,2} & \cdots & a_{i-1,j-1} & a_{i-1,j+1} & \cdots & a_{i-1,n} \\ a_{i+1,1} & a_{i+1,2} & \cdots & a_{i+1,j-1} & a_{i+1,j+1} & \cdots & a_{i+1,n} \\ \cdot & & & & & & \cdot \\ \cdot & & & & & & \cdot \\ \cdot & & & & & & \cdot \\ a_{n1} & a_{n2} & \cdots & a_{n,j-1} & a_{n,j+1} & \cdots & a_{nn} \end{vmatrix} \tag{3-13}$$

We have thus shown that the sum of all terms in $|\mathbf{A}|$ involving a_{11} as a factor is given by $a_{11}|\mathbf{A}_{11}|$.

Next we ask what is the sum of all terms in $|\mathbf{A}|$ involving a_{ij} as a factor? Consider the matrix **B** obtained from **A** by (1) interchanging row i of **A** with the row above it and repeating this process until after $i - 1$ interchanges; row i of **A** is now the first row, and the lower rows are in normal order except for the omission of row i; and (2) interchanging column j of **A** step by step with the one on its left until after $j - 1$ steps it is the first column. Thus

$$|\mathbf{B}| = (-1)^{i+j-2}|\mathbf{A}| = (-1)^{i+j}|\mathbf{A}|$$

$$b_{11} = a_{ij}$$

and $$|\mathbf{B}_{11}| = |\mathbf{A}_{ij}|$$

since

$$|\mathbf{B}_{11}| = \begin{vmatrix} a_{11} & \cdots & a_{1,j-1} & a_{1,j+1} & \cdots & a_{1n} \\ \cdot & & & & & \\ \cdot & & & & & \cdot \\ \cdot & & & & & \\ a_{i-1,1} & & & & & \cdot \\ a_{i+1,1} & & & & & \\ \cdot & & & & & \\ \cdot & & & & & \cdot \\ \cdot & & & & & \\ a_{n1} & & \cdot & \cdot & \cdot & a_{nn} \end{vmatrix}$$

Thus the sum of all terms in $|\mathbf{B}|$ which involve $a_{ij}(=b_{11})$ as a factor is $b_{11}|\mathbf{B}_{11}|$. It is seen above that when the terms in $|\mathbf{B}|$ are multiplied by $(-1)^{i+j}$, they become terms in $|\mathbf{A}|$. Thus the sum of all terms in $|\mathbf{A}|$ involving a_{ij} as a factor is

$$(-1)^{i+j}a_{ij}|\mathbf{A}_{ij}|$$

Co-factor. Let us define these co-factors (coefficients) as

$$c_{ij} = (-1)^{i+j}|\mathbf{A}_{ij}| \tag{3-14}$$

so that

$$c_{11} = |\mathbf{A}_{11}| \qquad c_{12} = -|\mathbf{A}_{12}| \qquad c_{22} = |\mathbf{A}_{22}| \qquad \text{etc.}$$

Now consider the expression

$$a_{i1}c_{i1} + a_{i2}c_{i2} + \cdots + a_{in}c_{in}$$

There are altogether $(n - 1)!n = n!$ terms in this expression, *all different* and all occurring with correct sign in **A**. But the expansion of **A** has only $n!$ terms, all different. Thus

$$|\mathbf{A}| = a_{i1}c_{i1} + a_{i2}c_{i2} + \cdots + a_{in}c_{in} \tag{3-15}$$

This gives us the expansion of $|\mathbf{A}|$ in terms of the elements of the ith row and their co-factors. $|\mathbf{A}|$ may be similarly expanded in terms of the elements of *any row* (or column).

A determinant is unaltered in value when to any row, or column, is added a constant multiple of any other row or column (3-16)

Proof: Consider

$$\begin{vmatrix} a_{11}+\lambda\alpha & a_{12}+\lambda\beta & a_{13}+\lambda\gamma \\ a_{21} & a_{22} & a_{23} \\ a_{31} & a_{32} & a_{33} \end{vmatrix}$$

Using (3-15) to expand this determinant, Δ, in terms of the elements of the first row gives

$$\Delta = (a_{11}+\lambda\alpha)\begin{vmatrix} a_{22} & a_{23} \\ a_{32} & a_{33} \end{vmatrix} - (a_{12}+\lambda\beta)\begin{vmatrix} a_{21} & a_{23} \\ a_{31} & a_{33} \end{vmatrix} + (a_{13}+\lambda\gamma)\begin{vmatrix} a_{21} & a_{22} \\ a_{31} & a_{32} \end{vmatrix}$$

$$= \begin{vmatrix} a_{11} & a_{12} & a_{13} \\ a_{21} & a_{22} & a_{23} \\ a_{31} & a_{32} & a_{33} \end{vmatrix} + \lambda \begin{vmatrix} \alpha & \beta & \gamma \\ a_{21} & a_{22} & a_{23} \\ a_{31} & a_{32} & a_{33} \end{vmatrix}$$

If $\qquad [\alpha \quad \beta \quad \gamma] = [a_{21} \quad a_{22} \quad a_{23}]$

or $\qquad [\alpha \quad \beta \quad \gamma] = [a_{31} \quad a_{32} \quad a_{33}]$

the last determinant on the right-hand side vanishes because of two identical rows, and thus the right-hand side reduces to the value of the original determinant. This result is often useful in the numerical evaluation of determinants.

Example. Evaluate

$$|\mathbf{A}| = \begin{vmatrix} 2 & 4 & 6 \\ 3 & 2 & 3 \\ 1 & 4 & 9 \end{vmatrix}$$

Expanding in terms of the elements of the first row,

$$\begin{aligned} |\mathbf{A}| &= 2\begin{vmatrix} 2 & 3 \\ 4 & 9 \end{vmatrix} - 4\begin{vmatrix} 3 & 3 \\ 1 & 9 \end{vmatrix} + 6\begin{vmatrix} 3 & 2 \\ 1 & 4 \end{vmatrix} \\ &= 2(6) - 4(24) + 6(10) \\ &= -24 \end{aligned}$$

Alternatively, subtract twice the second row from the first to give

$$|\mathbf{A}| = \begin{vmatrix} -4 & 0 & 0 \\ 3 & 2 & 3 \\ 1 & 4 & 9 \end{vmatrix}$$

Expanding this in terms of the elements in the first row,

$$|\mathbf{A}| = -4(6) = -24$$

Expansions in Terms of Alien Co-factors Vanish Identically. Consider

$$a_{i1}c_{j1} + a_{i2}c_{j2} + \cdots + a_{in}c_{jn} \qquad i \neq j$$

The elements are those of row i, and the co-factors are those for row j. This is the expression we should obtain for the determinant of a matrix in which rows i and j are identical, which, from (3-9), is zero. Thus

$$\begin{aligned} \sum_{r=1}^{n} a_{ir}c_{jr} &= 0 \qquad i \neq j \\ \sum_{s=1}^{n} a_{sk}c_{sl} &= 0 \qquad k \neq l \end{aligned} \tag{3-17}$$

The Inverse, or Reciprocal, Matrix. In scalar algebra we have

$$xx^{-1} = x^{-1}x = 1 \qquad \text{(unity)}$$

This suggests that in matrix algebra we ask whether a *matrix* $\mathbf{A}^{-1}$ exists such that

$$\mathbf{AA}^{-1} = \mathbf{A}^{-1}\mathbf{A} = \mathbf{I} \qquad \text{(unit matrix)}$$

$\mathbf{A}^{-1}$ is defined as the inverse (or reciprocal) of $\mathbf{A}$.

The steps in its construction are as follows:

1. From $\mathbf{A}$ form a new matrix where a_{ij} is replaced by its co-factor c_{ij} and transpose this new matrix. The resulting matrix is called the *adjugate*, or *adjoint*, of $\mathbf{A}$.

$$(\text{adj } \mathbf{A}) = \begin{bmatrix} c_{11} & c_{21} & \cdots & c_{n1} \\ c_{12} & c_{22} & \cdots & c_{n2} \\ \cdot & & & \cdot \\ \cdot & & & \cdot \\ \cdot & & & \cdot \\ c_{1n} & c_{2n} & \cdots & c_{nn} \end{bmatrix}$$

We can then see that

$$\mathbf{A}\,(\text{adj } \mathbf{A}) = (\text{adj } \mathbf{A})\,\mathbf{A} = \begin{bmatrix} |\mathbf{A}| & 0 & \cdots & 0 \\ 0 & |\mathbf{A}| & \cdots & 0 \\ \cdot & & & \cdot \\ \cdot & & & \cdot \\ \cdot & & & \cdot \\ 0 & 0 & \cdots & |\mathbf{A}| \end{bmatrix} = |\mathbf{A}|\mathbf{I}$$

using the result about expansions in terms of alien co-factors.

2. Define $\mathbf{A}^{-1}$ as

$$\frac{1}{|\mathbf{A}|}(\text{adj } \mathbf{A}) = \begin{bmatrix} \frac{c_{11}}{|\mathbf{A}|} & \frac{c_{21}}{|\mathbf{A}|} & \cdots & \frac{c_{n1}}{|\mathbf{A}|} \\ \cdot & & & \cdot \\ \cdot & & & \cdot \\ \cdot & & & \cdot \\ \frac{c_{1n}}{|\mathbf{A}|} & \cdot & \cdot \quad \cdot & \frac{c_{nn}}{|\mathbf{A}|} \end{bmatrix}$$

This last step is possible only if $|\mathbf{A}| \neq 0$, in which case the matrix **A** is said to be nonsingular. When $|\mathbf{A}| = 0$, the matrix **A** is said to be singular.

$\mathbf{A}^{-1}$ is also unique; for suppose **B** exists such that $\mathbf{AB} = \mathbf{I}$, then

$$\begin{aligned} \mathbf{A}^{-1} &= \mathbf{A}^{-1}\mathbf{I} \\ &= \mathbf{A}^{-1}\mathbf{AB} \\ &= \mathbf{B} \end{aligned}$$

Likewise, if **C** exists such that $\mathbf{CA} = \mathbf{I}$, $\mathbf{C} = \mathbf{A}^{-1}$.

Example. The calculation of an inverse matrix.

$$\mathbf{A} = \begin{bmatrix} 1 & 2 & 3 \\ 1 & 3 & 5 \\ 1 & 5 & 12 \end{bmatrix}$$

Replacing elements by co-factors gives

$$\begin{bmatrix} \begin{vmatrix} 3 & 5 \\ 5 & 12 \end{vmatrix} & -\begin{vmatrix} 1 & 5 \\ 1 & 12 \end{vmatrix} & \begin{vmatrix} 1 & 3 \\ 1 & 5 \end{vmatrix} \\ -\begin{vmatrix} 2 & 3 \\ 5 & 12 \end{vmatrix} & \begin{vmatrix} 1 & 3 \\ 1 & 12 \end{vmatrix} & -\begin{vmatrix} 1 & 2 \\ 1 & 5 \end{vmatrix} \\ \begin{vmatrix} 2 & 3 \\ 3 & 5 \end{vmatrix} & -\begin{vmatrix} 1 & 3 \\ 1 & 5 \end{vmatrix} & \begin{vmatrix} 1 & 2 \\ 1 & 3 \end{vmatrix} \end{bmatrix} = \begin{bmatrix} 11 & -7 & 2 \\ -9 & 9 & -3 \\ 1 & -2 & 1 \end{bmatrix}$$

Therefore

$$\text{adj } \mathbf{A} = \begin{bmatrix} 11 & -9 & 1 \\ -7 & 9 & -2 \\ 2 & -3 & 1 \end{bmatrix}$$

$$\begin{aligned} |\mathbf{A}| &= \begin{vmatrix} 1 & 2 & 3 \\ 0 & 1 & 2 \\ 0 & 3 & 9 \end{vmatrix} \quad \text{subtracting first row from second and third} \\ &= 3 \end{aligned}$$

Therefore

$$\mathbf{A}^{-1} = \begin{bmatrix} 1\frac{2}{3} & -3 & \frac{1}{3} \\ -\frac{7}{3} & 3 & -\frac{2}{3} \\ \frac{2}{3} & -1 & \frac{1}{3} \end{bmatrix}$$

Check

$$\mathbf{AA}^{-1} = \begin{bmatrix} 1 & 2 & 3 \\ 1 & 3 & 5 \\ 1 & 5 & 12 \end{bmatrix} \begin{bmatrix} 1\frac{1}{3} & -3 & \frac{1}{3} \\ -\frac{7}{3} & 3 & -\frac{2}{3} \\ \frac{2}{3} & -1 & \frac{1}{3} \end{bmatrix}$$

$$= \begin{bmatrix} 1 & 0 & 0 \\ 0 & 1 & 0 \\ 0 & 0 & 1 \end{bmatrix}$$

Second Example. Leontief Statical Input-output System.

Let a_{ij} = input of product i per unit output of product j
X_i = total (gross) output of product i
C_i = consumption (final demand) of product i

Suppose we have just two products. Then we may write

$$\begin{aligned} a_{11}X_1 + a_{12}X_2 + C_1 &= X_1 \\ a_{21}X_1 + a_{22}X_2 + C_2 &= X_2 \end{aligned}$$

assuming no waste or excess production. Rearranging gives

$$\begin{aligned} (1 - a_{11})X_1 - a_{12}X_2 &= C_1 \\ -a_{21}X_1 + (1 - a_{22})X_2 &= C_2 \end{aligned}$$

or

$$\mathbf{AX} = \mathbf{C}$$

where

$$\mathbf{A} = \begin{bmatrix} 1 - a_{11} & -a_{12} \\ -a_{21} & 1 - a_{22} \end{bmatrix}$$

We may solve for **X** in terms of **C**; that is, we can find what total gross outputs X_1 and X_2 would be required to support a given program of final demand C_1, C_2.

$$\mathbf{X} = \mathbf{A}^{-1}\mathbf{C}$$

where

$$\mathbf{A}^{-1} = \frac{1}{(1 - a_{11})(1 - a_{22}) - a_{12}a_{21}} \begin{bmatrix} 1 - a_{22} & a_{12} \\ a_{21} & 1 - a_{11} \end{bmatrix}$$

so that

$$X_1 = \frac{1 - a_{22}}{\Delta} C_1 + \frac{a_{12}}{\Delta} C_2$$

$$X_2 = \frac{a_{21}}{\Delta} C_1 + \frac{1 - a_{11}}{\Delta} C_2$$

where

$$\Delta = (1 - a_{11})(1 - a_{22}) - a_{12}a_{21}$$

Cramer's Rule. If $\mathbf{Ax} = \mathbf{h}$, where **A** is a nonsingular matrix, premultiplication of both sides by $\mathbf{A}^{-1}$ gives

$$\mathbf{x} = \mathbf{A}^{-1}\mathbf{h}$$

For the 3 × 3 case this gives

$$\begin{bmatrix} x_1 \\ x_2 \\ x_3 \end{bmatrix} = \frac{1}{|\mathbf{A}|}\begin{bmatrix} c_{11} & c_{21} & c_{31} \\ c_{12} & c_{22} & c_{32} \\ c_{13} & c_{23} & c_{33} \end{bmatrix}\begin{bmatrix} h_1 \\ h_2 \\ h_3 \end{bmatrix}$$

where the c's denote co-factors. Thus

$$x_1 = \frac{h_1c_{11} + h_2c_{21} + h_3c_{31}}{|\mathbf{A}|}$$

The numerator in this expression for x_1 is the expansion of a determinant by the elements of the first column, where this column is $h_1 \quad h_2 \quad h_3$ and the remaining two columns are the second and third columns of **A**. Thus in a set of simultaneous equations, x_i is found as the ratio of two determinants, the first being that of the matrix of coefficients, in which the **h** vector has replaced the ith column, and the second being the determinant of the coefficient matrix.

$$x_1 = \frac{\begin{vmatrix} h_1 & a_{12} & a_{13} \\ h_2 & a_{22} & a_{23} \\ h_3 & a_{32} & a_{33} \end{vmatrix}}{|\mathbf{A}|} \qquad x_2 = \frac{\begin{vmatrix} a_{11} & h_1 & a_{13} \\ a_{21} & h_2 & a_{23} \\ a_{31} & h_3 & a_{33} \end{vmatrix}}{|\mathbf{A}|} \qquad x_3 = \frac{\begin{vmatrix} a_{11} & a_{12} & h_1 \\ a_{21} & a_{22} & h_2 \\ a_{31} & a_{32} & h_3 \end{vmatrix}}{|\mathbf{A}|}$$

Properties of Inverse Matrices

$$(\mathbf{AB})^{-1} = \mathbf{B}^{-1}\mathbf{A}^{-1} \tag{3-18}$$

Proof:

$$\begin{aligned} (\mathbf{AB})(\mathbf{B}^{-1}\mathbf{A}^{-1}) &= \mathbf{A}(\mathbf{BB}^{-1})\mathbf{A}^{-1} \\ &= \mathbf{AIA}^{-1} \\ &= \mathbf{AA}^{-1} \\ &= \mathbf{I} \end{aligned}$$

Similarly,

$$(\mathbf{B}^{-1}\mathbf{A}^{-1})(\mathbf{AB}) = \mathbf{I}$$

It is easy to extend this result to obtain

$$(\mathbf{ABC})^{-1} = \mathbf{C}^{-1}\mathbf{B}^{-1}\mathbf{A}^{-1} \tag{3-19}$$

By the definition of an inverse,

$$(\mathbf{A}^{-1})(\mathbf{A}^{-1})^{-1} = \mathbf{I}$$

Premultiplying both sides by $\mathbf{A}$,

$$\mathbf{AA}^{-1}(\mathbf{A}^{-1})^{-1} = \mathbf{AI}$$

$$\mathbf{I}(\mathbf{A}^{-1})^{-1} = \mathbf{A}$$

Thus
$$(\mathbf{A}^{-1})^{-1} = \mathbf{A} \tag{3-20}$$

$$(\mathbf{A}')^{-1} = (\mathbf{A}^{-1})' \tag{3-21}$$

i.e., the inverse of the transpose equals the transpose of the inverse.

Proof:
$$\mathbf{AA}^{-1} = \mathbf{I}$$

Transposing,
$$(\mathbf{A}^{-1})'\mathbf{A}' = \mathbf{I}$$

Postmultiply by $(\mathbf{A}')^{-1}$.

$$(\mathbf{A}^{-1})'\mathbf{A}'(\mathbf{A}')^{-1} = (\mathbf{A}')^{-1}$$

Thus
$$(\mathbf{A}^{-1})' = (\mathbf{A}')^{-1}$$

$$|\mathbf{A}^{-1}| = \frac{1}{|\mathbf{A}|} \tag{3-22}$$

There is an important result on determinants that $|\mathbf{AB}| = |\mathbf{A}| \cdot |\mathbf{B}|$.† We have $\mathbf{A}^{-1}\mathbf{A} = \mathbf{I}$.

Therefore
$$|\mathbf{I}| = 1 = |\mathbf{A}^{-1}\mathbf{A}| = |\mathbf{A}^{-1}| \cdot |\mathbf{A}|$$

Therefore
$$|\mathbf{A}^{-1}| = \frac{1}{|\mathbf{A}|}$$

3-3. Vector Differentiation

Suppose we have

$$\begin{aligned}\mathbf{a}'\mathbf{x} &= [a_1 \quad a_2 \quad \cdots \quad a_n]\{x_1 \quad x_2 \quad \cdots \quad x_n\} \\ &= a_1x_1 + a_2x_2 + \cdots + a_nx_n\end{aligned}$$

If we take the partial derivatives of $\mathbf{a}'\mathbf{x}$ with respect to the scalar x_i, we have

$$\frac{\partial(\mathbf{a}'\mathbf{x})}{\partial x_1} = a_1$$

$$\frac{\partial(\mathbf{a}'\mathbf{x})}{\partial x_2} = a_2$$

$$\vdots$$

$$\frac{\partial(\mathbf{a}'\mathbf{x})}{\partial x_n} = a_n$$

† See G. Hadley, *Linear Algebra*, Addison-Wesley, Reading, Mass., 1961, pp. 99–100.

and we see that the partial derivatives are simply the elements of the vector **a**. Thus if we form the n partial derivatives in turn and then arrange these as a vector **a**, we may consider the process to be one of vector differentiation, defined by

$$\frac{\partial(\mathbf{a}'\mathbf{x})}{\partial\mathbf{x}} = \mathbf{a} \tag{3-23}$$

where the left-hand side (LHS) indicates the operation of differentiating with respect to the elements of the **x** vector.

Consider now the quadratic form

$$\mathbf{x}'\mathbf{A}\mathbf{x} = [x_1 \quad x_2 \quad \cdots \quad x_n] \begin{bmatrix} a_{11} & a_{12} & \cdots & a_{1n} \\ a_{12} & a_{22} & \cdots & a_{2n} \\ \cdot & & & \cdot \\ \cdot & & & \cdot \\ \cdot & & & \cdot \\ a_{1n} & a_{2n} & \cdots & a_{nn} \end{bmatrix} \begin{bmatrix} x_1 \\ x_2 \\ \cdot \\ \cdot \\ \cdot \\ x_n \end{bmatrix}$$

$$\begin{aligned} = a_{11}x_1^2 + 2a_{12}x_1x_2 + 2a_{13}x_1x_3 + \cdots + 2a_{1n}x_1x_n \\ + \; a_{22}x_2^2 + 2a_{23}x_2x_3 + \cdots + 2a_{2n}x_2x_n \\ \cdot \\ \cdot \\ \cdot \\ + \; a_{nn}x_n^2 \end{aligned}$$

Taking partial derivatives with respect to the elements of **x** gives

$$\frac{\partial}{\partial x_1}(\mathbf{x}'\mathbf{A}\mathbf{x}) = 2(a_{11}x_1 + a_{12}x_2 + a_{13}x_3 + \cdots + a_{1n}x_n)$$

$$\frac{\partial}{\partial x_2}(\mathbf{x}'\mathbf{A}\mathbf{x}) = 2(a_{12}x_1 + a_{22}x_2 + a_{23}x_3 + \cdots + a_{2n}x_n)$$

$$\cdots \qquad \cdots$$

$$\frac{\partial}{\partial x_n}(\mathbf{x}'\mathbf{A}\mathbf{x}) = 2(a_{1n}x_1 + a_{2n}x_2 + a_{3n}x_3 + \cdots + a_{nn}x_n)$$

Apart from the multiplying factor 2, the right-hand sides (RHS) of the above equations contain the elements of the matrix product **Ax**, which give a *column* vector of n elements. Alternatively, we may regard the RHS of the above equations as the elements of the matrix product **x′A**, a *row* vector of n elements. Thus

$$\frac{\partial}{\partial x}(\mathbf{x}'\mathbf{A}\mathbf{x}) = 2\mathbf{A}\mathbf{x} \tag{3-24}$$

or

$$\frac{\partial}{\partial x}(\mathbf{x}'\mathbf{A}\mathbf{x}) = 2\mathbf{x}'\mathbf{A} \tag{3-25}$$

The choice between (3-24) and (3-25) is usually determined by the context in which differentiation takes place, for in matrix equations we can equate only matrices of the same order, and we cannot set a row vector equal to a column vector.

3-4. Partitioned Matrices

Since a matrix is a rectangular array of elements, we may divide it by means of horizontal and vertical lines into smaller arrays or submatrices. For example,

$$\mathbf{A} = \left[\begin{array}{ccc:c} a_{11} & a_{12} & a_{13} & a_{14} \\ a_{21} & a_{22} & a_{23} & a_{24} \\ \hdashline a_{31} & a_{32} & a_{33} & a_{34} \end{array}\right]$$

may be partitioned by means of the two lines shown to give the four submatrices

$$\begin{aligned} \mathbf{A}_{11} &= \begin{bmatrix} a_{11} & a_{12} & a_{13} \\ a_{21} & a_{22} & a_{23} \end{bmatrix} & \mathbf{A}_{12} &= \begin{bmatrix} a_{14} \\ a_{24} \end{bmatrix} \\ \mathbf{A}_{21} &= [a_{31} \quad a_{32} \quad a_{33}] & \mathbf{A}_{22} &= a_{34} \end{aligned} \tag{3-26}$$

and $\mathbf{A}$ may then be written

$$\mathbf{A} = \begin{bmatrix} \mathbf{A}_{11} & \mathbf{A}_{12} \\ \mathbf{A}_{21} & \mathbf{A}_{22} \end{bmatrix}$$

Notice that the partitioning lines must extend all the way across or up and down the original matrix.

The basic operations of addition and multiplication still apply to partitioned matrices, but the matrices must have been partitioned conformably. For example, if $\mathbf{B}$ is also of order 3×4 and is partitioned,

$$\mathbf{B} = \begin{bmatrix} \mathbf{B}_{11} & \mathbf{B}_{12} \\ \mathbf{B}_{21} & \mathbf{B}_{22} \end{bmatrix}$$

where $\mathbf{B}_{ij}$ is of the same order as $\mathbf{A}_{ij}$, then the sum $\mathbf{A} + \mathbf{B}$ can be written

$$\mathbf{A} + \mathbf{B} = \begin{bmatrix} \mathbf{A}_{11} + \mathbf{B}_{11} & \mathbf{A}_{12} + \mathbf{B}_{12} \\ \mathbf{A}_{21} + \mathbf{B}_{21} & \mathbf{A}_{22} + \mathbf{B}_{22} \end{bmatrix}$$

To consider multiplication, suppose **B** is of order 4 × 2:

$$\mathbf{B} = \begin{bmatrix} b_{11} & b_{12} \\ b_{21} & b_{22} \\ b_{31} & b_{32} \\ b_{41} & b_{42} \end{bmatrix}$$

The product **AB** can be formed and will be of order 3 × 2. For the product to be expressed in terms of partitioned matrices, the only condition is that the partitioning of the *rows* of **B** should conform to the partitioning of the *columns* of **A**. For example, let us partition **B** as follows:

$$\mathbf{B} = \begin{bmatrix} \mathbf{B}_{11} \\ \mathbf{B}_{21} \end{bmatrix}$$

$$\text{where} \qquad \mathbf{B}_{11} = \begin{bmatrix} b_{11} & b_{12} \\ b_{21} & b_{22} \\ b_{31} & b_{32} \end{bmatrix} \qquad \text{and} \qquad \mathbf{B}_{21} = [b_{41} \quad b_{42}] \tag{3-27}$$

If we treated the submatrices as ordinary elements, we should write the product **AB** as

$$\begin{aligned} \mathbf{AB} &= \begin{bmatrix} \mathbf{A}_{11} & \mathbf{A}_{12} \\ \mathbf{A}_{21} & \mathbf{A}_{22} \end{bmatrix} \begin{bmatrix} \mathbf{B}_{11} \\ \mathbf{B}_{21} \end{bmatrix} \\ &= \begin{bmatrix} \mathbf{A}_{11}\mathbf{B}_{11} + \mathbf{A}_{12}\mathbf{B}_{21} \\ \mathbf{A}_{21}\mathbf{B}_{11} + \mathbf{A}_{22}\mathbf{B}_{21} \end{bmatrix} \end{aligned} \tag{3-28}$$

Inspection of the elements in the products of the submatrices shows that (3-28) does in fact give the same result as would be obtained by straightforward multiplication of the original unpartitioned matrices. Thus the submatrices can be treated as ordinary elements provided the matrices have been partitioned conformably.

The condition for conformable partitioning would also have been satisfied by

$$\mathbf{B} = \begin{bmatrix} \mathbf{B}_{11} & \mathbf{B}_{12} \\ \mathbf{B}_{21} & \mathbf{B}_{22} \end{bmatrix}$$

where

$$\mathbf{B}_{11} = \begin{bmatrix} b_{11} \\ b_{21} \\ b_{31} \end{bmatrix} \qquad \mathbf{B}_{12} = \begin{bmatrix} b_{12} \\ b_{22} \\ b_{32} \end{bmatrix} \qquad \mathbf{B}_{21} = b_{41} \qquad \mathbf{B}_{22} = b_{42}$$

and the product would then appear as

$$\mathbf{AB} = \begin{bmatrix} \mathbf{A}_{11}\mathbf{B}_{11} + \mathbf{A}_{12}\mathbf{B}_{21} & \mathbf{A}_{11}\mathbf{B}_{12} + \mathbf{A}_{12}\mathbf{B}_{22} \\ \mathbf{A}_{21}\mathbf{B}_{11} + \mathbf{A}_{22}\mathbf{B}_{21} & \mathbf{A}_{21}\mathbf{B}_{12} + \mathbf{A}_{22}\mathbf{B}_{22} \end{bmatrix}$$

in terms of the new submatrices.

3-5. Linear Dependence and Rank

Consider a set of m vectors $\mathbf{a}_1, \mathbf{a}_2, \ldots, \mathbf{a}_m$, each of order $n \times 1$. If there exist scalars λ_i, not all zero, such that

$$\lambda_1\mathbf{a}_1 + \lambda_2\mathbf{a}_2 + \cdots + \lambda_m\mathbf{a}_m = \mathbf{0} \tag{3-29}$$

then the set of vectors is said to be *linearly dependent*. If the only scalars for which (3-29) holds are $\lambda_1 = \lambda_2 = \cdots = \lambda_m = 0$, then the set of vectors is said to be *linearly independent*.

For example, consider the vectors

$$\mathbf{a}_1 = \begin{bmatrix} 2 \\ 1 \\ 5 \end{bmatrix} \qquad \mathbf{a}_2 = \begin{bmatrix} 10 \\ 5 \\ 25 \end{bmatrix}$$

where, by inspection, $5\mathbf{a}_1 - \mathbf{a}_2 = \mathbf{0}$, so that the vectors are linearly dependent. Likewise, the vectors

$$\mathbf{a}_1 = \begin{bmatrix} 2 \\ 1 \\ 5 \end{bmatrix} \qquad \mathbf{a}_2 = \begin{bmatrix} 0 \\ 0 \\ 0 \end{bmatrix}$$

are linearly dependent since we can write $0\mathbf{a}_1 + \lambda_2\mathbf{a}_2 = \mathbf{0}$ for some $\lambda_2 \neq 0$. Notice that the definition of (3-29) is satisfied if only a single λ is nonzero. The vectors

$$\mathbf{a}_1 = \begin{bmatrix} 2 \\ 1 \\ 5 \end{bmatrix} \qquad \mathbf{a}_2 = \begin{bmatrix} 10 \\ 5 \\ 20 \end{bmatrix}$$

are linearly independent, since it is clearly impossible to find scalars λ_1 and λ_2 such that $\lambda_1\mathbf{a}_1 + \lambda_2\mathbf{a}_2 = \mathbf{0}$.

A set of m column vectors each of order $n \times 1$ may be arranged in the form of a matrix $\mathbf{A}$. The *rank* of the matrix, denoted by $\rho(\mathbf{A})$, is then defined as the maximum number of linearly independent columns. Thus

$$\mathbf{A}_1 = \begin{bmatrix} 2 & 10 \\ 1 & 5 \\ 5 & 25 \end{bmatrix} \quad \text{and} \quad \mathbf{A}_2 = \begin{bmatrix} 2 & 0 \\ 1 & 0 \\ 5 & 0 \end{bmatrix}$$

have each rank 1, while

$$\mathbf{A}_3 = \begin{bmatrix} 2 & 10 \\ 1 & 5 \\ 5 & 20 \end{bmatrix}$$

has rank 2. The rank of a matrix is a unique number and may also be defined as the maximum number of linearly independent rows.[1] By inspection of the above matrices we see that any two rows of $\mathbf{A}_1$ are linearly dependent, and the same holds for $\mathbf{A}_2$. For $\mathbf{A}_3$ the three rows are linearly dependent since, for example,

$$\text{1st row} - 2(\text{2d row}) + 0(\text{3d row}) = \mathbf{0}$$

Likewise, the first two rows are linearly dependent, but rows 1 and 3 are linearly independent and likewise rows 2 and 3 are linearly independent. Thus the rank of $\mathbf{A}_3$ is 2.

It follows from this definition of rank that the rank of a matrix cannot exceed the number of its rows or columns, whichever is the smaller.

It can be shown that the rank of an $m \times n$ matrix $\mathbf{A}$ is k if and only if every minor in $\mathbf{A}$ of order $k + 1$ vanishes, while at least one minor of order k does not vanish.[2] By inspection it can be seen that all second-order minors in $\mathbf{A}_1$ and $\mathbf{A}_2$ above are zero, but each possesses nonzero first-order minors and so has rank 1. In $\mathbf{A}_3$,

$$\begin{vmatrix} 2 & 10 \\ 1 & 5 \end{vmatrix} = 0$$

but

$$\begin{vmatrix} 2 & 10 \\ 5 & 20 \end{vmatrix} = -10 \quad \text{and} \quad \begin{vmatrix} 1 & 5 \\ 5 & 20 \end{vmatrix} = -5$$

so that the rank of $\mathbf{A}_3$ is 2. Thus one method of computing the rank of a matrix $\mathbf{A}$ is to look for the largest nonvanishing determinant, and the order of this determinant is the rank of $\mathbf{A}$.

[1] *Ibid.*, p. 142.
[2] *Ibid.*, pp. 140–141.

Two important remarks follow from this definition of rank in terms of nonvanishing determinants. First, a nonsingular matrix of order $n \times n$ has rank n, for the definition of a nonsingular matrix is one whose determinant is nonzero. Second, if an $n \times n$ matrix $\mathbf{A}$ has rank k, it is possible to express all other columns (or rows) as linear functions of a set of k linearly independent columns (or rows). Without loss of generality we may take the linearly independent columns as the first k columns $\mathbf{a}_1, \mathbf{a}_2, \ldots, \mathbf{a}_k$. Then for any column $\mathbf{a}_p (p > k)$, scalars λ_i exist, not all zero, such that

$$\lambda_1 \mathbf{a}_1 + \cdots + \lambda_k \mathbf{a}_k + \lambda_p \mathbf{a}_p = \mathbf{0}$$

But λ_p cannot be zero or the above equation would imply that $\mathbf{a}_1, \ldots, \mathbf{a}_k$ are linearly dependent, which contradicts our assumption. Thus $\mathbf{a}_p$ can be expressed as a linear function of the linearly independent set $\mathbf{a}_1, \ldots, \mathbf{a}_k$.

Next we state an important theorem on the rank of the product of two matrices.[1]

$$\rho(\mathbf{AB}) \leq \min [\rho(\mathbf{A}), \rho(\mathbf{B})] \tag{3-30}$$

This states that the rank of the product $\mathbf{AB}$ cannot exceed the smaller of the ranks of $\mathbf{A}$, $\mathbf{B}$. An important corollary of this result may be derived as follows. Suppose $\mathbf{B}$ is an $m \times n$ matrix $(m < n)$ with rank k $(k \leq m)$ and we premultiply $\mathbf{B}$ by a nonsingular matrix $\mathbf{A}$ of order m (and rank m).

Let $\rho(\mathbf{AB}) = K$.

By (3-30),

$$K \leq \min [m,k]$$

that is, $$K \leq k \tag{3-31}$$

But $$\mathbf{B} = \mathbf{A}^{-1}(\mathbf{AB})$$

therefore $$\rho(\mathbf{B}) \leq \min [\rho(\mathbf{A}^{-1}), \rho(\mathbf{AB})]$$

that is, $$k \leq K \tag{3-32}$$

Relations (3-31) and (3-32) together imply

$$K = k$$

A similar proof holds for the case of postmultiplication by a nonsingular matrix so that we have

$$\rho(\mathbf{AB}) = \rho(\mathbf{BC}) = \rho(\mathbf{B}) \tag{3-33}$$

if $\mathbf{A}$ and $\mathbf{C}$ are nonsingular matrices.

[1] *Ibid.*, p. 138.

This is a very important result, and it also leads to another method of determining the rank of a matrix. If we can multiply a matrix by a series of nonsingular matrices, we can obtain, by a suitable choice of nonsingular matrices, a new matrix whose rank is obvious from inspection, and hence we have obtained the rank of the original matrix.

Consider the matrix

$$\mathbf{A} = \begin{bmatrix} 2 & 10 \\ 1 & 5 \\ 5 & 20 \end{bmatrix}$$

Interchange the first and third rows to give

$$\begin{bmatrix} 5 & 20 \\ 1 & 5 \\ 2 & 10 \end{bmatrix}$$

Subtract twice the second row from the third:

$$\begin{bmatrix} 5 & 20 \\ 1 & 5 \\ 0 & 0 \end{bmatrix}$$

Divide through the first row by 5:

$$\begin{bmatrix} 1 & 4 \\ 1 & 5 \\ 0 & 0 \end{bmatrix}$$

Subtract the first row from the second:

$$\begin{bmatrix} 1 & 4 \\ 0 & 1 \\ 0 & 0 \end{bmatrix}$$

Subtract four times the first column from the second:

$$\begin{bmatrix} 1 & 0 \\ 0 & 1 \\ 0 & 0 \end{bmatrix}$$

Each of the above constitute *elementary operations* on the rows and columns, and the operations can be achieved by pre- or post-multiplication of the matrix by suitably chosen *elementary matrices.*

An elementary matrix is one obtained by performing elementary operations on the unit matrix. For example, to interchange the first and third rows of **A** we interchange the first and third rows of $\mathbf{I}_3$ to give

$$\mathbf{E}_1 = \begin{bmatrix} 0 & 0 & 1 \\ 0 & 1 & 0 \\ 1 & 0 & 0 \end{bmatrix}$$

and then form the product $\mathbf{E}_1\mathbf{A}$ to give

$$\begin{bmatrix} 5 & 20 \\ 1 & 5 \\ 2 & 10 \end{bmatrix}$$

as in the first step above. The next step is to form $\mathbf{E}_2$ by subtracting twice the second row of $\mathbf{I}_3$ from the third:

$$\mathbf{E}_2 = \begin{bmatrix} 1 & 0 & 0 \\ 0 & 1 & 0 \\ 0 & -2 & 1 \end{bmatrix}$$

The first four steps above thus correspond to the premultiplication of **A** by

$$\mathbf{E} = \overset{\mathbf{E}_4}{\begin{bmatrix} 1 & 0 & 0 \\ -1 & 1 & 0 \\ 0 & 0 & 1 \end{bmatrix}} \overset{\mathbf{E}_3}{\begin{bmatrix} \frac{1}{5} & 0 & 0 \\ 0 & 1 & 0 \\ 0 & 0 & 1 \end{bmatrix}} \overset{\mathbf{E}_2}{\begin{bmatrix} 1 & 0 & 0 \\ 0 & 1 & 0 \\ 0 & -2 & 1 \end{bmatrix}} \overset{\mathbf{E}_1}{\begin{bmatrix} 0 & 0 & 1 \\ 0 & 1 & 0 \\ 1 & 0 & 0 \end{bmatrix}}$$

$$= \begin{bmatrix} 0 & 0 & \frac{1}{5} \\ 0 & 1 & -\frac{1}{5} \\ 1 & -2 & 0 \end{bmatrix} \tag{3-34}$$

Operations on the columns of **A** are achieved by postmultiplying **A** by elementary matrices in which the appropriate elementary operations have been carried out on the columns of **I**. In the above example only a single operation is required, which may be indicated by

$$\mathbf{F} = \begin{bmatrix} 1 & -4 \\ 0 & 1 \end{bmatrix} \tag{3-35}$$

Thus the above transformation of **A** has been achieved by forming the product

$$\mathbf{EAF}$$

These elementary matrices are all nonsingular, and hence elementary operations do not change the rank of a matrix.

Thus $\rho(\mathbf{EAF}) = \rho(\mathbf{A})$, and since

$$\mathbf{EAF} = \begin{bmatrix} 1 & 0 \\ 0 & 1 \\ 0 & 0 \end{bmatrix}$$

it is obvious that the rank of **A** is 2.

In general, for any matrix **A** elementary row and column operations exist, summarized in the nonsingular matrices **E** and **F**, such that

$$\mathbf{EAF} = \begin{bmatrix} \mathbf{I}_k & \mathbf{0} \\ \mathbf{0} & \mathbf{0} \end{bmatrix} \tag{3-36}$$

and $\rho(\mathbf{A}) = k$. Depending on the order and rank of **A**, some or all of the **0** submatrices on the right-hand side of (3-36) may not exist. If **A** is $n \times n$ and nonsingular, then $\mathbf{EAF} = \mathbf{I}_n$.

3-6. Characteristic Roots and Vectors

When we add to the above results on rank some results on characteristic values, we are in a position to derive some important results on quadratic forms which have a direct application in linear statistical models.

The characteristic-value problem is defined as that of finding values of a scalar λ and an associated vector $\mathbf{x} \neq \mathbf{0}$ which satisfy

$$\mathbf{Ax} = \lambda\mathbf{x} \tag{3-37}$$

where **A** is a given $n \times n$ matrix. λ is called a characteristic root of **A**, and **x** a characteristic vector. Alternative names are latent roots and vectors and eigenvalues and eigenvectors. If we take the 2×2 case as an illustration of (3-37), we have

$$\begin{aligned} (a_{11} - \lambda)x_1 + a_{12}x_2 &= 0 \\ a_{21}x_1 + (a_{22} - \lambda)x_2 &= 0 \end{aligned} \tag{3-38}$$

which may be put back in matrix form as

$$(\mathbf{A} - \lambda\mathbf{I})\mathbf{x} = \mathbf{0} \tag{3-39}$$

For **A** and **x** of appropriate order, (3-39) is an alternative form of (3-37). If the matrix $(\mathbf{A} - \lambda\mathbf{I})$ were nonsingular, we could multiply through (3-39) by its inverse, and the only solution to (3-39) would be the null vector $\mathbf{x} = \mathbf{0}$. Thus there will be a solution $\mathbf{x} \neq \mathbf{0}$ only if $(\mathbf{A} - \lambda\mathbf{I})$ is singular, that is, if

$$|\mathbf{A} - \lambda\mathbf{I}| = 0 \tag{3-40}$$

Equation (3-40) yields a polynomial in the unknown λ, which may then be solved for λ, and then the characteristic vectors obtained.

For example, in the 2×2 case, (3-40) gives

$$\begin{vmatrix} a_{11} - \lambda & a_{12} \\ a_{21} & a_{22} - \lambda \end{vmatrix} = 0 \tag{3-41}$$

that is,

$$(a_{11} - \lambda)(a_{22} - \lambda) - a_{12}a_{21} = 0$$

$$\lambda^2 - (a_{11} + a_{22})\lambda + (a_{11}a_{22} - a_{12}a_{21}) = 0$$

with roots

$$\begin{aligned} \lambda_1 &= \tfrac{1}{2}\left[(a_{11} + a_{22}) + \sqrt{(a_{11} + a_{22})^2 - 4(a_{11}a_{22} - a_{12}a_{21})}\right] \\ \lambda_2 &= \tfrac{1}{2}\left[(a_{11} + a_{22}) - \sqrt{(a_{11} + a_{22})^2 - 4(a_{11}a_{22} - a_{12}a_{21})}\right] \end{aligned} \tag{3-42}$$

In the special case of a symmetric matrix, $a_{12} = a_{21}$ and the roots become

$$\begin{aligned} \lambda_1 &= \tfrac{1}{2}\left[(a_{11} + a_{22}) + \sqrt{(a_{11} - a_{22})^2 + 4a_{12}^2}\right] \\ \lambda_2 &= \tfrac{1}{2}\left[(a_{11} + a_{22}) - \sqrt{(a_{11} - a_{22})^2 + 4a_{12}^2}\right] \end{aligned} \tag{3-43}$$

and since the content of the square-root sign is the sum of two squares, the roots λ_1 and λ_2 are necessarily real in the symmetric case.

For a numerical example, consider

$$\mathbf{A} = \begin{bmatrix} 4 & 2 \\ 2 & 1 \end{bmatrix}$$

Substitution in (3-43) gives $\lambda_1 = 5$, and $\lambda_2 = 0$. To find the characteristic vector associated with each root, we return to (3-39). For $\lambda_1 = 5$,

$$(\mathbf{A} - \lambda\mathbf{I}) = \begin{bmatrix} -1 & 2 \\ 2 & -4 \end{bmatrix}$$

and Eq. (3-39) gives

$$\begin{aligned} -x_1 + 2x_2 &= 0 \\ 2x_1 - 4x_2 &= 0 \end{aligned}$$

that is,

$$x_1 = 2x_2$$

Thus one element in the characteristic vector is arbitrary, and so if $\mathbf{x}$ satisfies (3-39) for a given λ, then so does $k\mathbf{x}$, where k is an arbitrary constant. We may standardize the vector by making the sum of the squares of its elements unity, i.e.,

$$x_1^2 + x_2^2 = 1$$

which with $x_1 = 2x_2$ gives

$$x_2 = \frac{1}{\sqrt{5}} \quad \text{and} \quad x_1 = \frac{2}{\sqrt{5}}$$

so that the characteristic vector associated with $\lambda_1 = 5$ is

$$\mathbf{u}_1 = \{2/\sqrt{5} \quad 1/\sqrt{5}\}$$

Similarly, it may be shown that the characteristic vector associated with $\lambda_2 = 0$ is

$$\mathbf{u}_2 = \{1/\sqrt{5} \quad -2/\sqrt{5}\}$$

We notice that $\mathbf{u}_1'\mathbf{u}_2 = 0$, which means that the characteristic vectors of this symmetric matrix are *orthogonal.*[1] These two results of real characteristic roots and orthogonal characteristic vectors hold for all symmetric matrices.[2] Furthermore, if a characteristic root λ_j has multiplicity k (i.e., is repeated k times), there will be exactly k orthogonal characteristic vectors corresponding to this root.[3]

The nth-order symmetric matrix $\mathbf{A}$ has characteristic roots $\lambda_1, \lambda_2, \ldots, \lambda_n$, possibly not all distinct. Corresponding to these roots are a set of orthogonal characteristic vectors $\mathbf{u}_1, \mathbf{u}_2, \ldots, \mathbf{u}_n$ such that

$$\mathbf{u}_i'\mathbf{u}_j = 0 \qquad i \neq j; i,j = 1, 2, \ldots, n$$

We can, without loss of generality, normalize the vectors so that $\mathbf{u}_i'\mathbf{u}_i = 1$ for all i. A set of normalized orthogonal vectors is called an *orthonormal* set. Let $\mathbf{Q}$ be the nth-order matrix whose columns consist of the vectors $\mathbf{u}_i$, and we can write these two conditions as

$$\mathbf{u}_i'\mathbf{u}_j = \delta_{ij} \qquad \delta_{ij} = \begin{cases} 0 & i \neq j \\ 1 & i = j \end{cases} \tag{3-44}$$

It then follows that

$$\mathbf{Q}'\mathbf{Q} = \mathbf{I}_n \tag{3-45}$$

so that

$$\mathbf{Q}' = \mathbf{Q}^{-1} \tag{3-46}$$

[1] Two vectors $\mathbf{x}$ and $\mathbf{y}$ are said to be orthogonal if $\mathbf{x}'\mathbf{y} = \mathbf{y}'\mathbf{x} = 0$.

[2] See Hadley, *op. cit.*, pp. 240–241.

[3] *Ibid.*, pp. 243–245.

that is, the transpose of **Q** is equal to its inverse. Such a matrix is said to be an *orthogonal* matrix.

If we now form the product $\mathbf{Q'AQ}$, the ijth element in the resulting nth-order matrix is

$$\mathbf{u}_i'\mathbf{A}\mathbf{u}_j = \mathbf{u}_i'\lambda_j\mathbf{u}_j$$

applying (3-37), since $\mathbf{u}_j$ is the characteristic vector corresponding to λ_j. Thus

$$\begin{aligned} \mathbf{u}_i'\mathbf{A}\mathbf{u}_j &= \lambda_j\mathbf{u}_i'\mathbf{u}_j \\ &= \lambda_j\delta_{ij} \qquad \text{using (3-44)} \end{aligned}$$

Hence

$$\mathbf{Q'AQ} = \begin{bmatrix} \lambda_1 & 0 & 0 & \cdots & 0 \\ 0 & \lambda_2 & 0 & \cdots & 0 \\ 0 & 0 & \lambda_3 & \cdots & 0 \\ \cdot & & & & \cdot \\ \cdot & & & & \cdot \\ \cdot & & & & \cdot \\ 0 & 0 & 0 & \cdots & \lambda_n \end{bmatrix} \tag{3-47}$$

Thus assembling the characteristic vectors of **A** as the columns of **Q** and forming the product $\mathbf{Q'AQ}$ has produced a diagonal matrix with the characteristic roots of **A** displayed on the principal diagonal.

Equation (3-47) represents the diagonalization of the matrix **A**. The same technique may be applied to the diagonalization of quadratic forms. Consider the quadratic form $\mathbf{x'Ax}$. As shown on page 74 above, this involves terms in x_i^2 and cross-product terms in x_ix_j. Now let us define a nonsingular transformation of variables

$$\mathbf{x} = \mathbf{Qy} \tag{3-48}$$

where **Q** is the matrix of characteristic vectors of **A**. Substituting (3-48) in the quadratic form gives

$$\mathbf{y'Q'AQy} \tag{3-49}$$

which is a quadratic form in **y** with matrix $\mathbf{Q'AQ}$. Since this matrix is shown in (3-47) to be a diagonal matrix, we have

$$\mathbf{x'Ax} = \lambda_1y_1^2 + \lambda_2y_2^2 + \cdots + \lambda_ny_n^2 \tag{3-50}$$

that is, the quadratic form in the x's has been shown equivalent to a weighted sum of squares of y's, where the y's are linear functions of the x's.

Suppose the **x** vector consists of normally and independently distributed variables with zero mean and constant variance; that is,

$$\begin{aligned} E(x_i) &= 0 \qquad i = 1, \ldots, n \\ E(x_i^2) &= \sigma^2 \qquad i = 1, \ldots, n \\ E(x_ix_j) &= 0 \qquad i \neq j \end{aligned}$$

Then the transformation (3-48) ensures that the **y** vector consists of independent normal variables with the same mean and variance. The transformation (3-48) gives

$$\mathbf{y} = \mathbf{Q}'\mathbf{x} \qquad \text{since } \mathbf{Q} \text{ is orthogonal}$$

Thus

$$y_i = \mathbf{q}_i'\mathbf{x}$$

where $\mathbf{q}_i$ is the *i*th characteristic vector of **A**; that is,

$$y_i = \sum_{s=1}^{n} q_{is}x_s$$

Therefore

$$\begin{aligned} E(y_i) &= 0 \qquad \text{for all } i \\ E(y_i^2) &= q_{i1}^2E(x_1^2) + q_{i2}^2E(x_2^2) + \cdots + q_{in}^2E(x_n^2) \\ &\qquad + 2q_{i1}q_{i2}E(x_1x_2) + \cdots + 2q_{i,n-1}q_{in}E(x_{n-1}x_n) \\ &= \sigma^2 \end{aligned}$$

since $\sum_{s=1}^{n} q_{is}^2 = 1$ as characteristic vectors form an orthonormal set and $E(x_ix_j) = 0$, for $i \neq j$.

$$\begin{aligned} E(y_iy_j) &= q_{i1}q_{j1}E(x_1^2) + q_{i2}q_{j2}E(x_2^2) + \cdots + q_{in}q_{jn}E(x_n^2) \\ &\qquad + \text{cross-product terms} \\ &= 0 \end{aligned}$$

since $\sum_{s=1}^{n} q_{is}q_{js} = 0$ for orthonormal vectors.

An especially important case of (3-50) arises when **A** is an *idempotent* matrix. We are concerned only with symmetric idempotent matrices which are defined as

$$\begin{aligned} \mathbf{A} &= \mathbf{A}' \\ \mathbf{A}^2 &= \mathbf{A} \end{aligned} \tag{3-51}$$

that is, an idempotent matrix is one which on multiplication by itself remains unchanged.

The characteristic roots of an idempotent matrix are either zero or unity. For

$$\mathbf{Ax} = \lambda\mathbf{x}$$

Therefore

$$\mathbf{A}^2\mathbf{x} = \lambda\mathbf{Ax} = \lambda^2\mathbf{x}$$

But

$$\mathbf{A}^2\mathbf{x} = \mathbf{Ax} = \lambda\mathbf{x}$$

Hence

$$\lambda^2\mathbf{x} = \lambda\mathbf{x}$$

But

$$\mathbf{x} \neq \mathbf{0}$$

Hence

$$\lambda^2 - \lambda = 0 \quad \text{and} \quad \lambda = 0 \quad \text{or} \quad \lambda = 1$$

It then follows from (3-47) that when an idempotent matrix of order n and of rank $n - k$ $(0 \leq k < n)$ is diagonalized, there will be $n - k$ units in the principal diagonal, and k zeros for the rank of the matrix on the right-hand side must be $n - k$, since the multiplication of **A** by nonsingular matrices cannot change the rank. We thus have the important result that if $\mathbf{x}'\mathbf{Ax}$ is a quadratic form in n independent normal variables with zero mean and common variance σ^2, and if **A** is idempotent of rank $n - k$, then

$$\mathbf{x}'\mathbf{Ax} = y_1^2 + \cdots + y_{n-k}^2 \tag{3-52}$$

where the y's are also independent normal variables with zero mean and variance σ^2.

Example. The following rather lengthy example should be worked through carefully since it illustrates many points of importance for Chap. 4. Consider

$$\mathbf{X} = \begin{bmatrix} 1 & 1 \\ 1 & 2 \\ 1 & 3 \end{bmatrix}$$

Then

$$(\mathbf{X}'\mathbf{X}) = \begin{bmatrix} 3 & 6 \\ 6 & 14 \end{bmatrix} \quad \text{and} \quad |\mathbf{X}'\mathbf{X}| = 6$$

$$(\mathbf{X}'\mathbf{X})^{-1} = \begin{bmatrix} 14/6 & -1 \\ -1 & 3/6 \end{bmatrix}$$

and

$$\mathbf{X}(\mathbf{X}'\mathbf{X})^{-1}\mathbf{X}' = \begin{bmatrix} 5/6 & 2/6 & -1/6 \\ 2/6 & 2/6 & 2/6 \\ -1/6 & 2/6 & 5/6 \end{bmatrix}$$

Define a new matrix **A** as

$$\mathbf{A} = \mathbf{I}_3 - \mathbf{X}(\mathbf{X}'\mathbf{X})^{-1}\mathbf{X}' = \begin{bmatrix} 1/6 & -2/6 & 1/6 \\ -2/6 & 4/6 & -2/6 \\ 1/6 & -2/6 & 1/6 \end{bmatrix}$$

A is seen to be a symmetric matrix. It is also an idempotent matrix, for $\mathbf{A}^2 = \mathbf{A}$. We notice also that **A** has rank 1, since all second-order minors vanish.

We now wish to find the characteristic roots and vectors of **A**. The characteristic equation

$$|\mathbf{A} - \lambda\mathbf{I}| = 0$$

gives, on expansion by the first row (or column) of $(\mathbf{A} - \lambda\mathbf{I})$,

$$(\tfrac{1}{6} - \lambda)[(\tfrac{4}{6} - \lambda)(\tfrac{1}{6} - \lambda) - \tfrac{4}{36}] + \tfrac{2}{6}[-\tfrac{2}{6}(\tfrac{1}{6} - \lambda) + \tfrac{2}{36}] + \tfrac{1}{6}[\tfrac{4}{36} - \tfrac{1}{6}(\tfrac{4}{6} - \lambda)] = 0$$

that is,

$$\lambda^3 - \lambda^2 = 0 \tag{3-53}$$

Equation (3-53) has roots $\lambda_1 = 1$ and $\lambda_2 = 0$ with multiplicity 2, which illustrate the result that the characteristic roots of an idempotent matrix are either zero or unity and that the number of unit roots is equal to the rank of the matrix. Corresponding to $\lambda_1 = 1$,

$$(\mathbf{A} - \lambda\mathbf{I}) = \begin{bmatrix} -\tfrac{5}{6} & -\tfrac{2}{6} & \tfrac{1}{6} \\ -\tfrac{2}{6} & -\tfrac{2}{6} & -\tfrac{2}{6} \\ \tfrac{1}{6} & -\tfrac{2}{6} & -\tfrac{5}{6} \end{bmatrix}$$

and the matrix equation $(\mathbf{A} - \lambda\mathbf{I})\mathbf{x} = \mathbf{0}$ gives

$$\begin{aligned} -5x_1 - 2x_2 + x_3 &= 0 \\ -2x_1 - 2x_2 - 2x_3 &= 0 \\ x_1 - 2x_2 - 5x_3 &= 0 \end{aligned} \tag{3-54}$$

To these three equations we append

$$x_1^2 + x_2^2 + x_3^2 = 1 \tag{3-55}$$

in order to normalize the **x** vector.

Equations (3-54) and (3-55) yield the **x** vector

$$\mathbf{x} = \left\{ \frac{1}{\sqrt{6}} \quad \frac{-2}{\sqrt{6}} \quad \frac{1}{\sqrt{6}} \right\} \tag{3-56}$$

For $\lambda = 0$ the equation $(\mathbf{A} - \lambda\mathbf{I})\mathbf{x} = \mathbf{0}$ gives only a single independent equation

$$x_1 - 2x_2 + x_3 = 0 \tag{3-57}$$

which, with the normalization equation (3-55), means that one of the x's can be set at an arbitrary value. For example, let $x_3 = 0$; then (3-55) and (3-57) give

$$\mathbf{x}^* = \left\{ \frac{2}{\sqrt{5}} \quad \frac{1}{\sqrt{5}} \quad 0 \right\} \tag{3-58}$$

which is one characteristic vector associated with the root $\lambda = 0$. Since this root has multiplicity 2, we expect another characteristic vector $\mathbf{x}^{**}$ associated with the root and orthogonal to $\mathbf{x}^*$. The orthogonality condition $(\mathbf{x}^*)'\mathbf{x}^{**} = 0$ implies

$$2x_1^{**} + x_2^{**} = 0 \tag{3-59}$$

Since $\mathbf{x}^{**}$ is associated with $\lambda = 0$, it must also satisfy (3-57) and, of course, the normalization condition (3-55). These three equations give

$$\mathbf{x}^{**} = \left\{\frac{1}{\sqrt{30}} \quad \frac{-2}{\sqrt{30}} \quad \frac{-5}{\sqrt{30}}\right\} \tag{3-60}$$

Now define the matrix $\mathbf{Q}$ whose columns consist of the three characteristic vectors (3-56), (3-58), and (3-60).

$$\mathbf{Q} = \begin{bmatrix} \frac{1}{\sqrt{6}} & \frac{2}{\sqrt{5}} & \frac{1}{\sqrt{30}} \\ \frac{-2}{\sqrt{6}} & \frac{1}{\sqrt{5}} & \frac{-2}{\sqrt{30}} \\ \frac{1}{\sqrt{6}} & 0 & \frac{-5}{\sqrt{30}} \end{bmatrix} \tag{3-61}$$

Letting q_i denote the ith column of $\mathbf{Q}$, we see that

$$q_i'q_j = \begin{cases} 0 & \text{for } i \neq j \\ 1 & \text{for } i = j \end{cases} \tag{3-62}$$

that is, $\mathbf{Q}$ is an orthogonal matrix and $\mathbf{Q}' = \mathbf{Q}^{-1}$.

If the reader now forms the product $\mathbf{Q}'\mathbf{A}\mathbf{Q}$, he will find

$$\mathbf{Q}'\mathbf{A}\mathbf{Q} = \begin{bmatrix} 1 & 0 & 0 \\ 0 & 0 & 0 \\ 0 & 0 & 0 \end{bmatrix}$$

as is to be expected from (3-47) above.

If we have a quadratic form $\mathbf{u}'\mathbf{A}\mathbf{u}$, where the u_i are independent standard normal variables, and we define

$$\mathbf{v} = \mathbf{Q}'\mathbf{u} \tag{3-63}$$

then the v_i will also be independent standard normal variables. We have

$$v_i = q_{i1}u_1 + q_{i2}u_2 + q_{i3}u_3 \qquad i = 1, 2, 3$$

where q_{i1}, q_{i2}, q_{i3} are the elements in the ith column of $\mathbf{Q}$. Hence

$$\begin{aligned} E(v_i) &= 0 && \text{since } E(u_i) = 0 \text{ for all } i \\ E(v_i^2) &= \sum_{j=1}^{3} q_{ij}^2 && \text{since } E(u_i^2) = 1 \text{ for all } i \\ &= 1 && \text{from (3-62)} \end{aligned} \tag{3-64}$$

and

$$\begin{aligned} E(v_iv_j) &= \sum_{r=1}^{3} q_{ir}q_{jr} \\ &= q_i'q_j \\ &= 0 && \text{from (3-62)} \end{aligned}$$

Substituting (3-63) in the quadratic form u′Au gives

$$\begin{aligned} \mathbf{u'Au} &= \mathbf{v'Q'AQv} \\ &= v_1^2 \end{aligned} \tag{3-65}$$

The original quadratic form involved terms in u_1^2, u_2^2, u_3^2 and cross-product terms in u_iu_j. However, on the assumption that the matrix **A** of the form is idempotent of rank 1, we have shown that it is possible to define an orthogonal transformation $\mathbf{u} = \mathbf{Qv}$ such that $\mathbf{u'Au} = v_1^2$.

References

There are many introductory books on matrix algebra available, but one of the best for social science students is

1. G. Hadley: *Linear Algebra,* Addison-Wesley, Reading, Mass., 1961.

A very useful summary of matrix results, though mostly without proofs, is contained in the first chapter of

2. Franklin A. Graybill: *An Introduction to Linear Statistical Models,* McGraw-Hill, New York, 1961, vol. I.

Exercises

3-1. Expand (A + B)(A − B) and (A − B)(A + B). Are these expansions the same? If not, why not? How many terms in each?

3-2. Given

$$\mathbf{A} = \begin{bmatrix} 1 & 0 & 3 \\ 2 & -1 & 1 \end{bmatrix}$$

$$\mathbf{B} = \begin{bmatrix} 3 & 4 & 1 \\ 0 & -1 & 5 \\ 1 & 2 & -2 \end{bmatrix} \qquad \mathbf{C} = \begin{bmatrix} 2 \\ -1 \\ 4 \end{bmatrix}$$

Calculate (AB)′, B′A′, (AC)′, and C′A′.

3-3. Find all matrices **B** obeying the equation

$$\begin{bmatrix} 0 & 1 \\ 0 & 2 \end{bmatrix} \mathbf{B} = \begin{bmatrix} 0 & 0 & 1 \\ 0 & 0 & 2 \end{bmatrix}$$

3-4. Find all matrices **B** which commute with

$$\mathbf{A} = \begin{bmatrix} 0 & 1 \\ 0 & 2 \end{bmatrix}$$

to give AB = BA.

3-5. Write down a few matrices of order 3 × 3 with numerical elements. Find first their squares and then their cubes, checking the latter by using the two processes $\mathbf{A}(\mathbf{A}^2)$ and $\mathbf{A}^2(\mathbf{A})$.

3-6. Prove that diagonal matrices of the same order are commutative in multiplication with each other.

3-7. Let

$$\mathbf{J} = \begin{bmatrix} 0 & 0 & 1 \\ 0 & 1 & 0 \\ 1 & 0 & 0 \end{bmatrix}$$

Write out in full some products **JA**, where **A** is a rectangular matrix. Describe in words the effect on **A**. Do the same with products of type **AJ**. Find $\mathbf{J}^2$.

3-8. If

$$\mathbf{V} = \begin{bmatrix} 0 & 1 & 0 \\ 0 & 0 & 1 \\ 0 & 0 & 0 \end{bmatrix}$$

find $\mathbf{V}^2$ and $\mathbf{V}^3$. Examine some products of type **VA**, $\mathbf{V}^2\mathbf{A}$, and $\mathbf{V}'\mathbf{A}$.

3-9. Prove that if **A** and **B** are such that **AB** and **BA** coexist, then **AB** and **BA** have the same sum of diagonal elements [tr (**AB**) = tr (**BA**)].

3-10. Given

$$\mathbf{A} = \begin{bmatrix} 1 & 3 & 2 \\ 2 & 6 & 9 \\ 7 & 6 & 1 \end{bmatrix} \quad \text{and} \quad \mathbf{E} = \begin{bmatrix} 0 & 1 & 0 \\ 1 & 0 & 0 \\ 0 & 0 & 1 \end{bmatrix}$$

Calculate $|\mathbf{A}|$, $|\mathbf{E}|$, and $|\mathbf{B}|$, where $\mathbf{B} = \mathbf{EA}$.
Verify that $|\mathbf{B}| = |\mathbf{E}|\,|\mathbf{A}|$.

3-11. Show that

$$\begin{vmatrix} 1 & 1 & 1 \\ a & b & c \\ a^2 & b^2 & c^2 \end{vmatrix} = (c - b)(c - a)(b - a)$$

3-12. If (x_1y_1) and (x_2y_2) are points on the x, y plane, show that the equation

$$\begin{vmatrix} x & y & 1 \\ x_1 & y_1 & 1 \\ x_2 & y_2 & 1 \end{vmatrix} = 0$$

represents a straight line through these two points.

3-13. Prove that

$$\begin{vmatrix} a_{11} & a_{12} & \cdots & a_{1n} \\ 0 & a_{22} & \cdots & a_{2n} \\ \cdot & & & \cdot \\ \cdot & & & \cdot \\ 0 & 0 & \cdots & a_{nn} \end{vmatrix} = a_{11} \quad a_{22} \quad \ldots \quad a_{nn}$$

3-14. Prove that the determinant of a skew-symmetric matrix of odd order vanishes identically. (If **A** is a skew-symmetric matrix, then $\mathbf{A}' = -\mathbf{A}$.)

3-15. Show that the matrix

$$\mathbf{Q} = \begin{bmatrix} \frac{1}{\sqrt{6}} & \frac{2}{\sqrt{5}} & \frac{1}{\sqrt{30}} \\ \frac{-2}{\sqrt{6}} & \frac{1}{\sqrt{5}} & \frac{-2}{\sqrt{30}} \\ \frac{1}{\sqrt{6}} & 0 & \frac{-5}{\sqrt{30}} \end{bmatrix}$$

is orthogonal, i.e., that $\mathbf{Q}' = \mathbf{Q}^{-1}$.

3-16. If the u_i are normal variables with

$$\begin{aligned} E(u_i) &= 0 \qquad & i &= 1, \ldots, n \\ E(u_i^2) &= \sigma^2 \qquad & i &= 1, \ldots, n \\ E(u_i u_j) &= 0 \qquad & i &\neq j \end{aligned}$$

show that $E(\mathbf{u}'\mathbf{A}\mathbf{u}) = \sigma^2 \operatorname{tr}(\mathbf{A})$.

3-17. Given

$$\mathbf{X} = \begin{bmatrix} 1 & 1 \\ 1 & 2 \\ 1 & 1 \\ 1 & 3 \end{bmatrix}$$

Compute $\qquad \mathbf{A} = (\mathbf{I}_4 - \mathbf{X}(\mathbf{X}'\mathbf{X})^{-1}\mathbf{X}')$

Show that A is idempotent and determine its rank. Find the characteristic roots and associated characteristic vectors of A, and hence obtain the orthogonal matrix which diagonalizes A.

3-18. If A is an $n \times k$ matrix of rank k, show that

$$\rho(\mathbf{A}'\mathbf{A}) = \rho(\mathbf{A}') = \rho(\mathbf{A})$$

3-19. Extend the result of Exercise 3-9 to show that

$$\operatorname{tr}(\mathbf{ABC}) = \operatorname{tr}(\mathbf{BCA}) = \operatorname{tr}(\mathbf{CAB})$$

provided the matrices are conformable for multiplication.

4

The General Linear Model

We now set out as compactly as possible the general linear model in k variables. To do so we shall use the matrix notation developed in Chap. 3 and also make use of many of the results obtained in that chapter.

4-1. Assumptions

Let us assume that a linear relationship exists between a variable Y and $k - 1$ explanatory variables $X_2, X_3, \ldots, X_k$ and a disturbance term u. If we have a sample of n observations on Y and the X's we can write

$$Y_i = \beta_1 + \beta_2 X_{2i} + \cdots + \beta_k X_{ki} + u_i \qquad i = 1, 2, \ldots, n \tag{4-1}$$

The β coefficients and the parameters of the u distribution are unknown, and our problem is to obtain estimates of these unknowns. The n equations in (4-1) can be set out compactly in matrix notation as

$$\mathbf{Y} = \mathbf{X}\boldsymbol{\beta} + \mathbf{u} \tag{4-2}$$

where

$$\mathbf{Y} = \begin{bmatrix} Y_1 \\ Y_2 \\ \cdot \\ \cdot \\ \cdot \\ Y_n \end{bmatrix} \qquad \mathbf{X} = \begin{bmatrix} 1 & X_{21} & \cdots & X_{k1} \\ 1 & X_{22} & \cdots & X_{k2} \\ \cdot & & & \cdot \\ \cdot & & & \cdot \\ \cdot & & & \cdot \\ 1 & X_{2n} & \cdots & X_{kn} \end{bmatrix}$$

$$\boldsymbol{\beta} = \begin{bmatrix} \beta_1 \\ \beta_2 \\ \cdot \\ \cdot \\ \cdot \\ \beta_k \end{bmatrix} \qquad \mathbf{u} = \begin{bmatrix} u_1 \\ u_2 \\ \cdot \\ \cdot \\ \cdot \\ u_n \end{bmatrix} \tag{4-3}$$

The intercept term β_1 requires the insertion of a column of units in the $\mathbf{X}$ matrix. The convention of using X_{ki} to denote the ith observation on the variable X_k means that the subscripts in the $\mathbf{X}$ matrix follow the reverse of the normal pattern, where the first subscript usually indicates the row, and the second the column, of the matrix.

To make any progress with the estimation of the vector of coefficients $\boldsymbol{\beta}$, we must make some further assumptions about how the observations in (4-1) have been generated. These assumptions are crucial for the estimation process, and we commence with the simplest set, leaving for later chapters a detailed treatment of the cases where one or more of these assumptions is not fulfilled. The simplest set of crucial assumptions is

$$E(\mathbf{u}) = \mathbf{0} \tag{4-4a}$$

$$E(\mathbf{uu}') = \sigma^2\mathbf{I}_n \tag{4-4b}$$

$$\mathbf{X} \text{ is a set of fixed numbers} \tag{4-4c}$$

$$\mathbf{X} \text{ has rank } k < n \tag{4-4d}$$

The first assumption states that $E(u_i) = 0$ for all i, that is, that the u_i are random variables with zero expectation. Assumption (4-4b) is a compact way of writing a very important double assumption. Since $\mathbf{u}$ is an $n \times 1$ column vector and $\mathbf{u}'$ a row vector, the product $\mathbf{uu}'$ is a symmetric matrix of order n and, since the operation of taking expected values is to be applied to each element of the matrix, we have

$$E(\mathbf{uu}') = \begin{bmatrix} E(u_1^2) & E(u_1u_2) & \cdots & E(u_1u_n) \\ E(u_2u_1) & E(u_2^2) & \cdots & E(u_2u_n) \\ \cdot & & & \cdot \\ \cdot & & & \cdot \\ \cdot & & & \cdot \\ E(u_nu_1) & E(u_nu_2) & \cdots & E(u_n^2) \end{bmatrix} = \begin{bmatrix} \sigma^2 & 0 & \cdots & 0 \\ 0 & \sigma^2 & \cdots & 0 \\ \cdot & & & \cdot \\ \cdot & & & \cdot \\ \cdot & & & \cdot \\ 0 & 0 & \cdots & \sigma^2 \end{bmatrix}$$

The terms on the main diagonal show that $E(u_i^2) = \sigma^2$ for all i; that is, the u_i have constant variance σ^2, which property is referred to as homoscedasticity. The off-diagonal terms give $E(u_tu_{t+s}) = 0$ for $s \neq 0$; that is, the u_i values are pairwise uncorrelated. Assumption (4-4c) that the $\mathbf{X}$ matrix denotes a set of fixed numbers parallels that made in Chap. 1. This means that in repeated sampling the sole source of variation in the $\mathbf{Y}$ vector is variation in the $\mathbf{u}$ vector and the properties of our estimators and tests are *conditional* upon $\mathbf{X}$. But as in Chap. 1, we shall examine how these properties hold up when this assumption is relaxed. The final assumption about **X** is that the number of observations exceeds the number of parameters to be estimated and that no exact linear relations exist between any of the X variables, where it is convenient to extend the list of X variables to include X_1, whose value is always unity, corresponding to the first column in **X**. If, for example, one explanatory variable were a multiple of another, or one were an exact linear function of several others, then the rank of **X** would be less than k, and likewise the rank of **X′X** would be less than k.† Since **X′X** is a symmetric matrix of order k, this would mean that its inverse did not exist, and as we shall see, this inverse $(\mathbf{X}'\mathbf{X})^{-1}$ plays a crucial role in the estimation procedure.

4-2. Least-squares Estimators

Taking (4-1) and (4-4*a*) to (4-4*d*), we now apply the least-squares principle to estimate the parameters of (4-1). Let

$$\hat{\boldsymbol{\beta}} = \{\hat{\beta}_1, \hat{\beta}_2, \ldots, \hat{\beta}_k\}$$

denote a column vector of estimates of $\boldsymbol{\beta}$. Then we may write

$$\mathbf{Y} = \mathbf{X}\hat{\boldsymbol{\beta}} + \mathbf{e} \tag{4-5}$$

where **e** denotes the column vector of n residuals $(\mathbf{Y} - \mathbf{X}\hat{\boldsymbol{\beta}})$. Notice carefully the distinction between (4-2) and (4-5). In the former the unknown coefficients $\boldsymbol{\beta}$ and the unknown disturbances **u** appear, while in the latter we have some set of estimates $\hat{\boldsymbol{\beta}}$ and the corresponding set of residuals **e**. From (4-5) the sum of squared residuals is

$$\begin{aligned} \sum_{i=1}^{n} e_i^2 &= \mathbf{e}'\mathbf{e} \\ &= (\mathbf{Y} - \mathbf{X}\hat{\boldsymbol{\beta}})'(\mathbf{Y} - \mathbf{X}\hat{\boldsymbol{\beta}}) \\ &= \mathbf{Y}'\mathbf{Y} - 2\hat{\boldsymbol{\beta}}'\mathbf{X}'\mathbf{Y} + \hat{\boldsymbol{\beta}}'\mathbf{X}'\mathbf{X}\hat{\boldsymbol{\beta}} \end{aligned} \tag{4-6}$$

which follows from noting that $\hat{\boldsymbol{\beta}}'\mathbf{X}'\mathbf{Y}$ is a scalar and thus equal to its transpose $\mathbf{Y}'\mathbf{X}\hat{\boldsymbol{\beta}}$. To find the value of $\hat{\boldsymbol{\beta}}$ which minimizes the sum of squared residuals we differentiate (4-6).

$$\frac{\partial}{\partial \hat{\boldsymbol{\beta}}}(\mathbf{e}'\mathbf{e}) = -2\mathbf{X}'\mathbf{Y} + 2\mathbf{X}'\mathbf{X}\hat{\boldsymbol{\beta}}$$

† $\rho(\mathbf{X}'\mathbf{X}) = \rho(\mathbf{X}\mathbf{X}') = \rho(\mathbf{X}) = \rho(\mathbf{X}')$. See Exercise 3-18.

Equating to zero gives

$$\mathbf{X}'\mathbf{X}\hat{\boldsymbol{\beta}} = \mathbf{X}'\mathbf{Y}$$

and from assumption (4-4*d*),

$$\hat{\boldsymbol{\beta}} = (\mathbf{X}'\mathbf{X})^{-1}\mathbf{X}'\mathbf{Y} \tag{4-7}$$

This is the fundamental result for the least-squares estimators. As expressed in (4-7) it gives $\hat{\boldsymbol{\beta}}$ as a column vector. Alternatively, we might have written

$$\frac{\partial}{\partial\hat{\boldsymbol{\beta}}}(\mathbf{e}'\mathbf{e}) = -2\mathbf{Y}'\mathbf{X} + 2\hat{\boldsymbol{\beta}}'\mathbf{X}'\mathbf{X}$$

which would give

$$\hat{\boldsymbol{\beta}}' = \mathbf{Y}'\mathbf{X}(\mathbf{X}'\mathbf{X})^{-1}$$

Transposing both sides of this last result takes us back directly to (4-7).

To establish the mean and variance of $\hat{\boldsymbol{\beta}}$, we substitute (4-2) into (4-7), which gives

$$\begin{aligned}\hat{\boldsymbol{\beta}} &= (\mathbf{X}'\mathbf{X})^{-1}\mathbf{X}'[\mathbf{X}\boldsymbol{\beta} + \mathbf{u}] \\ &= \boldsymbol{\beta} + (\mathbf{X}'\mathbf{X})^{-1}\mathbf{X}'\mathbf{u}\end{aligned} \tag{4-8}$$

since $(\mathbf{X}'\mathbf{X})^{-1}(\mathbf{X}'\mathbf{X}) = \mathbf{I}_k$. This expresses $\hat{\boldsymbol{\beta}}$ as a linear function of the true but unknown $\boldsymbol{\beta}$ and the disturbance values $u_1, u_2, \ldots, u_n$. If we consider the sampling process to be repeated, then the X values remain fixed from sample to sample by assumption (4-4*c*), but each sample will give a different set of u's and hence a different vector $\hat{\boldsymbol{\beta}}$. Taking expected values of both sides of (4-8) gives

$$\begin{aligned}E(\hat{\boldsymbol{\beta}}) &= E(\boldsymbol{\beta}) + E[(\mathbf{X}'\mathbf{X})^{-1}\mathbf{X}'\mathbf{u}] \\ &= \boldsymbol{\beta} + (\mathbf{X}'\mathbf{X})^{-1}\mathbf{X}'E(\mathbf{u})\end{aligned}$$

since $\mathbf{X}$ remains fixed. Thus

$$E(\hat{\boldsymbol{\beta}}) = \boldsymbol{\beta} \tag{4-9}$$

since $E(\mathbf{u}) = \mathbf{0}$ by assumption (4-4*a*). Thus the least-squares estimators are unbiased.

Now consider

$$E[(\hat{\boldsymbol{\beta}} - \boldsymbol{\beta})(\hat{\boldsymbol{\beta}} - \boldsymbol{\beta})'] = \begin{bmatrix} E(\hat{\beta}_1 - \beta_1)^2 & E(\hat{\beta}_1 - \beta_1)(\hat{\beta}_2 - \beta_2) & \cdots & E(\hat{\beta}_1 - \beta_1)(\hat{\beta}_k - \beta_k) \\ E(\hat{\beta}_2 - \beta_2)(\hat{\beta}_1 - \beta_1) & E(\hat{\beta}_2 - \beta_2)^2 & \cdots & E(\hat{\beta}_2 - \beta_2)(\hat{\beta}_k - \beta_k) \\ \vdots & & & \\ E(\hat{\beta}_k - \beta_k)(\hat{\beta}_1 - \beta_1) & E(\hat{\beta}_k - \beta_k)(\hat{\beta}_2 - \beta_2) & \cdots & E(\hat{\beta}_k - \beta_k)^2 \end{bmatrix} \tag{4-10}$$

Since (4-9) shows that $E(\hat{\beta}_i) = \beta_i$ for $i = 1, 2, \ldots, k$, it follows that $E(\hat{\beta}_i - \beta_i)^2$ is the variance of $\hat{\beta}_i$ and $E(\hat{\beta}_i - \beta_i)(\hat{\beta}_j - \beta_j)$ is the covariance of $\hat{\beta}_i$ and $\hat{\beta}_j$. Thus the symmetric matrix in (4-10) contains variances along its main diagonal and covariances everywhere else. We refer to it as the variance-covariance matrix of the $\hat{\beta}$s and denote it by var $(\hat{\boldsymbol{\beta}})$.

From (4-8)

$$(\hat{\boldsymbol{\beta}} - \boldsymbol{\beta}) = (\mathbf{X}'\mathbf{X})^{-1}\mathbf{X}'\mathbf{u}$$

Thus

$$\begin{aligned} \text{var}\,(\hat{\boldsymbol{\beta}}) &= E[(\hat{\boldsymbol{\beta}} - \boldsymbol{\beta})(\hat{\boldsymbol{\beta}} - \boldsymbol{\beta})'] \\ &= E[(\mathbf{X}'\mathbf{X})^{-1}\mathbf{X}'\mathbf{u}\mathbf{u}'\mathbf{X}(\mathbf{X}'\mathbf{X})^{-1}] \end{aligned}$$

using the rule that $(\mathbf{ABC})' = \mathbf{C}'\mathbf{B}'\mathbf{A}'$ and noting that $(\mathbf{X}'\mathbf{X})^{-1}$ is a symmetric matrix, for $(\mathbf{X}'\mathbf{X})$ is a symmetric matrix. Thus

$$\begin{aligned} \text{var}\,(\hat{\boldsymbol{\beta}}) &= (\mathbf{X}'\mathbf{X})^{-1}\mathbf{X}'E(\mathbf{u}\mathbf{u}')\mathbf{X}(\mathbf{X}'\mathbf{X})^{-1} \\ &= (\mathbf{X}'\mathbf{X})^{-1}\mathbf{X}'\sigma^2\mathbf{I}_n\mathbf{X}(\mathbf{X}'\mathbf{X})^{-1} \qquad \text{by assumption (4-4}b\text{)} \\ &= \sigma^2(\mathbf{X}'\mathbf{X})^{-1} \end{aligned}$$

since σ^2, a scalar, can be moved from in front of a matrix to behind, or vice versa, and $\mathbf{I}_n$ can be suppressed. So

$$\text{var}\,(\hat{\boldsymbol{\beta}}) = \sigma^2(\mathbf{X}'\mathbf{X})^{-1} \tag{4-11}$$

and the variance of any coefficient $\hat{\beta}_i$ may be obtained by taking the ith term from the principal diagonal of $(\mathbf{X}'\mathbf{X})^{-1}$ and multiplying by σ^2, the variance of u_i.

We have shown that the least-squares estimators are linear unbiased, the linearity property indicating here that the estimators are linear functions of $\mathbf{Y}$, as is shown by (4-7). It can also be shown, as in Chap. 1, that they possess a smaller variance than any other linear unbiased estimators and hence are best linear unbiased.

We shall do this by proving a more general result, of which this is a special case. The more general result also has applications in prediction problems. Let us assume that

$$\mathbf{Y} = \mathbf{X}\boldsymbol{\beta} + \mathbf{u}$$

as before and also make assumptions (4-4a) to (4-4d). Consider $\mathbf{C}\boldsymbol{\beta}$, where $\mathbf{C}$ is an $r \times k$ matrix of known constants with $r \leq k$. $\mathbf{C}\boldsymbol{\beta}$ thus represents a set of linear functions of the β parameters. In the special case where $\mathbf{C} = \mathbf{I}_k$, these functions simply reduce to the column vector $\boldsymbol{\beta}$ itself. Define an arbitrary linear function of $\mathbf{Y}$, say,

$$\mathbf{b} = \mathbf{AY} \tag{4-12}$$

where $\mathbf{A}$ is an $r \times n$ matrix. If $\mathbf{b}$ is to be an unbiased estimator of $\mathbf{C}\boldsymbol{\beta}$, we have

$$\begin{aligned} E(\mathbf{b}) &= E(\mathbf{AX}\boldsymbol{\beta} + \mathbf{Au}) \\ &= \mathbf{AX}\boldsymbol{\beta} \\ &= \mathbf{C}\boldsymbol{\beta} \end{aligned}$$

if and only if

$$\mathbf{AX} = \mathbf{C} \tag{4-13}$$

The variance-covariance matrix of $\mathbf{b}$ is given by

$$\begin{aligned} \text{var}(\mathbf{b}) &= E[(\mathbf{b} - \mathbf{C}\boldsymbol{\beta})(\mathbf{b} - \mathbf{C}\boldsymbol{\beta})'] \\ &= E(\mathbf{Auu'A'}) \qquad \text{since } \mathbf{b} = \mathbf{AY} = \mathbf{AX}\boldsymbol{\beta} + \mathbf{Au} \\ &\qquad\qquad\qquad\qquad\qquad\quad = \mathbf{C}\boldsymbol{\beta} + \mathbf{Au} \\ &= \sigma^2\mathbf{AA'} \end{aligned} \tag{4-14}$$

To minimize the variances of our unbiased linear estimators we must choose the elements of $\mathbf{A}$ such that $\mathbf{AX} = \mathbf{C}$ and the elements in the main diagonal of $\mathbf{AA'}$ are as small as possible. Consider the identity

$$\begin{aligned} \mathbf{AA'} \equiv\ & [\mathbf{C}(\mathbf{X'X})^{-1}\mathbf{X'}][\mathbf{C}(\mathbf{X'X})^{-1}\mathbf{X'}]' \\ & + [\mathbf{A} - \mathbf{C}(\mathbf{X'X})^{-1}\mathbf{X'}][\mathbf{A} - \mathbf{C}(\mathbf{X'X})^{-1}\mathbf{X'}]' \end{aligned} \tag{4-15}$$

This identity may be established by multiplying out the terms on the right-hand side and using $\mathbf{AX} = \mathbf{C}$. The two terms on the right-hand side are each in the form of a matrix multiplied by its transpose. Thus the diagonal elements in each product are necessarily nonnegative. Considering the first product, we see that the elements in $\mathbf{C}$ and $\mathbf{X}$ are known constants. Hence the diagonal terms in the first product are given constants. These represent the minimum possible values for the variances of our estimators in (4-12), and the only way to prevent the estimators having greater variances than these is to set

$$\mathbf{A} = \mathbf{C}(\mathbf{X'X})^{-1}\mathbf{X'} \tag{4-16}$$

so that the last term on the right-hand side of (4-15) consists of a null matrix multiplied by its transpose, yielding, of course, a null matrix. Substituting in (4-12), the best linear unbiased estimators of $\mathbf{C}\boldsymbol{\beta}$ are given by

$$\mathbf{b} = \mathbf{C}(\mathbf{X'X})^{-1}\mathbf{X'Y}$$

This is exactly what we should have obtained if we had estimated $\mathbf{C\beta}$ by replacing $\boldsymbol{\beta}$ by its least-squares estimator defined in (4-7). Thus

$$\text{LS estimator of } \mathbf{C\beta} = \mathbf{C(X'X)^{-1}X'Y}$$

Hence the least-squares estimators are best linear unbiased. In the special case where $\mathbf{C} = \mathbf{I}_k$, $\mathbf{C\beta} = \boldsymbol{\beta}$, and the best linear unbiased estimator of $\boldsymbol{\beta}$ is thus $\mathbf{(X'X)^{-1}X'Y}$, the least-squares estimator defined in (4-7) above.[1]

Turning now to the residual sum of squares, we have from (4-5)

$$\begin{aligned}
\mathbf{e} &= \mathbf{Y} - \mathbf{X}\hat{\boldsymbol{\beta}} \\
&= \mathbf{X\beta} + \mathbf{u} - \mathbf{X}[\mathbf{(X'X)^{-1}X'(X\beta + u)}] \qquad \text{using (4-2) and (4-7)} \\
&= \mathbf{u} - \mathbf{X(X'X)^{-1}X'u} \\
&= [\mathbf{I}_n - \mathbf{X(X'X)^{-1}X'}]\mathbf{u} \qquad (4\text{-}17)
\end{aligned}$$

which expresses the observed residuals as a linear function of the unknown disturbances. Defining the matrix in (4-17) as

$$\mathbf{A} = \mathbf{I}_n - \mathbf{X(X'X)^{-1}X'} \qquad (4\text{-}18)$$

it can be seen that $\mathbf{A}$ is a symmetric, idempotent matrix, for

$$\begin{aligned}
\mathbf{A}' &= \mathbf{I}_n - \mathbf{X(X'X)^{-1}X'} = \mathbf{A} \\
\text{and} \qquad \mathbf{A}^2 &= [\mathbf{I}_n - \mathbf{X(X'X)^{-1}X'}][\mathbf{I}_n - \mathbf{X(X'X)^{-1}X'}] \\
&= \mathbf{I}_n - 2\mathbf{X(X'X)^{-1}X'} + \mathbf{X(X'X)^{-1}X'X(X'X)^{-1}X'} \\
&= \mathbf{I}_n - \mathbf{X(X'X)^{-1}X'} \\
&= \mathbf{A}
\end{aligned}$$

Thus the sum of squared residuals is

$$\begin{aligned}
\mathbf{e'e} &= \mathbf{u'A'Au} \\
&= \mathbf{u'Au} \\
&= \mathbf{u'}[\mathbf{I}_n - \mathbf{X(X'X)^{-1}X'}]\mathbf{u} \qquad (4\text{-}19)
\end{aligned}$$

Taking expected values of both sides,

$$\begin{aligned}
E(\mathbf{e'e}) &= \sigma^2 \operatorname{tr} [\mathbf{I}_n - \mathbf{X(X'X)^{-1}X'}] \qquad \text{see Exercise (3-16)} \\
&= \sigma^2\{\operatorname{tr} \mathbf{I}_n - \operatorname{tr} [\mathbf{X(X'X)^{-1}X'}]\} \\
&= \sigma^2\{n - \operatorname{tr} [\mathbf{(X'X)^{-1}(X'X)}]\} \qquad \text{see Exercise (3-19)} \\
&= (n - k)\sigma^2 \qquad (4\text{-}20)
\end{aligned}$$

since $\mathbf{(X'X)}$ is of order k so that $\mathbf{(X'X)^{-1}(X'X)} = \mathbf{I}_k$. Thus

$$S^2 = \frac{\mathbf{e'e}}{n - k} \qquad (4\text{-}21)$$

[1] The above method of proof is due to R. L. Plackett, "A Historical Note on the Method of Least Squares," *Biometrika*, vol. 36, p. 458, 1949.

provides us with an unbiased estimator of the disturbance variance.

The calculation of S^2 is easily achieved by using

$$\begin{aligned} \mathbf{e}'\mathbf{e} &= \mathbf{Y}'\mathbf{Y} - 2\hat{\boldsymbol{\beta}}'\mathbf{X}'\mathbf{Y} + \hat{\boldsymbol{\beta}}'\mathbf{X}'\mathbf{X}\hat{\boldsymbol{\beta}} \qquad \text{from (4-6)} \\ &= \mathbf{Y}'\mathbf{Y} - \hat{\boldsymbol{\beta}}'\mathbf{X}'\mathbf{Y} \end{aligned} \tag{4-22}$$

since $(\mathbf{X}'\mathbf{X})\hat{\boldsymbol{\beta}} = \mathbf{X}'\mathbf{Y}$ from the least-squares derivation of $\hat{\boldsymbol{\beta}}$. Using small letters to denote deviations from arithmetic means,

$$\begin{aligned} \sum_{i=1}^{n} y_i^2 &= \sum_{i=1}^{n} Y_i^2 - \frac{1}{n}\Big(\sum_{i=1}^{n} Y_i\Big)^2 \\ &= \mathbf{Y}'\mathbf{Y} - \frac{1}{n}(\Sigma Y)^2 \end{aligned}$$

$$\sum_{i=1}^{n} e_i^2 = \mathbf{e}'\mathbf{e}$$

Notice that a property of the least-squares fit is that $\bar{e} = 0$.[1] Partitioning the total sum of squares in Y in the manner of Chaps. 1 and 2 into the "explained" sum of squares, due to the linear influence of the explanatory variables, and the residual sum of squares, we have

$$\begin{aligned} \text{"Explained" } SS &= \Sigma y_i^2 - \Sigma e_i^2 \\ &= \mathbf{Y}'\mathbf{Y} - \mathbf{e}'\mathbf{e} - \frac{1}{n}(\Sigma Y)^2 \\ &= \hat{\boldsymbol{\beta}}'\mathbf{X}'\mathbf{Y} - \frac{1}{n}(\Sigma Y)^2 \qquad \text{using (4-22)} \end{aligned}$$

The coefficient of multiple correlation ($R_{1\cdot 23\ldots k}$) is then defined by

$$R^2_{1\cdot 23\cdots k} = \frac{\hat{\boldsymbol{\beta}}'\mathbf{X}'\mathbf{Y} - (1/n)(\Sigma Y)^2}{\mathbf{Y}'\mathbf{Y} - (1/n)(\Sigma Y)^2} \tag{4-23}$$

It is customary to compute a correlation coefficient only for random variables which possess some joint distribution. We have introduced it here for two reasons. First, even in the case of fixed **X**, it is a useful summary statistic for the analysis-of-variance tables that will be given later, and second, the assumption of fixed **X** can

[1] This may be seen by differentiating the sum of squares partially with respect to $\hat{\beta}_1$ and setting the result equal to zero.

$$\begin{aligned} \frac{\partial}{\partial\hat{\beta}_1}\Sigma e_i^2 &= \frac{\partial}{\partial\hat{\beta}_1}\Sigma(Y_i - \hat{\beta}_1 - \hat{\beta}_2 X_{2i} - \cdots - \hat{\beta}_k X_{ki})^2 \\ &= -2\Sigma(Y_i - \hat{\beta}_1 - \hat{\beta}_2 X_{2i} - \cdots - \hat{\beta}_k X_{ki}) = 0 \end{aligned}$$

that is, $\Sigma e_i = 0$ therefore $\bar{e} = 0$

be relaxed later. In any case, a summary statistic measuring the proportion of the total variance accounted for by the linear relation fitted often serves a useful descriptive purpose.

Collecting results so far we have

$$
\begin{aligned}
\mathbf{Y} &= \mathbf{X}\boldsymbol{\beta} + \mathbf{u} = \mathbf{X}\hat{\boldsymbol{\beta}} + \mathbf{e} \\
\hat{\boldsymbol{\beta}} &= (\mathbf{X}'\mathbf{X})^{-1}\mathbf{X}'\mathbf{Y} \\
E(\hat{\boldsymbol{\beta}}) &= \boldsymbol{\beta} \\
\operatorname{var}(\hat{\boldsymbol{\beta}}) &= \sigma^2(\mathbf{X}'\mathbf{X})^{-1} \\
E(\mathbf{e}'\mathbf{e}) &= (n-k)\sigma^2 \\
R^2 &= \frac{\hat{\boldsymbol{\beta}}'\mathbf{X}'\mathbf{Y} - (1/n)(\Sigma Y)^2}{\mathbf{Y}'\mathbf{Y} - (1/n)(\Sigma Y)^2}
\end{aligned}
$$

These formulas have all been developed from the initial relation (4-1), where the variables are measured from zero origin. Averaging (4-1) and (4-5) over the n sample observations gives

$$\bar{Y} = \beta_1 + \beta_2\bar{X}_2 + \cdots + \beta_k\bar{X}_k + \bar{u} = \hat{\beta}_1 + \hat{\beta}_2\bar{X}_2 + \cdots + \hat{\beta}_k\bar{X}_k$$

since $\bar{u}$ will not, in general, disappear, but, as shown above, a consequence of the least-squares fit is that $\bar{e}$ is identically zero.

Subtracting from the original relations and using lowercase letters to denote deviations from arithmetic means gives

$$
\begin{aligned}
y_i = \beta_2 x_{2i} + \cdots + \beta_k x_{ki} + u_i - \bar{u} &= \hat{\beta}_2 x_{2i} + \cdots \\
&\quad + \hat{\beta}_k x_{ki} + e_i \qquad i = 1, \ldots, n
\end{aligned}
$$

or in matrix notation,

$$\mathbf{Y} = \mathbf{X}\boldsymbol{\beta} + \mathbf{u} - \bar{\mathbf{u}} = \mathbf{X}\hat{\boldsymbol{\beta}} + \mathbf{e} \tag{4-24}$$

where now

$$
\mathbf{Y} = \begin{bmatrix} y_1 \\ y_2 \\ \cdot \\ \cdot \\ \cdot \\ y_n \end{bmatrix} \quad
\mathbf{X} = \begin{bmatrix} x_{21} & x_{31} & \cdots & x_{k1} \\ x_{22} & x_{32} & \cdots & x_{k2} \\ \cdot & & & \cdot \\ \cdot & & & \cdot \\ \cdot & & & \cdot \\ x_{2n} & x_{3n} & \cdots & x_{kn} \end{bmatrix} \quad
\boldsymbol{\beta} = \begin{bmatrix} \beta_2 \\ \beta_3 \\ \cdot \\ \cdot \\ \cdot \\ \beta_k \end{bmatrix} \quad
\hat{\boldsymbol{\beta}} = \begin{bmatrix} \hat{\beta}_2 \\ \hat{\beta}_3 \\ \cdot \\ \cdot \\ \cdot \\ \hat{\beta}_k \end{bmatrix}
$$

$$
\mathbf{u} = \begin{bmatrix} u_1 \\ u_2 \\ \cdot \\ \cdot \\ \cdot \\ u_n \end{bmatrix} \quad
\bar{\mathbf{u}} = \begin{bmatrix} \bar{u} \\ \bar{u} \\ \cdot \\ \cdot \\ \cdot \\ \bar{u} \end{bmatrix} \quad
\mathbf{e} = \begin{bmatrix} e_1 \\ e_2 \\ \cdot \\ \cdot \\ \cdot \\ e_n \end{bmatrix} \tag{4-25}
$$

The contrast between (4-25) and the original formulation (4-3) is that now the elements of **Y** and **X** are in deviation form, the column of units no longer appears in the **X** matrix, and the $\boldsymbol{\beta}$ and $\hat{\boldsymbol{\beta}}$ vectors contain $k - 1$ elements rather than k because the intercept term disappears in the new formulation.

It is clear from (4-24) that we could proceed exactly as in the development of (4-7) to derive the formula

$$\hat{\boldsymbol{\beta}} = (\mathbf{X}'\mathbf{X})^{-1}\mathbf{X}'\mathbf{Y}$$

so that this result still holds when **X** and **Y** are in deviation form. In obtaining the results $E(\hat{\boldsymbol{\beta}}) = \boldsymbol{\beta}$ and $\text{var}\ (\hat{\boldsymbol{\beta}}) = \sigma^2(\mathbf{X}'\mathbf{X})^{-1}$, we made the substitution $\mathbf{Y} = \mathbf{X}\boldsymbol{\beta} + \mathbf{u}$. Now we have to substitute $\mathbf{Y} = \mathbf{X}\boldsymbol{\beta} + \mathbf{u} - \bar{\mathbf{u}}$. For example,

$$\begin{aligned} \boldsymbol{\beta} &= (\mathbf{X}'\mathbf{X})^{-1}\mathbf{X}'\mathbf{Y} \\ &= (\mathbf{X}'\mathbf{X})^{-1}\mathbf{X}'(\mathbf{X}\boldsymbol{\beta} + \mathbf{u} - \bar{\mathbf{u}}) \\ &= \boldsymbol{\beta} + (\mathbf{X}'\mathbf{X})^{-1}\mathbf{X}'\mathbf{u} - (\mathbf{X}'\mathbf{X})^{-1}\mathbf{X}'\bar{\mathbf{u}} \end{aligned}$$

This gives an additional term $(\mathbf{X}'\mathbf{X})^{-1}\mathbf{X}'\bar{\mathbf{u}}$, which, however, is zero, for

$$\begin{aligned} \mathbf{X}'\bar{\mathbf{u}} &= \{\bar{u}\Sigma x_{2i} \quad \bar{u}\Sigma x_{3i} \quad \cdots \quad \bar{u}\Sigma x_{ki}\} \\ &= \mathbf{0} \end{aligned}$$

since the sum of deviations about the mean is identically zero. Thus $E(\hat{\boldsymbol{\beta}}) = \boldsymbol{\beta}$ and $\text{var}\ (\hat{\boldsymbol{\beta}}) = \sigma^2(\mathbf{X}'\mathbf{X})^{-1}$ also hold for the formulation in terms of deviations. The residuals **e** are exactly the same as before, so that $E(\mathbf{e}'\mathbf{e}) = (n - k)\sigma^2$ and $\mathbf{e}'\mathbf{e} = \mathbf{Y}'\mathbf{Y} - \hat{\boldsymbol{\beta}}'\mathbf{X}'\mathbf{Y}$. The one change is in the formula for R^2, which now becomes

$$R^2 = \frac{\hat{\boldsymbol{\beta}}'\mathbf{X}'\mathbf{Y}}{\mathbf{Y}'\mathbf{Y}} \tag{4-26}$$

and the sum of squares due to the linear influence of the explanatory variables is

$$\hat{\boldsymbol{\beta}}'\mathbf{X}'\mathbf{Y} = \hat{\beta}_2 \sum_{i=1}^{n} x_{2i}y_i + \cdots + \hat{\beta}_k \sum_{i=1}^{n} x_{ki}y_i \tag{4-27}$$

4-3. Significance Tests and Confidence Intervals

So far no assumption has been made about the form of the distribution of the u_i. To derive significance tests and confidence intervals for the $\hat{\beta}_i$, we may proceed either by assuming the u_i to be normally distributed, in which case the following results will hold exactly, or by making no explicit assumption about the form of the distribution and appealing to the Central Limit Theorem to justify our regarding the tests as approximately correct.[1] To derive the tests we shall add to assumptions (4-4*a*) to (4-4*d*) the assumption

$$u_i \text{ has a normal distribution} \qquad i = 1, 2, \ldots, n \qquad (4\text{-}4e)$$

Assumptions (4-4*a*), (4-4*b*), and (4-4*e*) may now be compactly written

$$\mathbf{u} \text{ is } N(\mathbf{0}, \sigma^2 \mathbf{I}_n) \qquad (4\text{-}28)$$

It follows from (4-28) that the likelihood for the sample values is

$$\begin{aligned} L &= \frac{1}{(2\pi\sigma^2)^{n/2}} \exp\left(\frac{-\mathbf{u}'\mathbf{u}}{2\sigma^2}\right) \\ &= \frac{1}{(2\pi\sigma^2)^{n/2}} \exp\left[-\frac{(\mathbf{Y} - \mathbf{X}\boldsymbol{\beta})'(\mathbf{Y} - \mathbf{X}\boldsymbol{\beta})}{2\sigma^2}\right] \end{aligned}$$

Maximizing the likelihood with respect to $\boldsymbol{\beta}$ is equivalent to choosing $\boldsymbol{\beta}$ to minimize the sum of squares $(\mathbf{Y} - \mathbf{X}\boldsymbol{\beta})'(\mathbf{Y} - \mathbf{X}\boldsymbol{\beta})$. This is exactly the least-squares criterion already set up in (4-6), and so the maximum-likelihood estimator of $\boldsymbol{\beta}$ is simply the least-squares estimator already obtained, $\hat{\boldsymbol{\beta}} = (\mathbf{X}'\mathbf{X})^{-1}\mathbf{X}'\mathbf{Y}$.

From (4-8) it is seen that any estimate $\hat{\beta}_i$ is equal to β_i plus a linear function of $\mathbf{u}$, which has a multivariate normal distribution. Thus $\hat{\beta}_i$ has a normal distribution.[2] Its mean and variance are already known from (4-9) and (4-11) as β_i and $a_{ii}\sigma^2$, where a_{ii} is the *i*th element in the principal diagonal of $(\mathbf{X}'\mathbf{X})^{-1}$. In fact, (4-8), (4-9), and (4-11), together with assumption (4-28), mean that $\hat{\boldsymbol{\beta}}$ has a multivariate normal distribution specified by

$$\hat{\boldsymbol{\beta}} \text{ is } N[\boldsymbol{\beta}, \sigma^2(\mathbf{X}'\mathbf{X})^{-1}] \qquad (4\text{-}29)$$

If σ^2 were known, this result would enable us to carry out tests of significance and estimate confidence intervals for $\boldsymbol{\beta}$ in the usual way. However, σ^2 is unknown, and we require one further step to obtain a practical procedure.

[1] See W. Feller, *An Introduction to Probability Theory and Its Applications*, 2d ed., Wiley, New York, 1957, vol. I, pp. 229, 238–241.

[2] See, for example, Franklin A. Graybill, *An Introduction to Linear Statistical Models*, McGraw-Hill, New York, 1961, vol. I, pp. 56–57.

We have shown in (4-19) that the residual sum of squares, $\mathbf{e}'\mathbf{e}$, is a quadratic form in $\mathbf{u}$.

$$\mathbf{e}'\mathbf{e} = \mathbf{u}'\mathbf{A}\mathbf{u} = \mathbf{u}'[\mathbf{I}_n - \mathbf{X}(\mathbf{X}'\mathbf{X})^{-1}\mathbf{X}']\mathbf{u}$$

We have further shown that $\mathbf{A}$ is a symmetric idempotent matrix and, in (4-20), that its trace is $n - k$. Thus it follows that the rank of $\mathbf{A}$ is $n - k$, and it is possible to find an orthogonal matrix $\mathbf{P}$ such that $\mathbf{P}'\mathbf{A}\mathbf{P} = \mathbf{E}_{n-k}$, where $\mathbf{E}_{n-k}$ is a diagonal matrix with $n - k$ units and k zeros in the main diagonal.[1] This orthogonal matrix $\mathbf{P}$ may also be used to define a transformation from the $\mathbf{u}$ vector to a $\mathbf{v}$ vector, namely,

$$\mathbf{u} = \mathbf{P}\mathbf{v} \qquad \text{or} \qquad \mathbf{v} = \mathbf{P}'\mathbf{u} \qquad \text{since } \mathbf{P}^{-1} = \mathbf{P}' \tag{4-30}$$

Substituting in (4-19) gives

$$\begin{aligned} \mathbf{e}'\mathbf{e} &= \mathbf{u}'\mathbf{A}\mathbf{u} \\ &= \mathbf{v}'\mathbf{P}'\mathbf{A}\mathbf{P}\mathbf{v} \\ &= \mathbf{v}'\mathbf{E}_{n-k}\mathbf{v} \\ &= v_1^2 + v_2^2 + \cdots + v_{n-k}^2 \end{aligned} \tag{4-31}$$

where, without any loss of generality, we have taken the $n - k$ unit elements to occupy the first $n - k$ places in the main diagonal of $\mathbf{E}_{n-k}$. It follows from the properties of orthogonal matrices that if the u_i are normally and independently distributed with zero mean and constant variance σ^2, then so are the v_i.† Thus (4-31) expresses the residual sum of squares as the sum of the squares of $n - k$ independent normal variates with zero mean and variance σ^2. Hence $\mathbf{e}'\mathbf{e}/\sigma^2$ has a χ^2 distribution with $n - k$ degrees of freedom.[2]

It remains finally to show that $\mathbf{e}'\mathbf{e}$ is distributed independently of $\hat{\boldsymbol{\beta}}$. This may be done by showing that $\mathbf{e}$ is distributed independently of $\hat{\boldsymbol{\beta}}$. Consider the symmetric matrix

$$E[\mathbf{e}(\hat{\boldsymbol{\beta}} - \boldsymbol{\beta})'] = \begin{bmatrix} E[e_1(\hat{\beta}_1 - \beta_1)] & E[e_1(\hat{\beta}_2 - \beta_2)] & \cdots & E[e_1(\hat{\beta}_k - \beta_k)] \\ E[e_2(\hat{\beta}_1 - \beta_1)] & E[e_2(\hat{\beta}_2 - \beta_2)] & \cdots & E[e_2(\hat{\beta}_k - \beta_k)] \\ \cdot & & & \cdot \\ \cdot & & & \cdot \\ \cdot & & & \cdot \\ E[e_n(\hat{\beta}_1 - \beta_1)] & E[e_n(\hat{\beta}_2 - \beta_2)] & \cdots & E[e_n(\hat{\beta}_k - \beta_k)] \end{bmatrix}$$

[1] This follows from the results on idempotent matrices in Chap. 3. See pp. 98–100.

† See pp. 102–103.

[2] See P. G. Hoel, *Introduction to Mathematical Statistics*, 2d ed., Wiley, New York, 1954, pp. 216–217.

This represents all possible covariances between the e_i and the $\hat{\beta}_j$, since $E(\mathbf{e}) = \mathbf{0}$. We have shown in (4-17) that

$$\mathbf{e} = [\mathbf{I}_n - \mathbf{X}(\mathbf{X}'\mathbf{X})^{-1}\mathbf{X}']\mathbf{u}$$

and in (4-8) that $(\hat{\boldsymbol{\beta}} - \boldsymbol{\beta}) = (\mathbf{X}'\mathbf{X})^{-1}\mathbf{X}'\mathbf{u}$. Substituting these values gives

$$\begin{aligned} E[\mathbf{e}(\hat{\boldsymbol{\beta}} - \boldsymbol{\beta})'] &= E\{[\mathbf{I}_n - \mathbf{X}(\mathbf{X}'\mathbf{X})^{-1}\mathbf{X}']\mathbf{uu}'\mathbf{X}(\mathbf{X}'\mathbf{X})^{-1}\} \\ &= \sigma^2\mathbf{X}(\mathbf{X}'\mathbf{X})^{-1} - \sigma^2\mathbf{X}(\mathbf{X}'\mathbf{X})^{-1} \\ &= \mathbf{0} \end{aligned} \tag{4-32}$$

Since $\mathbf{e}$ and $\hat{\boldsymbol{\beta}}$ are each linear functions of normal variates, they are also normally distributed, and since we have shown their covariance to be zero, it follows that they are independently distributed.[1]

This final result enables us to use the t distribution to derive tests for individual regression coefficients:

$\hat{\beta}_i$ is $N(\beta_i, a_{ii}\sigma^2)$

$\sum_{i=1}^{n} e_i^2/\sigma^2$ has a χ^2 distribution with $n - k$ degrees of freedom

Hence, from the definition of the t distribution,

$$t = \frac{\hat{\beta}_i - \beta_i}{\sqrt{\sum_{i=1}^{n} e_i^2/(n-k)}\,\sqrt{a_{ii}}} \tag{4-33}$$

has the t distribution with $n - k$ degrees of freedom, where a_{ii} is the ith diagonal element in $(\mathbf{X}'\mathbf{X})^{-1}$. To test any particular hypothesis about β_i, we substitute the hypothetical value of β_i in (4-33), and if the resultant value of t lies in an appropriate critical region, we reject the hypothesis under test. For example, to test the hypothesis that $\beta_i = 0$, that is, that X_i has no linear influence on Y, we compute the test statistic

$$t = \frac{\hat{\beta}_i}{\sqrt{\Sigma e_i^2/(n-k)}\,\sqrt{a_{ii}}} \tag{4-34}$$

It also follows from (4-33) that a $100(1 - \epsilon)$ per cent confidence interval for β_i is given by

$$\hat{\beta}_i \pm t_{\epsilon/2}\sqrt{\frac{\Sigma e_i^2}{n-k}}\,\sqrt{a_{ii}} \tag{4-35}$$

[1] See Graybill, *op. cit.*, pp. 57–58.

To obtain a joint test for several or all β_i, we need one further theoretical development. This may be fairly simply obtained by a further use of orthogonal variables. Define $k - 1$ new variables $z_2, \ldots, z_k$ in terms of the deviations $x_2, \ldots, x_k$.

$$\begin{aligned} z_{2i} &= w_{22}x_{2i} \\ z_{3i} &= w_{32}x_{2i} + w_{33}x_{3i} \qquad i = 1, 2, \ldots, n \\ &\cdot \\ &\cdot \\ &\cdot \\ z_{ki} &= w_{k2}x_{2i} + \cdots + w_{kk}x_{ki} \end{aligned} \tag{4-36}$$

where the w's are chosen so as to make

$$\begin{aligned} \sum_{i=1}^{n} z_{ji}^2 &= 1 \qquad j = 2, 3, \ldots, k \\ \sum_{i=1}^{n} z_{ji}z_{li} &= 0 \qquad j,l = 2, \ldots, k; j \neq l \end{aligned} \tag{4-37}$$

that is, the z's are orthogonal variables, and condition (4-37) may be written

$$\mathbf{Z'Z} = \mathbf{I}_{k-1} \tag{4-38}$$

The relations (4-36) may be set in matrix form as

$$\mathbf{Z} = \mathbf{XW} \tag{4-39}$$

that is,

$$\begin{bmatrix} z_{21} & z_{31} & \cdots & z_{k1} \\ z_{22} & z_{32} & \cdots & z_{k2} \\ \cdot & & & \cdot \\ \cdot & & & \cdot \\ \cdot & & & \cdot \\ z_{2n} & z_{3n} & \cdots & z_{kn} \end{bmatrix} = \begin{bmatrix} x_{21} & x_{31} & \cdots & x_{k1} \\ x_{22} & x_{32} & \cdots & x_{k2} \\ \cdot & & & \cdot \\ \cdot & & & \cdot \\ \cdot & & & \cdot \\ x_{2n} & x_{3n} & \cdots & x_{kn} \end{bmatrix} \begin{bmatrix} w_{22} & w_{32} & \cdots & w_{k2} \\ 0 & w_{33} & \cdots & w_{k3} \\ \cdot & & & \cdot \\ \cdot & & & \cdot \\ \cdot & & & \cdot \\ 0 & 0 & \cdots & w_{kk} \end{bmatrix} \tag{4-40}$$

Recalling from (4-24) the equations in deviation form,

$$\mathbf{Y} = \mathbf{X}\boldsymbol{\beta} + \mathbf{u} - \bar{\mathbf{u}} = \mathbf{X}\hat{\boldsymbol{\beta}} + \mathbf{e}$$

and substituting $\mathbf{ZW}^{-1}$ for $\mathbf{X}$ gives

$$\mathbf{Y} = \mathbf{ZW}^{-1}\boldsymbol{\beta} + \mathbf{u} - \bar{\mathbf{u}} = \mathbf{ZW}^{-1}\hat{\boldsymbol{\beta}} + \mathbf{e} \tag{4-41}$$

Defining $$\boldsymbol{\beta}^* = \mathbf{W}^{-1}\boldsymbol{\beta} \quad \text{and} \quad \hat{\boldsymbol{\beta}}^* = \mathbf{W}^{-1}\hat{\boldsymbol{\beta}} \tag{4-42}$$

gives $$\mathbf{Y} = \mathbf{Z}\boldsymbol{\beta}^* + \mathbf{u} - \bar{\mathbf{u}} = \mathbf{Z}\hat{\boldsymbol{\beta}}^* + \mathbf{e} \tag{4-43}$$

From (4-43) we see that $\mathbf{Y}$ has now been expressed as a linear function of the orthogonal variables $\mathbf{Z}$ with coefficients $\boldsymbol{\beta}^*$ and the disturbances, or alternatively, $\mathbf{Y}$ may be written as the sum of a linear function of the orthogonal variables with coefficients $\hat{\boldsymbol{\beta}}^*$ and the residuals $\mathbf{e}$, which are exactly the residuals of the original least-squares relation $\mathbf{Y} = \mathbf{X}\hat{\boldsymbol{\beta}} + \mathbf{e}$. It is intuitively clear from (4-43) that $\hat{\boldsymbol{\beta}}^*$ is the least-squares estimator of $\boldsymbol{\beta}^*$, but it may be proved as follows:

$$\hat{\boldsymbol{\beta}} = (\mathbf{X}'\mathbf{X})^{-1}\mathbf{X}'\mathbf{Y}$$

Therefore

$$\begin{aligned} \hat{\boldsymbol{\beta}}^* &= \mathbf{W}^{-1}(\mathbf{X}'\mathbf{X})^{-1}\mathbf{X}'\mathbf{Y} && \text{using (4-42)} \\ &= \mathbf{W}^{-1}(\mathbf{X}'\mathbf{X})^{-1}(\mathbf{W}^{-1})'\mathbf{Z}'\mathbf{Y} && \text{using (4-39)} \end{aligned}$$

But from $\mathbf{Z} = \mathbf{XW}$ we have

$$\mathbf{Z}'\mathbf{Z} = \mathbf{W}'\mathbf{X}'\mathbf{XW}$$

Therefore

$$\begin{aligned} (\mathbf{Z}'\mathbf{Z})^{-1} &= \mathbf{W}^{-1}(\mathbf{X}'\mathbf{X})^{-1}(\mathbf{W}')^{-1} && \text{using } (\mathbf{ABC})^{-1} = \mathbf{C}^{-1}\mathbf{B}^{-1}\mathbf{A}^{-1} \\ &= \mathbf{W}^{-1}(\mathbf{X}'\mathbf{X})^{-1}(\mathbf{W}^{-1})' \end{aligned}$$

using the result that the inverse of the transpose is equal to the transpose of the inverse. Hence

$$\hat{\boldsymbol{\beta}}^* = (\mathbf{Z}'\mathbf{Z})^{-1}\mathbf{Z}'\mathbf{Y}$$

which is the least-squares estimator of $\boldsymbol{\beta}^*$ in (4-43).

As we have seen in (4-38), $\mathbf{Z}'\mathbf{Z} = \mathbf{I}_{k-1}$, and so $(\mathbf{Z}'\mathbf{Z})^{-1} = \mathbf{I}_{k-1}$, which on substitution in the formula for $\hat{\boldsymbol{\beta}}^*$ gives the very simple result

$$\hat{\boldsymbol{\beta}}^* = \mathbf{Z}'\mathbf{Y} \tag{4-44}$$

that is,

$$\hat{\beta}_2^* = \sum_{i=1}^{n} z_{2i}y_i$$

$$\hat{\beta}_3^* = \sum_{i=1}^{n} z_{3i}y_i$$

$$\cdot$$
$$\cdot$$
$$\cdot$$

$$\hat{\beta}_k^* = \sum_{i=1}^{n} z_{ki}y_i$$

It is very important to notice that (4-36) and (4-44) mean that $\hat{\beta}_i$ is independent of whether z_i is the last orthogonal variable included in the relation or whether z_{i+1}, z_{i+2}, etc., also appear, for in

$$z_{it} = w_{i2}x_{2t} + w_{i3}x_{3t} + \cdots + w_{ii}x_{it}$$

the weights w_{ij} depend only on $x_2 \cdots x_i$ and remain unchanged if we then introduce

$$z_{i+1,t} = w_{i+1,2}x_{2t} + w_{i+1,3}x_{3t} + \cdots + w_{i+1,i+1}x_{i+1,t}$$

etc.

From (4-11) we have directly

$$\begin{aligned} \operatorname{var}(\hat{\boldsymbol{\beta}}^*) &= \sigma^2(\mathbf{Z}'\mathbf{Z})^{-1} \\ &= \sigma^2 I_{k-1} \end{aligned} \tag{4-45}$$

Thus the $\hat{\beta}_i^*$ are normally and *independently* distributed about β_i^* with variance σ^2, for all the covariance terms in (4-45) are zero. Thus

$$\frac{\hat{\beta}_i^* - \beta_i^*}{\sigma} \text{ is } N(0,1)$$

and from the property of independence, $\sum_{i=2}^{k} (\hat{\beta}_i^* - \beta_i^*)^2/\sigma^2$ has a χ^2 distribution with $k - 1$ degrees of freedom. Since $\sum_{i=1}^{n} e_i^2/\sigma^2$ has an independent χ^2 distribution, the quantity

$$F = \frac{\sum_{i=2}^{k} (\hat{\beta}_i^* - \beta_i^*)^2/(k-1)}{\sum_{i=1}^{n} e_i^2/(n-k)} \tag{4-46}$$

has the F distribution with $k - 1$ and $n - k$ degrees of freedom.

Consider the hypothesis $\beta_2^* = \beta_3^* = \cdots = \beta_k^* = 0$. From (4-42) we have $\boldsymbol{\beta} = \mathbf{W}\boldsymbol{\beta}^*$, and so this hypothesis is equivalent to the hypothesis $\beta_2 = \beta_3 = \cdots = \beta_k = 0$. The initial hypothesis $\boldsymbol{\beta}^* = \mathbf{0}$ thus provides a test of the overall relation, that is, a test of whether $X_2, X_3, \ldots, X_k$ exercise any influence upon Y. The appropriate test statistic then becomes

$$F = \frac{\sum_{i=2}^{k} \hat{\beta}_i^{*2}/(k-1)}{\sum_{i=1}^{n} e_i^2/(n-k)} \tag{4-47}$$

One way of computing this test statistic would be first to compute the values of the orthogonal variables $\mathbf{Z}$, then to fit a least-squares regression to them, and finally to sum the squared coefficients of this regression to obtain the term $\sum_{i=2}^{k} \hat{\beta}_i^{*2}$. Fortunately there is no need to follow such an arduous course, for

$$\begin{aligned}
\sum_{i=2}^{k} \hat{\beta}_i^{*2} &= \hat{\boldsymbol{\beta}}^{*\prime}\hat{\boldsymbol{\beta}}^* \\
&= (\mathbf{W}^{-1}\hat{\boldsymbol{\beta}})'\mathbf{Z}'\mathbf{Y} && \text{since } \hat{\boldsymbol{\beta}}^* = \mathbf{W}^{-1}\hat{\boldsymbol{\beta}} = \mathbf{Z}'\mathbf{Y} \\
&= \hat{\boldsymbol{\beta}}'(\mathbf{W}^{-1})'\mathbf{W}'\mathbf{X}'\mathbf{Y} && \text{since } \mathbf{Z} = \mathbf{X}\mathbf{W} \\
&= \hat{\boldsymbol{\beta}}'(\mathbf{W}')^{-1}\mathbf{W}'\mathbf{X}'\mathbf{Y} \\
&= \hat{\boldsymbol{\beta}}'\mathbf{X}'\mathbf{Y}
\end{aligned}$$

Thus the required quantity is expressed in terms of the least-squares coefficients of the regression on the original X_i variables. Moreover, as shown in the development of (4-27) above, $\hat{\boldsymbol{\beta}}'\mathbf{X}'\mathbf{Y}$ measures the reduction in the sum of squares due to the explanatory variables. Also, using (4-22) and (4-26), we may write

$$\begin{aligned}
\hat{\boldsymbol{\beta}}'\mathbf{X}'\mathbf{Y} &= \mathbf{Y}'\mathbf{Y} \cdot R^2 \\
\mathbf{e}'\mathbf{e} &= \mathbf{Y}'\mathbf{Y}(1 - R^2)
\end{aligned}$$

which yield the following alternative form for the test statistic:

$$F = \frac{R^2/(k-1)}{(1-R^2)/(n-k)} \tag{4-48}$$

These results provide the basis for the conventional analysis-of-variance treatment outlined in Table 4-1. The ratio of the first mean square to the second gives (4-47) or (4-48), and an appropriate critical region is selected from the F distribution with $k-1$ and $n-k$ degrees of freedom.

TABLE 4-1. ANALYSIS OF VARIANCE

Source of variation	Sum of squares	Degrees of freedom	Mean square
$X_2, X_3, \ldots, X_k$	$\hat{\boldsymbol{\beta}}'\mathbf{X}'\mathbf{Y} = \mathbf{Y}'\mathbf{Y}\cdot R^2$	$k-1$	$\hat{\boldsymbol{\beta}}'\mathbf{X}'\mathbf{Y}/(k-1)$
Residual	$\mathbf{e}'\mathbf{e} = \mathbf{Y}'\mathbf{Y}(1-R^2)$	$n-k$	$\mathbf{e}'\mathbf{e}/(n-k)$
Total	$\mathbf{Y}'\mathbf{Y} = \sum_{i=1}^{n} y_i^2$	$n-1$	

An alternative procedure for testing a single coefficient may also be developed in an analysis-of-variance framework. We shall show that it is equivalent to the test already developed in (4-34), but the analysis-of-variance approach can also be extended to cover any subgroup of several coefficients. From (4-42) we have $\boldsymbol{\beta}^* = \mathbf{W}^{-1}\boldsymbol{\beta}$. Since the $\mathbf{W}$ matrix is triangular, with zeros everywhere below the main diagonal, its inverse is of the same form, and thus

$$\begin{aligned}
\beta_2^* &= f_2(\beta_2, \beta_3, \ldots, \beta_k) \\
\beta_3^* &= f_3(\beta_3, \ldots, \beta_k) \\
&\cdot \\
&\cdot \\
&\cdot \\
\beta_{k-1}^* &= f_{k-1}(\beta_{k-1}, \beta_k) \\
\beta_k^* &= f_k(\beta_k)
\end{aligned}$$

where the f_i are linear, homogeneous functions of the β_i. Thus $\beta_k = 0$ implies $\beta_k^* = 0$. To test the hypothesis that $\beta_k^* = 0$, we have $\hat{\beta}_k^{*2}/\sigma^2$ has the χ^2 distribution with 1 degree of freedom and

$\sum_{i=1}^{n} e_i^2/\sigma^2$ has an independent χ^2 distribution with $n - k$ degrees of freedom. Hence

$$F = \frac{\hat{\beta}_k^{*2}}{\Sigma e_i^2/(n-k)} \tag{4-49}$$

has the F distribution with $(1, n - k)$ degrees of freedom. Now $\sum_{i=2}^{k-1} \hat{\beta}_i^{*2}$ measures the explained sum of squares when the variables $z_2, \ldots, z_{k-1}$ (or equivalently $X_2, \ldots, X_{k-1}$) have been included. $\sum_{i=2}^{k} \hat{\beta}_i^{*2}$ measures the sum of squares when all variables $X_2, \ldots, X_{k-1}, X_k$ have been included. Thus $\hat{\beta}_k^{*2}$ measures the *increment* in the explained sum of squares due to the addition of X_k to the list of variables. The analysis-of-variance setup is given in Table 4-2, and the test of the net X_k effect is made by computing the two indicated mean squares and comparing the resultant F value with a preselected point on the F distribution with $(1, n - k)$ degrees of freedom.

TABLE 4-2

Source of variation	Sum of squares	Degrees of freedom	Mean square
$X_2, \ldots, X_{k-1}$	$\sum_{i=2}^{k-1} \hat{\beta}_i^{*2}$	$k - 2$	
X_k	$\hat{\beta}_k^{*2}$	1	$\hat{\beta}_k^{*2}$
Total due to $X_2, \ldots, X_k$	$\sum_{i=2}^{k} \hat{\beta}_i^{*2}$	$k - 1$	
Residual	$\sum_{i=1}^{n} e_i^2$	$n - k$	$\sum_{i=1}^{n} e_i^2/(n-k)$
Total	$\sum_{i=1}^{n} y_i^2$	$n - 1$	

This test, however, is formally equivalent to the one developed earlier. In (4-34) the test quantity suggested for the hypothesis $\beta_k = 0$ is

$$t = \frac{\hat{\beta}_k}{\sqrt{\sum_{i=1}^{n} e_i^2/(n-k)}\,\sqrt{a_{kk}}}$$

with $n - k$ degrees of freedom, where a_{kk} is the kth element in the main diagonal of $(\mathbf{X}'\mathbf{X})^{-1}$. But since a t quantity is the ratio of a standard normal variable to the square root of a χ^2 variable, which has been divided by its degrees of freedom r, squaring a t quantity gives an F quantity with $(1,r)$ degrees of freedom. Thus our earlier test gives rise to the test statistic

$$F = \frac{\hat{\beta}_k^2}{\left[\sum_{i=1}^{n} e_i^2/(n-k)\right] a_{kk}}$$

The analysis-of-variance statistic in (4-49) is

$$F = \frac{\hat{\beta}_k^{*2}}{\Sigma e_i^2/(n-k)}$$

Thus the two are equivalent if

$$\hat{\beta}_k^2 = a_{kk}\hat{\beta}_k^{*2}$$

From

$$\hat{\boldsymbol{\beta}}^* = \mathbf{W}^{-1}\hat{\boldsymbol{\beta}}$$

$$\hat{\boldsymbol{\beta}} = \mathbf{W}\hat{\boldsymbol{\beta}}^*$$

therefore

$$\hat{\beta}_k = w_{kk}\hat{\beta}_k^*$$

Thus we simply have to show that $w_{kk}^2 = a_{kk}$.

$$\mathbf{Z}'\mathbf{Z} = \mathbf{W}'\mathbf{X}'\mathbf{X}\mathbf{W} = \mathbf{I}_{k-1}$$

therefore

$$(\mathbf{X}'\mathbf{X})\mathbf{W} = (\mathbf{W}')^{-1}$$

therefore

$$(\mathbf{X}'\mathbf{X}) = (\mathbf{W}')^{-1}\mathbf{W}^{-1}$$

therefore

$$(\mathbf{X}'\mathbf{X})^{-1} = \mathbf{W}\mathbf{W}'$$

and from the definition of $\mathbf{W}$ in (4-40), we see that the bottom element in the principal diagonal of $\mathbf{W}\mathbf{W}'$ is w_{kk}^2. Hence $w_{kk}^2 = a_{kk}$, and the two tests are identical. The above exposition has been in terms of X_k, the last variable to be included in the set, but clearly the net contribution of any variable can be assessed in this way. Thus the conventional t test of a regression coefficient is equivalent to asking whether the addition to the explained sum of squares due to adding X_i to the set $X_2, X_3, \ldots, X_{i-1}, X_{i+1}, \ldots, X_k$ is significantly large in relation to the residual sum of squares. The calculations for Table 4-2 can be carried out by using the formulas of Table 4-1. The expression $\hat{\boldsymbol{\beta}}'\mathbf{X}'\mathbf{Y}$ or $\mathbf{Y}'\mathbf{Y}R^2$ gives the explained sum of squares for the set of variables included in $\mathbf{X}$. Thus this quantity is found first of all for the set of variables *excluding* the one under test and then for the complete set. Differencing gives the increment in the explained sum of squares due to the variable under test.

The analysis-of-variance treatment exemplified in Table 4-2 may be extended to test the contribution to the explained sum of squares of a subgroup of variables, say, $X_{r+1}, \ldots, X_k$. Since the $\hat{\beta}_i^*$ are normally and *independently* distributed about β_i^* with variance σ^2, the ratio

$$F = \frac{\sum_{i=r+1}^{k} (\hat{\beta}_i^* - \beta_i^*)^2/(k-r)}{\sum_{i=1}^{n} e_i^2/(n-k)}$$

has the F distribution with $(k - r, n - k)$ degrees of freedom. The hypothesis $\beta_{r+1} = \cdots = \beta_k = 0$ implies from (4-42) that

$$\beta_{r+1}^* = \cdots = \beta_k^* = 0$$

and this latter hypothesis is tested by computing

$$F = \frac{\sum_{i=r+1}^{k} \hat{\beta}_i^{*2}/(k-r)}{\sum_{i=1}^{n} e_i^2/(n-k)}$$

This is the basis of the analysis of variance shown in Table 4-3. The test of the hypothesis $\beta_{r+1} = \cdots = \beta_k = 0$ is then made by

TABLE 4-3

Source of variation	Sum of squares	Degrees of freedom	Mean square
$X_2, X_3, \ldots, X_r$	$\sum_{i=2}^{r} \hat{\beta}_i^{*2}$	$r - 1$	
$X_{r+1}, \ldots, X_k$	$\sum_{i=r+1}^{k} \hat{\beta}_i^{*2}$	$k - r$	$\sum_{i=r+1}^{k} \hat{\beta}_i^{*2}/(k-r)$
$X_2, \ldots, X_k$	$\sum_{i=2}^{k} \hat{\beta}_i^{*2}$	$k - 1$	
Residual	$\sum_{i=1}^{n} e_i^2$	$n - k$	$\sum_{i=1}^{n} e_i^2/(n-k)$
Total	$\sum_{i=1}^{n} y_i^2$	$n - 1$	

taking the ratio of the first to the second mean square in the last column of Table 4-3 and referring to the F distribution with $(k - r, n - k)$ degrees of freedom.

As an illustration of practical computations, consider the data in Table 4-4.

TABLE 4-4

Year	Y	X_2	X_3
1948	100	100	100
1949	106	104	99
1950	107	106	110
1951	120	111	126
1952	110	111	113
1953	116	115	103
1954	123	120	102
1955	133	124	103
1956	137	126	98

where Y = index of imports of goods and services to United Kingdom at constant (1948) prices

X_2 = index of gross United Kingdom product at 1948 prices

X_3 = ratio of indices of prices of imports and general United Kingdom output, respectively

SOURCE: Oxford, Diploma, 1958.

We first of all compute

$$\begin{array}{llll} n = 9 & \Sigma Y = 1{,}052 & \Sigma X_2 = 1{,}017 & \Sigma X_3 = 954 \\ & \bar{Y} = 116.9 & \bar{X}_2 = 113 & \bar{X}_3 = 106 \\ & \Sigma Y^2 = 124{,}228 & \Sigma X_2^2 = 115{,}571 & \Sigma X_3^2 = 101{,}772 \\ & \Sigma YX_2 = 119{,}750 & \Sigma YX_3 = 111{,}433 & \Sigma X_2X_3 = 107{,}690 \end{array}$$

From these we construct the following quantities in terms of deviations around the means:

$$\begin{aligned} \Sigma y^2 &= 124{,}228 - \tfrac{1}{9}(1{,}052)^2 &&= 1{,}260.89 \\ \Sigma x_2^2 &= 115{,}571 - \tfrac{1}{9}(1{,}017)^2 &&= 650 \\ \Sigma x_3^2 &= 101{,}772 - \tfrac{1}{9}(954)^2 &&= 648 \\ \Sigma yx_2 &= 119{,}750 - \tfrac{1}{9}(1{,}052)(1{,}017) &&= 874 \\ \Sigma yx_3 &= 111{,}433 - \tfrac{1}{9}(1{,}052)(954) &&= -79 \\ \Sigma x_2x_3 &= 107{,}690 - \tfrac{1}{9}(1{,}017)(954) &&= -112 \end{aligned}$$

Hence we have

$$\mathbf{X'X} = \begin{bmatrix} 650 & -112 \\ -112 & 648 \end{bmatrix} \qquad \mathbf{X'Y} = \begin{bmatrix} 874 \\ -79 \end{bmatrix}$$

$$|\mathbf{X'X}| = 408{,}656$$

$$(\mathbf{X'X})^{-1} = \frac{1}{408{,}656}\begin{bmatrix} 648 & 112 \\ 112 & 650 \end{bmatrix} = \begin{bmatrix} 0.001{,}585{,}68 & 0.000{,}274{,}07 \\ 0.000{,}274{,}07 & 0.001{,}590{,}58 \end{bmatrix}$$

From (4-7) we have

$$\begin{bmatrix} \hat{\beta}_2 \\ \hat{\beta}_3 \end{bmatrix} = \hat{\boldsymbol{\beta}} = (\mathbf{X'X})^{-1}\mathbf{X'Y} = \begin{bmatrix} 1.364{,}232{,}79 \\ 0.113{,}881{,}40 \end{bmatrix}$$

and from the footnote on page 113 above,

$$\begin{aligned} \hat{\beta}_1 &= \bar{Y} - \hat{\beta}_2\bar{X}_2 - \hat{\beta}_3\bar{X}_3 \\ &= 116.9 - (1.364{,}232{,}79)(113) - (0.113{,}881{,}4)(106) \\ &= -49.3297 \end{aligned}$$

giving the estimated relation

$$\hat{Y} = -49.3297 + 1.3642X_2 + 0.1139X_3$$

From (4-27) the explained sum of squares is

$$\hat{\boldsymbol{\beta}}'\mathbf{X'Y} = 1183.3428$$

which gives the analysis of variance shown in Table 4-5.

TABLE 4-5

Source of variation	Sum of squares	Degrees of freedom	Mean square
X_2 and X_3	1,183.34	2	591.67
Residual	77.55	6	12.93
Total	1,260.89	8	

The resultant F value is

$$F = 591.67/12.93 = 45.76$$

with (2,6) degrees of freedom. $F_{0.01} = 10.925$, so that a highly significant association exists between these three variables.

The analysis may also be conducted in a stepwise fashion, and the separate contributions of each variable analyzed.

Let b_2 = coefficient of X_2 in simple regression of Y on X_2
b_3 = coefficient of X_3 in simple regression of Y on X_3

Then
$$b_2 = \frac{\Sigma yx_2}{\Sigma x_2^2} = \frac{874}{650} = 1.344{,}615$$
$$b_3 = \frac{\Sigma yx_3}{\Sigma x_3^2} = \frac{-79}{648} = -0.121{,}914$$

The explained sum of squares due to X_2 alone is

$$b_2\Sigma yx_2 = (1.344{,}615)(874) = 1{,}175.19$$

and the explained sum of squares due to X_3 alone is

$$b_3\Sigma yx_3 = (-0.121{,}914)(-79) = 9.63$$

From these quantities we may set up Tables 4-6 and 4-7.

TABLE 4-6

Source of variation	Sum of squares	Degrees of freedom	Mean square
X_2	1,175.19	1	1,175.19
Addition of X_3	8.15	1	8.15
X_2 and X_3	1,183.34	2	
Residual	77.55	6	12.93
Total	1,260.89	8	

TABLE 4-7

Source of variation	Sum of squares	Degrees of freedom	Mean square
X_3	9.63	1	9.63
Addition of X_2	1,173.71	1	1,173.71
X_2 and X_3	1,183.34	2	
Residual	77.55	6	12.93
Total	1,260.89	8	

The total sum of squares due to X_2 *and* X_3 is known from Table 4-5 as 1,183.34. The X_2 sum of squares is 1,175.19, and the *additional* effect due to the inclusion of X_3 as well as X_2 is found by subtraction to be 8.15. The additional X_3 effect is then tested by the F ratio,

$$F = 8.15/12.93 = 0.63$$

with (1,6) degrees of freedom, which is evidently insignificant. The significance of X_2 alone can be tested by computing the residual sum of squares after X_2 as 1,260.89 − 1,175.19 = 85.70 with 7 degrees of freedom, giving a mean square of 12.24. The appropriate F ratio is then

$$F = 1{,}175.19/12.24 = 96.01$$

with (1,7) degrees of freedom, which is highly significant.

Alternatively, we may construct Table 4-7. The direct effect of X_3 is clearly insignificant, and the additional effect of X_2 highly significant.

The net (additional) effect of X_2 or X_3 might, alternatively, have been tested by using (4-33).

$$t = \frac{\hat{\beta}_i - \beta_i}{\sqrt{\sum_{i=1}^{n} e_i^2/(n-k)}\ \sqrt{a_{ii}}}$$

where a_{ii} is the appropriate diagonal element from $(\mathbf{X}'\mathbf{X})^{-1}$. For $\hat{\beta}_2$ we have, on the hypothesis that $\beta_2 = 0$,

$$t = \frac{1.364{,}232{,}79}{\sqrt{12.93}\ \sqrt{0.001{,}585{,}68}}$$

since $\Sigma e^2/(n - k) = 12.93$, as shown in Table 4-5, and 0.001,585,68 is the first element, and hence the element corresponding to X_2, in the principal diagonal of $(\mathbf{X}'\mathbf{X})^{-1}$. On squaring,

$$t^2 = 90.8$$

The additional effect of X_2 from Table 4-7 is given by

$$F = 1{,}173.71/12.93 = 90.8$$

and the tests are exactly equivalent.

Applying (4-35), we compute a 95 per cent confidence interval for β_2 as

$$1.364{,}232{,}8 \pm 2.4469\ \sqrt{12.93}\ \sqrt{0.001{,}585{,}68}$$

that is,

$$1.0143 \text{ to } 1.7141$$

As an alternative to the above, one might have started with the calculations from zero origin and written the $\mathbf{X'X}$ matrix as

$$\mathbf{X'X} = \begin{bmatrix} 9 & 1{,}017 & 954 \\ 1{,}017 & 115{,}571 & 107{,}690 \\ 954 & 107{,}690 & 101{,}772 \end{bmatrix}$$

The disadvantage of this approach, at any rate for work on desk calculators, is that the first row and column usually contain elements much smaller than the rest of the matrix, so that it is difficult to retain sufficient significant figures in all the elements in subsequent calculations.

Next we derive a result on linear functions of the β_i, which has several applications. We have already shown that if $\mathbf{C}$ is an $r \times k$ matrix of known constants, with $r \leq k$, the best linear unbiased estimators of $\mathbf{C}\boldsymbol{\beta}$ are given by $\mathbf{C}\hat{\boldsymbol{\beta}}$, where $\hat{\boldsymbol{\beta}}$ is the least-squares estimator of $\boldsymbol{\beta}$. Consider now the special case where $\mathbf{C}$ is simply a column vector of k constants,

$$\mathbf{c} = \{c_1 \quad c_2 \quad . \ . \ . \quad c_k\}$$

so that $\mathbf{c}'\boldsymbol{\beta}$ is a linear function of the β_i. In some econometric problems we are interested in testing whether certain coefficients satisfy a linear constraint, $\mathbf{c}'\boldsymbol{\beta} = r_0$. For example, if the hypothetical condition is $2\beta_2 - \beta_4 = 1$, the $\mathbf{c}$ vector is $\{0, 2, 0, -1, 0, \ . \ . \ . \ , 0\}$ and $r_0 = 1$. In prediction problems we may have a set of values $X_{2t}, X_{3t}, \ . \ . \ . \ , X_{kt}$, and the problem is to estimate the expected value of Y, $E(Y_t)$. Now

$$E(Y_t) = \beta_1 + \beta_2 X_{2t} + \cdots + \beta_k X_{kt}$$

since $\qquad E(u_t) = 0$

Thus $\qquad E(Y_t) = \mathbf{c}'\boldsymbol{\beta}$

where $\qquad \mathbf{c} = \{1 \quad X_{2t} \quad X_{3t} \quad . \ . \ . \quad X_{kt}\}$

Replacing the unknown $\boldsymbol{\beta}$ by $\hat{\boldsymbol{\beta}}$, we thus require to study the sampling distribution of the quantity $\mathbf{c}'\hat{\boldsymbol{\beta}}$ for use both in prediction problems and in problems involving linear restrictions on the coefficients of the explanatory variables.

$$E(\mathbf{c}'\hat{\boldsymbol{\beta}}) = \mathbf{c}'\boldsymbol{\beta} \qquad \text{since } E(\hat{\boldsymbol{\beta}}) = \boldsymbol{\beta} \tag{4-50}$$

Therefore $\qquad \text{var}\,(\mathbf{c}'\hat{\boldsymbol{\beta}}) = E\{[\mathbf{c}'(\hat{\boldsymbol{\beta}} - \boldsymbol{\beta})]^2\}$

$$= E[\mathbf{c}'(\hat{\boldsymbol{\beta}} - \boldsymbol{\beta})(\hat{\boldsymbol{\beta}} - \boldsymbol{\beta})'\mathbf{c}]$$

since $\mathbf{c}'(\hat{\boldsymbol{\beta}} - \boldsymbol{\beta})$ is a scalar, it is equal to its transpose, and so

$$[\mathbf{c}'(\hat{\boldsymbol{\beta}} - \boldsymbol{\beta})]^2 = \mathbf{c}'(\hat{\boldsymbol{\beta}} - \boldsymbol{\beta})(\hat{\boldsymbol{\beta}} - \boldsymbol{\beta})'\mathbf{c}$$

Thus $$\text{var}\,(\mathbf{c}'\hat{\boldsymbol{\beta}}) = \sigma^2\mathbf{c}'(\mathbf{X}'\mathbf{X})^{-1}\mathbf{c} \qquad \text{using (4-11)} \tag{4-51}$$

Since the $\hat{\beta}_i$ have a multivariate normal distribution, $\mathbf{c}'\hat{\boldsymbol{\beta}}$ is a normal variate; that is,

$$\mathbf{c}'\hat{\boldsymbol{\beta}} \text{ is } N(\mathbf{c}'\boldsymbol{\beta}, \sigma^2\mathbf{c}'(\mathbf{X}'\mathbf{X})^{-1}\mathbf{c}) \tag{4-52}$$

Shifting to the t distribution in the usual way,

$$t = \frac{\mathbf{c}'\hat{\boldsymbol{\beta}} - \mathbf{c}'\boldsymbol{\beta}}{\hat{s}\sqrt{\mathbf{c}'(\mathbf{X}'\mathbf{X})^{-1}\mathbf{c}}} \tag{4-53}$$

where $$\hat{s} = \sqrt{\sum_{i=1}^{n} e_i^2/(n-k)} \tag{4-54}$$

has the t distribution with $n - k$ degrees of freedom. The hypothesis $\mathbf{c}'\boldsymbol{\beta} = r_0$ may be tested by substituting this quantity in (4-53). It also follows from (4-53) that a $100(1 - \epsilon)$ per cent confidence interval for $\mathbf{c}'\boldsymbol{\beta}$ is given by

$$\mathbf{c}'\hat{\boldsymbol{\beta}} \pm t_{\epsilon/2}\hat{s}\sqrt{\mathbf{c}'(\mathbf{X}'\mathbf{X})^{-1}\mathbf{c}} \tag{4-55}$$

As an illustration, consider a three-variable relationship

$$Y = \beta_1 + \beta_2X_2 + \beta_3X_3 + u$$

and suppose we wish to test the hypothesis $\beta_2 = \beta_3$. Working with *deviations*, let us suppose that our data for 23 sample observations are[1]

$$\mathbf{X}'\mathbf{X} = \begin{bmatrix} 21.5 & 0 \\ 0 & 43.6 \end{bmatrix} \qquad \mathbf{X}'\mathbf{Y} = \begin{bmatrix} 17.3 \\ 25.4 \end{bmatrix} \qquad \Sigma y^2 = 49.2$$

The hypothesis under test is then

$$\mathbf{c}'\boldsymbol{\beta} = 0$$

where $$\mathbf{c} = \begin{bmatrix} 1 \\ -1 \end{bmatrix} \quad \text{and} \quad \boldsymbol{\beta} = \begin{bmatrix} \beta_2 \\ \beta_3 \end{bmatrix}$$

[1] L.S.E., 1959.

We require to compute the quantities entering into (4-53). Thus

$$(\mathbf{X}'\mathbf{X})^{-1} = \begin{bmatrix} 0.046{,}512 & 0 \\ 0 & 0.022{,}936 \end{bmatrix}$$

$$\hat{\boldsymbol{\beta}} = \begin{bmatrix} 0.804{,}658 \\ 0.582{,}574 \end{bmatrix} \qquad \hat{\boldsymbol{\beta}}'\mathbf{X}'\mathbf{Y} = 28.7$$

$$\mathbf{e}'\mathbf{e} = 49.2 - 28.7 = 20.5$$

$$\hat{s} = \sqrt{20.5/20} = 1.012 \qquad \mathbf{c}'(\mathbf{X}'\mathbf{X})^{-1}\mathbf{c} = 0.069{,}448$$

Substitution in (4-53) gives

$$t = \frac{0.222{,}084}{1.012\sqrt{0.069{,}448}} = 0.83$$

with 20 degrees of freedom. This low value does not lead to the rejection of the hypothesis $\beta_2 = \beta_3$.

So far all the results in this chapter have been derived under the assumption of fixed **X**. However, the argument already employed on pages 25–29 is equally valid here. This shows that all the confidence-interval statements still hold good, but the interpretation is changed to mean that if in repeated samples new values of **X** appear and the appropriate interval is computed, then $100(1 - \epsilon)$ per cent of these intervals will still include the true value. The essential condition for this extension of our results is that, whatever the joint distribution of X and Y, the *conditional* distribution of Y for given X should still satisfy the assumptions made in the derivation of the tests in this chapter. The probability of a type I error in hypothesis testing also involves the computation of probabilities for some test variable, under the assumption that the hypothesis under test is true. By exactly the same type of argument as used for confidence intervals, these probabilities remain unchanged when sampling is done from the joint distribution of X and Y. The difference between the case of **X** fixed and **X** random has an effect, not on the type I error or the truth of the confidence-interval statement, but on the power of the test and the expected width of the confidence interval.[1] In the special case where the joint distribution of **X** and **Y** is multivariate normal, the least-squares estimator $\hat{\boldsymbol{\beta}}$ is the maximum-likelihood estimator of the regression parameters in the regression of **Y** on **X** and has the properties of consistency, efficiency, minimum variance unbiased, and sufficiency.[2]

On pages 134 and 135 is a summary of the main formulas and results for the general linear model.

[1] See Graybill, *An Introduction to Linear Statistical Models*, pp. 204–206.

[2] *Ibid.*, pp. 197–200.

Variables in original form

$$\mathbf{Y} = \begin{bmatrix} Y_1 \\ Y_2 \\ \cdot \\ \cdot \\ \cdot \\ Y_n \end{bmatrix} \qquad \mathbf{X} = \begin{bmatrix} 1 & X_{21} & \cdots & X_{k1} \\ 1 & X_{22} & \cdots & X_{k2} \\ \cdot & \cdot & & \cdot \\ \cdot & \cdot & & \cdot \\ \cdot & \cdot & & \cdot \\ 1 & X_{2n} & \cdots & X_{kn} \end{bmatrix} \qquad \boldsymbol{\beta} = \begin{bmatrix} \beta_1 \\ \beta_2 \\ \cdot \\ \cdot \\ \cdot \\ \beta_k \end{bmatrix}$$

$$\hat{\boldsymbol{\beta}} = \begin{bmatrix} \hat\beta_1 \\ \hat\beta_2 \\ \cdot \\ \cdot \\ \cdot \\ \hat\beta_k \end{bmatrix} \qquad \mathbf{u} = \begin{bmatrix} u_1 \\ u_2 \\ \cdot \\ \cdot \\ \cdot \\ u_n \end{bmatrix} \qquad \mathbf{e} = \begin{bmatrix} e_1 \\ e_2 \\ \cdot \\ \cdot \\ \cdot \\ e_n \end{bmatrix}$$

$$\mathbf{Y} = \mathbf{X}\boldsymbol{\beta} + \mathbf{u} = \mathbf{X}\hat{\boldsymbol{\beta}} + \mathbf{e}$$

Least-squares estimator of β is

$$\hat{\boldsymbol{\beta}} = (\mathbf{X}'\mathbf{X})^{-1}\mathbf{X}'\mathbf{Y}$$

which is best linear unbiased with

$$\text{var}\ (\hat{\boldsymbol{\beta}}) = \sigma^2(\mathbf{X}'\mathbf{X})^{-1}$$

Unbiased estimator of σ^2 is

$$\hat{s}^2 = \mathbf{e}'\mathbf{e}/(n - k)$$

$$R^2_{1\cdot 23\cdots k} = \frac{\hat{\boldsymbol{\beta}}'\mathbf{X}'\mathbf{Y} - \dfrac{1}{n}(\Sigma Y)^2}{\mathbf{Y}'\mathbf{Y} - \dfrac{1}{n}(\Sigma Y)^2}$$

Variables in deviation form

$$\mathbf{Y} = \begin{bmatrix} y_1 \\ y_2 \\ \cdot \\ \cdot \\ \cdot \\ y_n \end{bmatrix} \qquad \mathbf{X} = \begin{bmatrix} x_{21} & \cdots & x_{k1} \\ x_{22} & & x_{k2} \\ \cdot & & \cdot \\ \cdot & & \cdot \\ \cdot & & \cdot \\ x_{2n} & \cdots & x_{kn} \end{bmatrix} \qquad \boldsymbol{\beta} = \begin{bmatrix} \beta_2 \\ \cdot \\ \cdot \\ \cdot \\ \beta_k \end{bmatrix}$$

$$\hat{\boldsymbol{\beta}} = \begin{bmatrix} \hat\beta_2 \\ \cdot \\ \cdot \\ \cdot \\ \hat\beta_k \end{bmatrix} \qquad \mathbf{u} = \begin{bmatrix} u_1 \\ u_2 \\ \cdot \\ \cdot \\ \cdot \\ u_n \end{bmatrix} \qquad \bar{\mathbf{u}} = \begin{bmatrix} \bar{u} \\ \bar{u} \\ \cdot \\ \cdot \\ \cdot \\ \bar{u} \end{bmatrix} \qquad \mathbf{e} = \begin{bmatrix} e_1 \\ e_2 \\ \cdot \\ \cdot \\ \cdot \\ e_n \end{bmatrix}$$

$$\mathbf{Y} = \mathbf{X}\boldsymbol{\beta} + \mathbf{u} - \bar{\mathbf{u}} = \mathbf{X}\hat{\boldsymbol{\beta}} + \mathbf{e}$$

Least-squares estimators are

$$\hat{\boldsymbol{\beta}} = (\mathbf{X}'\mathbf{X})^{-1}\mathbf{X}'\mathbf{Y}$$

and $\qquad \hat\beta_1 = \bar{Y} - \hat\beta_2\bar{X}_2 - \cdots - \hat\beta_k\bar{X}_k$

which are best linear unbiased with

$$\text{var}\ (\hat{\boldsymbol{\beta}}) = \sigma^2(\mathbf{X}'\mathbf{X})^{-1}$$

Unbiased estimator of σ^2 is

$$\hat{s}^2 = \mathbf{e}'\mathbf{e}/(n - k)$$

$$R^2_{1\cdot 23\cdots k} = \frac{\hat{\boldsymbol{\beta}}'\mathbf{X}'\mathbf{Y}}{\mathbf{Y}'\mathbf{Y}}$$

Variables in original form	Variables in deviation form
Test of $\beta_2 = \cdots = \beta_k = 0$ is based on $$F = \frac{R^2/(k-1)}{(1-R^2)/(n-k)}$$ with $(k-1, n-k)$ degrees of freedom. Test of $$\beta_i = 0 \qquad i = 1, \ldots, k$$ is based on $$t = \frac{\hat{\beta}_i - \beta_i}{\hat{s}\sqrt{a_{ii}}}$$ with $n-k$ degrees of freedom, where a_{ii} is ith element in principal diagonal of $(\mathbf{X}'\mathbf{X})^{-1}$.	Test of $\beta_2 = \cdots = \beta_k = 0$ is based on $$F = \frac{R^2/(k-1)}{(1-R^2)/(n-k)}$$ with $(k-1, n-k)$ degrees of freedom. Test of $$\beta_i = 0 \qquad i = 2, 3, \ldots, k$$ is based on $$t = \frac{\hat{\beta}_i - \beta_i}{\hat{s}\sqrt{a_{ii}}}$$ with $n-k$ degrees of freedom, where a_{ii} is element corresponding to X_i in principal diagonal of $(\mathbf{X}'\mathbf{X})^{-1}$. (Note this is now $(i-1)$st item in diagonal. For example, first item in diagonal refers to X_2.)
A $100(1-\epsilon)$ per cent confidence interval for β_i $(i = 1, 2, \ldots, k)$ is $$\hat{\beta}_i \pm t_{\epsilon/2}\,\hat{s}\sqrt{a_{ii}}$$	A $100(1-\epsilon)$ per cent confidence interval for β_i $(i = 2, 3, \ldots, k)$ is $$\hat{\beta}_i \pm t_{\epsilon/2}\,\hat{s}\sqrt{a_{ii}}$$
The hypothesis $\mathbf{c}'\boldsymbol{\beta} = r_0$, where $\mathbf{c}$ is a $k \times 1$ vector may be tested by $$t = \frac{\mathbf{c}'\hat{\boldsymbol{\beta}} - r_0}{\hat{s}\sqrt{\mathbf{c}'(\mathbf{X}'\mathbf{X})^{-1}\mathbf{c}}}$$ with $n-k$ degrees of freedom.	The hypothesis $\mathbf{c}'\boldsymbol{\beta} = r_0$, where $\mathbf{c}$ is a $(k-1) \times 1$ vector may be tested by $$t = \frac{\mathbf{c}'\hat{\boldsymbol{\beta}} - r_0}{\hat{s}\sqrt{\mathbf{c}'(\mathbf{X}'\mathbf{X})^{-1}\mathbf{c}}}$$ with $n-k$ degrees of freedom.
A $100(1-\epsilon)$ per cent confidence interval for $\mathbf{c}'\boldsymbol{\beta}$ is $$\mathbf{c}'\hat{\boldsymbol{\beta}} \pm t_{\epsilon/2}\,\hat{s}\sqrt{\mathbf{c}'(\mathbf{X}'\mathbf{X})^{-1}\mathbf{c}}$$	A $100(1-\epsilon)$ per cent confidence interval for $\mathbf{c}'\boldsymbol{\beta}$ is $$\mathbf{c}'\hat{\boldsymbol{\beta}} \pm t_{\epsilon/2}\,\hat{s}\sqrt{\mathbf{c}'(\mathbf{X}'\mathbf{X})^{-1}\mathbf{c}}$$

4-4. Tests of Equality between Coefficients in Two Relations

Suppose that we have n observations on X and Y, as assumed in the earlier part of this chapter, and that we obtain m ($> k$) additional observations. If we are uncertain whether the additional observations come from the same relation as the first set, we may write

$$\begin{aligned} \mathbf{Y}_1 &= \mathbf{X}_1\boldsymbol{\beta}_1 + \mathbf{u}_1 \\ \mathbf{Y}_2 &= \mathbf{X}_2\boldsymbol{\beta}_2 + \mathbf{u}_2 \end{aligned} \tag{4-56}$$

where the subscripts 1 and 2 denote the first and second set of observations, respectively, so that $\mathbf{X}_1$ is of order $n \times k$ and $\mathbf{X}_2$ of order $m \times k$. Let us assume that $\mathbf{u}_2$ has the same normal distribution as $\mathbf{u}_1$ with variance-covariance matrix $\sigma^2\mathbf{I}$.

Relations (4-56) may be written

$$\begin{bmatrix} \mathbf{Y}_1 \\ \mathbf{Y}_2 \end{bmatrix} = \begin{bmatrix} \mathbf{X}_1 & \mathbf{0} \\ \mathbf{0} & \mathbf{X}_2 \end{bmatrix} \begin{bmatrix} \boldsymbol{\beta}_1 \\ \boldsymbol{\beta}_2 \end{bmatrix} + \begin{bmatrix} \mathbf{u}_1 \\ \mathbf{u}_2 \end{bmatrix} \tag{4-57}$$

If we set up the hypothesis $\boldsymbol{\beta}_1 = \boldsymbol{\beta}_2 = \boldsymbol{\beta}$, the model becomes

$$\begin{bmatrix} \mathbf{Y}_1 \\ \mathbf{Y}_2 \end{bmatrix} = \begin{bmatrix} \mathbf{X}_1 \\ \mathbf{X}_2 \end{bmatrix} \boldsymbol{\beta} + \begin{bmatrix} \mathbf{u}_1 \\ \mathbf{u}_2 \end{bmatrix} \tag{4-58}$$

If we apply least squares to (4-58) and use (4-19), the sum of squared residuals from the fitted function is

$$Q_1 = [\mathbf{u}_1' \; \mathbf{u}_2'] \left[\mathbf{I} - \begin{pmatrix} \mathbf{X}_1 \\ \mathbf{X}_2 \end{pmatrix} (\mathbf{X}_1'\mathbf{X}_1 + \mathbf{X}_2'\mathbf{X}_2)^{-1} (\mathbf{X}_1' \; \mathbf{X}_2') \right] \begin{bmatrix} \mathbf{u}_1 \\ \mathbf{u}_2 \end{bmatrix} \tag{4-59}$$

This is a quadratic form in the u's. Result (4-31) applies directly, and so this quadratic form has rank $n + m - k$.

If we now apply least squares separately to each of the two relations in (4-56) and sum the squared residuals from each, we obtain

$$Q_2 = \mathbf{u}_1'[\mathbf{I} - \mathbf{X}_1(\mathbf{X}_1'\mathbf{X}_1)^{-1}\mathbf{X}_1']\mathbf{u}_1 + \mathbf{u}_2'[\mathbf{I} - \mathbf{X}_2(\mathbf{X}_2'\mathbf{X}_2)^{-1}\mathbf{X}_2']\mathbf{u}_2 \tag{4-60}$$

where the two quadratic forms on the right of (4-60) have ranks $n - k$ and $m - k$, respectively. Since $\mathbf{u}_1$ and $\mathbf{u}_2$ are independent, Q_2/σ^2 will have a χ^2 distribution with $m + n - 2k$ degrees of freedom.

Let us adopt the convenient notation that if $\mathbf{v}$ denotes a vector, the sum of squares $\mathbf{v}'\mathbf{v}$ is denoted by $\|\mathbf{v}\|^2$. Thus

$$Q_1 = \left\| \begin{matrix} \mathbf{Y}_1 - \mathbf{X}_1\hat{\boldsymbol{\beta}} \\ \mathbf{Y}_2 - \mathbf{X}_2\hat{\boldsymbol{\beta}} \end{matrix} \right\|^2 \qquad \text{and} \qquad Q_2 = \left\| \begin{matrix} \mathbf{Y}_1 - \mathbf{X}_1\hat{\boldsymbol{\beta}}_1 \\ \mathbf{Y}_2 - \mathbf{X}_2\hat{\boldsymbol{\beta}}_2 \end{matrix} \right\|^2$$

We have the identity

$$\begin{bmatrix} \mathbf{Y}_1 - \mathbf{X}_1\hat{\boldsymbol{\beta}} \\ \mathbf{Y}_2 - \mathbf{X}_2\hat{\boldsymbol{\beta}} \end{bmatrix} = \begin{bmatrix} \mathbf{Y}_1 - \mathbf{X}_1\hat{\boldsymbol{\beta}}_1 \\ \mathbf{Y}_2 - \mathbf{X}_2\hat{\boldsymbol{\beta}}_2 \end{bmatrix} + \begin{bmatrix} \mathbf{X}_1\hat{\boldsymbol{\beta}}_1 - \mathbf{X}_1\hat{\boldsymbol{\beta}} \\ \mathbf{X}_2\hat{\boldsymbol{\beta}}_2 - \mathbf{X}_2\hat{\boldsymbol{\beta}} \end{bmatrix} \tag{4-61}$$

Taking the sum of squares of both sides of (4-61), it can be seen by the definition of least-squares estimators in (4-7) above that the cross-product term on the right-hand side vanishes and we have

$$Q_1 = Q_2 + Q_3 \tag{4-62}$$

where

$$Q_3 = \left\| \begin{matrix} \mathbf{X}_1(\hat{\boldsymbol{\beta}}_1 - \hat{\boldsymbol{\beta}}) \\ \mathbf{X}_2(\hat{\boldsymbol{\beta}}_2 - \hat{\boldsymbol{\beta}}) \end{matrix} \right\|^2 \tag{4-63}$$

It can be shown that, under the hypothesis $\boldsymbol{\beta}_1 = \boldsymbol{\beta}_2 = \boldsymbol{\beta}$, Q_2/σ^2 and Q_3/σ^2 have independent χ^2 distributions with $m + n - 2k$ and k degrees of freedom, respectively.[1] Thus in the case where $m > k$, the hypothesis $\boldsymbol{\beta}_1 = \boldsymbol{\beta}_2 = \boldsymbol{\beta}$ may be tested by computing the F ratio,

$$F = \frac{Q_3/k}{Q_2/(m + n - 2k)} \tag{4-64}$$

with degrees of freedom $(k, m + n - 2k)$.

In a practical application of (4-64) the steps would be:

1. Pool all the $m + n$ observations and compute the least-squares estimate $\hat{\boldsymbol{\beta}}$. From this compute the sum of squared residuals $Q_1 = \mathbf{Y}'\mathbf{Y} - \hat{\boldsymbol{\beta}}'\mathbf{X}'\mathbf{Y}$.
2. Carry out step 1 for the two sets of data separately and total the two sums of squared residuals to obtain Q_2.
3. Compute $Q_3 = Q_1 - Q_2$, and hence compute F as defined in (4-64).
4. If $F > F_\epsilon$, reject the hypothesis $\boldsymbol{\beta}_1 = \boldsymbol{\beta}_2 = \boldsymbol{\beta}$.

The above test is applicable where the number of observations in the additional set, m, exceeds the number of parameters to be estimated, k. For the case of $m \leq k$ the hypothesis that the addi-

[1] See Gregory C. Chow, "Tests of Equality between Sets of Coefficients in Two Linear Regressions," *Econometrica*, vol. 28, no. 3, pp. 591–605, July, 1960, on which this section is based.

tional observations come from a linear structure with unchanged coefficients $\boldsymbol{\beta}$ may be tested by the ratio

$$F = \frac{\|\mathbf{X}_1\hat{\boldsymbol{\beta}}_1 - \mathbf{X}_1\hat{\boldsymbol{\beta}}\|^2 + \|\mathbf{Y}_2 - \mathbf{X}_2\hat{\boldsymbol{\beta}}\|^2}{\|\mathbf{Y}_1 - \mathbf{X}_1\hat{\boldsymbol{\beta}}_1\|^2} \frac{(n-k)}{m} \tag{4-65}$$

with degrees of freedom $(m, n - k)$.[1] A simple example of this test in the case of one extra observation and a single X variable has already been given in (1-53) at the end of Chap. 1. The practical steps in applying (4-65) would be:

1. From the first n observations on $\mathbf{Y}_1$ and $\mathbf{X}_1$, compute the least-squares coefficients $\hat{\boldsymbol{\beta}}_1$.
2. From the complete set of $n + m$ observations, compute the least-squares coefficients $\hat{\boldsymbol{\beta}}$.
3. Thence compute the three sums of squares appearing in (4-65).

References

The most comprehensive treatment of the topics covered in this chapter is available in

1. Franklin A. Graybill: *An Introduction to Linear Statistical Models,* McGraw-Hill, New York, 1961, vol. I, Chaps. 5–10.

Simpler and less extensive treatments are available in

2. R. L. Anderson and T. A. Bancroft: *Statistical Theory in Research,* McGraw-Hill, New York, 1952, Chaps. 14–16,

and in

3. Oscar Kempthorne: *The Design and Analysis of Experiments,* Wiley, New York, 1952, Chap. 5.

Exercises

4-1. A study of the demand for a particular commodity, based on annual data for 21 years, yields the following results:

Means	Standard deviations	Correlation coefficients
$\bar{X} = 51.843$	$S_X = 9.205$	$r_{XY} = -0.9158$
$\bar{Y} = 8.313$	$S_Y = 1.780$	$r_{YT} = -0.8696$
$\bar{T} = 0$	$S_T = 6.057$	$r_{XT} = 0.9304$

where X = per capita consumption, lb
Y = deflated price, cents per lb
T = time, years

(*a*) Compute the coefficient of time in the estimated relationship between Y and X and T.

(*b*) Test whether this coefficient differs significantly from zero.

[1] *Ibid.,* p. 598.

(*c*) Explain briefly the economic significance of the inclusion of time as an explanatory variable. (Manchester, 19 0)

4-2

Year	Production of sugar beet, 1,000 tons	Mean July temperature, °F	Mean rainfall, in.
1945	470	62	33
1946	520	62	42
1947	560	63	32
1948	510	61	38
1949	500	64	31
1950	550	61	40
1951	630	62	44
1952	640	63	36
1953	650	61	30
1954	620	58	43

Find the partial correlations of the production of sugar beet on the other two variables. Discuss the meaning of your results.

(Cambridge, Economics Tripos, Part II, 1956)

4-3. All the variables of a set X are standardized, and their matrix of correlations R is known. Find formulas for the set of regression equations and for the partial correlations in terms of matrices and determinants derived from R.

(Cambridge, Economics Tripos, Part II, 1956)

(*Note:* Standardization is the expression of a variable in standard-deviation units so that the standard deviation of the transformed variable is unity. This transformation affects the regression coefficients, but not the partial correlation coefficients. For example, if in the two-variable case we define $Y' = Y/S_Y$ and $X' = X/S_X$, the relation

$$Y = \hat{\alpha} + \hat{\beta}X$$

becomes

$$Y' = \frac{\hat{\alpha}}{S_Y} + \left(\hat{\beta}\frac{S_X}{S_Y}\right) X'$$

As shown in (1-41), $\hat{\beta} = rS_Y/S_X$; hence the coefficient of X' is simply r.)

4-4. It is desired to investigate the effect of climate, to be measured either by direct meteorological observation or by its secondary effects, such as plant development, on the incidence of a disease of bees.

X_1	X_2	X_3	Y
35	53	200	49
35	53	212	40
38	50	211	41
40	64	212	46
40	70	203	52
42	68	194	59
44	59	194	53
46	73	188	61
50	59	196	55
50	71	190	64

where X_1 = mean January temperature, °F
X_2 = mean June temperature, °F
X_3 = date of flowering of a particular summer-flowering species (days from Jan. 1)
Y = percentage of hives affected by disease

Investigate the regression of Y on X_1, X_2, and X_3. (Oxford, Diploma, 1955)

4-5. Commenting on the British demand for imported potatoes, Stone finds that "the own-price (substitution) elasticity is greater than unity—and is matched by a substitution elasticity of the same order of magnitude with respect to the price of home produced potatoes. A large negative trend is found . . . ." Assuming the two elasticities to be of equal magnitude, estimate that magnitude and also the percentage trend in the demand per annum from the figures given in the table.

QUANTITIES AND PRICES OF POTATOES PURCHASED IN GREAT BRITAIN, 1920–1938

Year	Imports purchased for final consumption or by producers: 1,000 tons Q	Imports purchased for final consumption or by producers: Pence per 7 lb P	Home produce, pence per 7 lb P'
1920	307	26.8	13.1
1922	155	26.6	7.8
1924	363	16.3	10.8
1926	273	14.5	7.4
1928	383	13.9	8.0
1930	232	12.5	5.7
1932	626	10.0	8.0
1934	124	18.4	6.2
1936	255	13.2	7.5
1938	117	19.0	6.8

SOURCE: J. R. N. Stone, *The Measurement of Consumers' Expenditure and Behaviour in the United Kingdom, 1920–1938*, Cambridge, London, 1954, vol. 1.

(Oxford, Diploma, 1955)

(*Note:* Stone's procedure is to fit functions linear in the logarithms of the variables, that is, constant elasticity functions.)

4-6. The table below shows the forecasts F_{1t} and F_{2t} made by two different forecasting techniques of the volume of United Kingdom imports of iron ore in a series of years, and also Y_t, the figure afterward published. Which would you consider the better technique? If you were to use a weighted average of the forecasts to obtain a better forecast, what weighted average would you use? It has been suggested that a useful standard by which to judge a technique of forecasting is to compare its performance with a "naïve" forecast $F_{3t} = Y_{t-1}$. Do you consider such a comparison useful?

United Kingdom Imports of Iron Ore, Million Tons

	1946	1947	1948	1949	1950	1951	1952	1953	1954
Y_t	6.5	6.8	8.7	8.7	8.4	8.8	9.7	11.0	11.6
F_{1t}	5.0	6.3	8.0	8.6	8.7	8.9	9.4	9.9	11.0
F_{2t}	6.2	6.7	8.5	9.0	9.0	9.2	9.9	11.1	12.0

(Oxford, Diploma, 1957)

4-7. The following weight measurements on a pig were taken at weekly intervals. Fit a polynomial growth curve up to the third degree, testing the necessity of the cubic term.

Week	Weight, lb	Week	Weight, lb	Week	Weight, lb
1	48	7	94	13	158
2	54	8	104	14	170
3	60	9	112	15	181
4	67	10	124	16	192
5	76	11	134	17	204
6	86	12	144		

(Oxford, Diploma, 1959)

4-8. In a certain chemical process the impurity Y present in the product varies considerably from day to day, and this is thought to be associated with the strength X_1 of one of the ingredients. From 67 pairs of values of Y and X_1 the following quantities are calculated:

$$\Sigma(Y - \bar{Y})^2 = 1.16 \qquad \Sigma(Y - \bar{Y})(X_1 - \bar{X}_1) = -8 \qquad \Sigma(X_1 - \bar{X}_1)^2 = 100$$

(*a*) Find the least-squares coefficient b, of Y on X_1, and estimate its standard error.

It is observed that the time X_2 for which the mixture has to be heated to complete the reaction also varies. For the same set of data,

$$\Sigma(X_2 - \bar{X}_2)^2 = 100 \qquad \Sigma(X_1 - \bar{X}_1)(X_2 - \bar{X}_2) = -80$$
$$\Sigma(Y - \bar{Y})(X_2 - \bar{X}_2) = 10$$

(*b*) Find the coefficients of X_1 and X_2 in the least-squares relationship of Y on X_1 and X_2 and estimate their standard errors.

(*c*) Why does the coefficient of X_1 in part (*b*) differ from that in part (*a*), and what conclusions about the process do you draw from your calculations in parts (*a*) and (*b*)? (R.S.S. Diploma, 1955)

4-9. In a study of 89 firms, the dependent variable was total cost (X_1) with explanatory variables, rate of output (X_2), and rate of absenteeism (X_3). The means were

$$\bar{X}_1 = 5.8 \qquad \bar{X}_2 = 2.9 \qquad \bar{X}_3 = 3.9$$

and the matrix showing sums of squares and cross products adjusted for means is

$$\begin{array}{c} \\ X_1 \\ X_2 \\ X_3 \end{array} \begin{array}{c} \begin{array}{ccc} X_1 & X_2 & X_3 \end{array} \\ \begin{bmatrix} 113.6 & 36.8 & 39.1 \\ & 50.5 & -66.2 \\ & & 967.1 \end{bmatrix} \end{array}$$

Estimate the relationship between X_1 and the other two variables. Set up an analysis-of-variance table to show the reduction in the total sum of squares due to fitting X_2, the additional reduction due to fitting X_3, and the total reduction due to X_2 and X_3 together. Test the overall effect and the partial X_3 effect, given X_2. (Manchester, 1960)

4-10. The following matrix gives the variances and covariances of the three variables:

$$X_1 = \text{log food consumption per capita}$$
$$X_2 = \text{log food price}$$
$$X_3 = \text{log disposable income per capita}$$

$$\begin{array}{c} \\ X_1 \\ X_2 \\ X_3 \end{array} \begin{array}{c} \begin{array}{ccc} X_1 & X_2 & X_3 \end{array} \\ \begin{bmatrix} 7.59 & -3.12 & 26.99 \\ & 29.16 & 30.80 \\ & & 133.00 \end{bmatrix} \end{array}$$

On the assumption that the demand relationship may be adequately represented by a function of the form $Y_1 = AY_2^{\alpha}Y_3^{\beta}$ (where $X_i = \log Y_i$), estimate the income elasticity of demand and compute a 95 per cent confidence interval for this coefficient, based on a sample of 20 observations.

4-11. In a study of production costs at 62 coal mines, data were obtained on costs per ton (X_1), degrees of mechanization (X_2), a measure of geological difficulty (X_3), and percentage of absenteeism (X_4). Defining

$$Z_i = \log X_i \qquad i = 1, 2, 3$$
$$Z_4 = X_4$$

the matrix of zero-order correlations for the Z's was

$$\begin{array}{c} \\ Z_1 \\ Z_2 \\ Z_3 \\ Z_4 \end{array} \begin{array}{c} \begin{array}{cccc} Z_1 & Z_2 & Z_3 & Z_4 \end{array} \\ \begin{bmatrix} 1.0000 & 0.3597 & 0.5749 & 0.4109 \\ & 1.0000 & 0.4630 & 0.3050 \\ & & 1.0000 & 0.2702 \\ & & & 1.0000 \end{bmatrix} \end{array}$$

Discuss the influence of these variables on production costs, performing any calculations or tests you consider desirable.

PART 2

The Theory of Econometrics

5

Introduction to the Theory of Econometrics

The single-equation model described in Part 1 has been widely used in econometric work, often without any strict examination of the validity of the technique for the application in question. Such applications were inevitable since the linear single-equation model was the one inherited from developments in mathematical statistics, where there was an early emphasis on the analysis of experimental data relating to situations in which the explanatory variables could be held at preassigned levels by the experimenter. However, in recent years a body of literature has developed which may appropriately be called the *theory of econometrics*. This body of literature stems directly from the single-equation linear model in that its basic preoccupation is with the assumptions of that model, with the applicability of these assumptions to the analysis of economic data, and with what, if anything, can be done if one or more of these assumptions is inappropriate.

Several related questions arise for examination. First, it is desirable to understand the types of situation likely to render various underlying assumptions of the single-equation linear model inappropriate, so that one can be on the alert for various kinds of trouble. For example, the model of Chap. 4 does not deal explicitly with errors of observation and measurement. Such errors in the "explained" variable Y can be dealt with by the model, since they merge automatically with the disturbance, but what happens if there are errors of measurement in the explanatory variables $X_2, \ldots, X_k$? We shall see in Chap. 6 that such errors set up a dependence between the disturbance term and the observed values of the explanatory variables, which invalidates one of the basic assumptions of the linear model. In the case of fixed **X** values, the assumptions made in (4-5) about the disturbance **u** ensured that **u** was independent of **X**, and in the case of random **X**, it was still assumed in Chap. 4 that the conditional distribution of **Y** about mean $\mathbf{X}\boldsymbol{\beta}$ did not involve **X**.

Another important assumption made in Chap. 4 was the serial independence of the disturbance term. If this does not hold, we have autocorrelated disturbances, and the problem of estimating the parameters of the relationship has to be considered afresh. It was also assumed that the disturbances were *homoscedastic*, that is, that they had a constant variance, independent of **X**. For many economic applications this may be an unrealistic formulation; the savings of households with high incomes may show much greater variation about some mean level than do the savings of households with low incomes. This state of affairs is described as heteroscedastic disturbances. Should we then use the formulas of Chap. 4 or not? The X_i variables may be very highly interrelated, which is described as the problem of *multicollinearity*. Does this make the estimation process simply more uncertain or downright dangerous and misleading? Some of the explanatory X_i variables may in fact be previous values of Y: this is the problem of *lagged variables*, and once again difficulties arise with the methods of Chap. 4.

It would appear that the most serious defect of the single-equation model is that attention is focused on a *single* equation, when the essence of economic theory is the interdependence of economic phenomena and the determination of the values of economic variables by the simultaneous interaction of relationships. As we shall see, the immediate consequence of the *simultaneous* nature of economic relations is that in any single relation of the system a dependence is set up between the disturbance term and some, at least, of the explanatory variables in that relation, which would seem to preclude the application of the methods of Part 1 to each relation in turn.

In all these cases a second set of questions arises. What, for example, are the consequences of applying the formulas of Chap. 4 to a relation where one or more of the basic assumptions is not fulfilled? It may be that some assumptions are more important than others, in the sense that their nonfulfillment has less harmful effects on the estimators described in Chap. 4. Thus one may sometimes use the methods of Chap. 4 with reasonable confidence. In other cases one may use those methods on grounds of computational convenience or because no alternative superior technique is available; in such cases it is all the more important to know what kinds of biases or inefficiencies to expect from the methods employed.

A further related question is whether there are any statistical tests available for detecting whether particular assumptions are likely to be wide of the mark or not; and finally, the very important question, what alternative estimation methods are available in various situations of difficulty, and what are the properties of the resultant estimators?

Discussion of this varied collection of questions constitutes the theory of econometrics. Unfortunately, the present stage of development of the subject might be likened to a primitive stage in medicine where a doctor is able to treat only *one* complaint at a time: he can reset a broken arm or prescribe for influenza, but if you come to him with both these troubles at once, the poor fellow is baffled and is forced to select one of your ailments, treat that, and leave the other alone. So in econometrics we have various methods of treating problems of errors in variables, and also methods of handling simultaneous-equation problems, but the methods for handling the first problem have been developed under assumptions which rule out the possibility of the second, and vice versa. Thus, if both problems arise simultaneously, we cannot treat them by somehow adding together the treatments appropriate for the cases in isolation; instead we require a properly developed, integrated treatment, designed for the case at hand, but this is not yet available.

Chapter 6 is devoted to the problem of errors in variables. Autocorrelation or, as it is sometimes called, the *time-series problem* is the subject of Chap. 7. Problems of multicollinearity, heteroscedasticity, and lagged and dummy variables are examined in Chap. 8. Finally, Chaps. 9 and 10 are given to an examination of the problems of identification and estimation in simultaneous-equation models.

6

Errors in Variables

To be realistic we must recognize that most economic statistics contain errors of measurement, so that they are only approximations to the underlying "true" values. Such errors may arise because totals are estimated on a sample basis or, even if a complete enumeration is attempted, errors and inaccuracies may creep in. Often, too, the published statistics may represent an attempt to measure concepts which are different from those postulated in the theory. What effect will these measurement errors have on the parameter estimates yielded by the conventional linear model of Chap. 4? Is this model still appropriate or not? If not, what alternative statistical models are available?

6-1. The Two-variable Linear Case

We shall illustrate the problem with reference to the two-variable linear case. Let us assume

$$X = \chi + u \tag{6-1}$$

$$Y = \psi + v \tag{6-2}$$

where X and Y indicate observed (measured) values, χ and ψ the true values, and u and v errors of observation. Suppose, further, that the true values are connected by the relation

$$\psi = \alpha + \beta\chi \tag{6-3}$$

This is an exact, functional relation and hardly seems appropriate for econometric work, since, if it were true, the only reason for points not lying exactly on a straight line would be errors of observation. A stochastic component of behavior would seem an essential in economics.[1] However, the statistical model of (6-1), (6-2),

[1] For the contrary case, see Milton Friedman, *A Theory of the Consumption Function,* National Bureau of Economic Research No. 63, General Series,

and (6-3) is the one most commonly discussed in the literature, and we shall analyze it before going on to discuss the possible extension of (6-3) to include a stochastic disturbance term.

Substituting (6-1) and (6-2) in (6-3) gives

$$Y = \alpha + \beta X + w \tag{6-4}$$

where $$w = v - \beta u$$

Even if the errors u and v are assumed to be mutually and serially independent with constant variances, and also to be independent of the true values χ and ψ, the full assumptions for the application of simple least squares to (6-4) to obtain estimates of α and β are not met, since w is not independent of X. The covariance of X and w is

$$\begin{aligned} E\{w[X - E(X)]\} &= E[(v - \beta u)(u)] \\ &= -\beta \text{ var } (u) \end{aligned}$$

on the assumption that $E(v) = E(u) = 0$, so that $E(X) = \chi$. Since this covariance does not vanish, a dependence exists between the error term and the explanatory variable in (6-4).

The consequence of this dependence is that the straightforward application of least squares to (6-4) would yield *biased* estimates of the parameters α and β. Furthermore, the bias will not disappear as the sample size becomes infinitely large; that is, the least-squares estimates are *inconsistent*.[1] For example, the least-squares esti-

---

Princeton University Press, Princeton, N.J., 1957, where Friedman bases his whole theory on a postulated exact, proportional relationship between permanent consumption and permanent income. There is an almost complete formal equivalence between Friedman's theory and the two-variable linear model with errors of observation. Measured income is the sum of permanent and transient income, measured consumption is the sum of permanent and transient consumption, and permanent consumption is proportional to permanent income. Friedman's assumptions about the probability distributions of the transient components also accord with those of the classical treatment of errors in variables, and a thorough grasp of the latter model is a great help in understanding the economic implications of Friedman's theory.

[1] An estimator t_n is said to be a consistent estimator of a parameter θ if

$$\lim_{n \to \infty} \Pr (|t_n - \theta| < \epsilon) = 1$$

In words, this condition states that if one chooses any arbitrarily small quantity ϵ, it becomes more and more certain, as the sample size becomes infinitely large, that the absolute discrepancy between t_n and θ will be less than ϵ. The estimator t_n is said to converge stochastically to θ as $n \to \infty$, and the condition is sometimes written as

$$\operatorname*{plim}_{n \to \infty} t_n = \theta$$

where plim stands for probability limit.

mator of β on the basis of n sample observations is

$$b_n = \frac{\sum_{i=1}^{n} (X_i - \bar{X})(Y_i - \bar{Y})}{\sum_{i=1}^{n} (X_i - \bar{X})^2}$$

$$= \frac{\Sigma(\chi - \bar{\chi})(\psi - \bar{\psi}) + \Sigma(\chi - \bar{\chi})(v - \bar{v}) + \Sigma(\psi - \bar{\psi})(u - \bar{u}) + \Sigma(u - \bar{u})(v - \bar{v})}{\Sigma(\chi - \bar{\chi})^2 + 2\Sigma(\chi - \bar{\chi})(u - \bar{u}) + \Sigma(u - \bar{u})^2}$$

On the assumption that the errors are distributed independently of one another and of the true values, the last three terms in the numerator and the middle term in the denominator will tend to zero as the sample size increases indefinitely. Thus the limiting value to which b_n tends in probability is

$$\text{plim } b_n = \frac{\beta\Sigma(\chi - \bar{\chi})^2}{\Sigma(\chi - \bar{\chi})^2 + \Sigma(u - \bar{u})^2}$$

$$= \frac{\beta}{1 + \sigma_u^2/\sigma_\chi^2} \qquad (6\text{-}5)$$

Thus plim $b_n \neq \beta$, but is in fact an underestimate of β. If the variance of the error term in X is, say, 10 per cent of the variance of the true values, then straightforward least squares would underestimate β by about 10 per cent, even for very large sample size.

There are three main alternative approaches to this problem, namely:

1. The classical approach, in which fairly strong assumptions are made about the probability distributions of the error terms
2. Other developments based on grouping the observations and making less stringent assumptions about the error terms
3. The use of instrumental variables

6-2. The Classical Approach

Within the classical approach there are two distinct subcases, according to the assumptions made about the true values, but some of the estimating formulas turn out to be identical. The first subcase of the classical approach starts with (6-1), (6-2), and (6-3). Assume further that u and v are normally and independently distributed variables with zero means and variances σ_u^2, σ_v^2. We may combine the three relations to give

$$X = \chi + u$$
$$Y = \alpha + \beta\chi + v$$

Then the X, Y values in a sample of n observations will be generated by the values $\chi_1, \chi_2, \ldots, \chi_n$ and the values $u_1, \ldots, u_n$, $v_1, \ldots, v_n$ drawn from the u, v distributions. Regarding the χ_i ($i = 1, \ldots, n$) as fixed numbers, the likelihood function for the sample observations is

$$L \propto \frac{1}{\sigma_u^n} e^{-\sum_{i=1}^{n} (X_i - \chi_i)^2/2\sigma_u^2} \frac{1}{\sigma_v^n} e^{-\sum_{i=1}^{n} (Y_i - \alpha - \beta\chi_i)^2/2\sigma_v^2}$$

which, on taking logarithms to base e, gives

$$L^* = \text{const} - \frac{n}{2}\log\sigma_u^2 - \frac{n}{2}\log\sigma_v^2 - \frac{1}{2\sigma_u^2}\sum_{i=1}^{n}(X_i - \chi_i)^2 - \frac{1}{2\sigma_v^2}\sum_{i=1}^{n}(Y_i - \alpha - \beta\chi_i)^2 \qquad (6\text{-}6)$$

We are primarily interested in the parameters α, β, σ_u^2, and σ_v^2. However, the estimating equations for these will involve the χ_i, which are unknown and indeed unobservable. Thus we must form maximum-likelihood estimates of the χ_i to obtain estimates of α and β.

Taking partial derivatives of L^* gives

$$\frac{\partial L^*}{\partial \sigma_u^2} = -\frac{n}{2\sigma_u^2} + \frac{1}{2\sigma_u^4}\sum_{i=1}^{n}(X_i - \chi_i)^2$$

$$\frac{\partial L^*}{\partial \sigma_v^2} = -\frac{n}{2\sigma_v^2} + \frac{1}{2\sigma_v^4}\sum_{i=1}^{n}(Y_i - \alpha - \beta\chi_i)^2$$

$$\frac{\partial L^*}{\partial \chi_i} = \frac{1}{\sigma_u^2}(X_i - \chi_i) + \frac{\beta}{\sigma_v^2}(Y_i - \alpha - \beta\chi_i) \qquad i = 1, 2, \ldots, n$$

$$\frac{\partial L^*}{\partial \alpha} = \frac{1}{\sigma_v^2}\sum_{i=1}^{n}(Y_i - \alpha - \beta\chi_i)$$

$$\frac{\partial L^*}{\partial \beta} = \frac{1}{\sigma_v^2}\sum_{i=1}^{n}\chi_i(Y_i - \alpha - \beta\chi_i)$$

Equating the first two partial derivatives to zero gives maximum-likelihood estimates of the error variances as

$$\tilde{\sigma}_u^2 = \frac{1}{n}\sum_{i=1}^{n}(X_i - \tilde{\chi}_i)^2 \tag{6-7}$$

and

$$\tilde{\sigma}_v^2 = \frac{1}{n}\sum_{i=1}^{n}(Y_i - \tilde{\alpha} - \tilde{\beta}\tilde{\chi}_i)^2 \tag{6-8}$$

using the tilde over a parameter to indicate the maximum-likelihood estimate of that parameter. However, if we equate $\partial L^*/\partial \chi_i$ to zero, we have

$$Y_i - \tilde{\alpha} - \tilde{\beta}\tilde{\chi}_i = -\frac{\tilde{\sigma}_v^2}{\tilde{\beta}\tilde{\sigma}_u^2}(X_i - \tilde{\chi}_i) \tag{6-9}$$

Squaring, summing over the sample observations, and dividing by n gives

$$\tilde{\sigma}_v^2 = \frac{\tilde{\sigma}_v^4}{\tilde{\beta}^2\tilde{\sigma}_u^4}\tilde{\sigma}_u^2$$

that is,

$$\tilde{\beta}^2 = \frac{\tilde{\sigma}_v^2}{\tilde{\sigma}_u^2}$$

This result shows that for any sample size the estimates of β, σ_v^2, and σ_u^2 will be such that the square of the first will equal the ratio of the other two. For infinitely large samples, maximum-likelihood estimates are consistent, and so we reach the ridiculous position of asserting that

$$\beta^2 = \frac{\sigma_v^2}{\sigma_u^2}$$

which, in general, will simply not be true. Thus the maximum-likelihood method breaks down in this application.

Instead of letting the ratio of the estimates of the error variances come out equal to the square of the estimate of β, it seems preferable to assume some plausible value for the ratio of the error variances, if it is possible from a knowledge of the sources of measurement error to make some estimate of the relative dispersion of the error distributions. Thus we assume

$$\frac{\sigma_u^2}{\sigma_v^2} = \lambda \tag{6-10}$$

where λ is a known number. Reverting to (6-9) and multiplying through by λ

$$(X_i - \tilde{\chi}_i) + \lambda\tilde{\beta}(Y_i - \tilde{\alpha} - \tilde{\beta}\tilde{\chi}_i) = 0$$

giving

$$\tilde{\chi}_i = \frac{X_i + \lambda\tilde{\beta}Y_i - \lambda\tilde{\alpha}\tilde{\beta}}{1 + \lambda\tilde{\beta}^2} \tag{6-11}$$

Setting $\partial L^*/\partial\alpha$ to zero gives

$$\tilde{\alpha} = \bar{Y} - \tilde{\beta}\bar{\tilde{\chi}} \tag{6-12}$$

where $\bar{\tilde{\chi}}$ indicates the mean of the n estimated values of χ. Setting $\partial L^*/\partial\beta$ to zero gives

$$\Sigma\tilde{\chi}_i(Y_i - \tilde{\alpha} - \tilde{\beta}\tilde{\chi}_i) = 0$$

which may be written

$$\Sigma(\tilde{\chi}_i - \bar{\tilde{\chi}})(Y_i - \tilde{\alpha} - \tilde{\beta}\tilde{\chi}_i) = 0 \tag{6-13}$$

since

$$\Sigma\bar{\tilde{\chi}}(Y_i - \tilde{\alpha} - \tilde{\beta}\tilde{\chi}_i) = \bar{\tilde{\chi}}\Sigma(Y_i - \tilde{\alpha} - \tilde{\beta}\tilde{\chi}_i)$$

$$= 0 \quad \text{since } \frac{\partial L^*}{\partial \alpha} = 0$$

On substituting (6-12) in (6-13), we obtain

$$\tilde{\beta} = \frac{\sum_{i=1}^{n} (\tilde{\chi}_i - \bar{\tilde{\chi}})(Y_i - \bar{Y})}{\sum_{i=1}^{n} (\tilde{\chi}_i - \bar{\tilde{\chi}})^2}$$

Notice that this is in the conventional form of a least-squares estimate, except that the estimated true values $\tilde{\chi}_i$ appear in place of the observed values X_i. Thus the maximum-likelihood approach corresponds to the least-squares regression of the observed Y values on the estimated true values $\tilde{\chi}_i$. From (6-11) we obtain

$$\tilde{\chi}_i - \bar{\tilde{\chi}} = \frac{1}{1 + \lambda\tilde{\beta}^2}[(X_i - \bar{X}) + \lambda\tilde{\beta}(Y_i - \bar{Y})]$$

Hence

$$\sum (\tilde{\chi}_i - \bar{\tilde{\chi}})(Y_i - \bar{Y}) = \frac{1}{1 + \lambda\tilde{\beta}^2}\left[\sum (X_i - \bar{X})(Y_i - \bar{Y}) + \lambda\tilde{\beta} \sum (Y_i - \bar{Y})^2\right]$$

and

$$\sum (\tilde{x}_i - \tilde{x})^2 = \frac{1}{(1 + \lambda\tilde{\beta}^2)^2}\Big[\sum (X_i - \bar{X})^2 + 2\lambda\tilde{\beta}\sum (X_i - \bar{X})(Y_i - \bar{Y}) + \lambda^2\tilde{\beta}^2 \sum (Y_i - \bar{Y})^2\Big]$$

Introducing the notation

$$m_{XY} = \frac{1}{n}\sum_{i=1}^{n} (X_i - \bar{X})(Y_i - \bar{Y})$$

$$m_{XX} = \frac{1}{n}\sum_{i=1}^{n} (X_i - \bar{X})^2$$

etc., we then have

$$\tilde{\beta} = \frac{(1 + \lambda\tilde{\beta}^2)(m_{XY} + \lambda\tilde{\beta}m_{YY})}{m_{XX} + 2\lambda\tilde{\beta}m_{XY} + \lambda^2\tilde{\beta}^2 m_{YY}}$$

which simplifies to a quadratic in $\tilde{\beta}$, namely,

$$\lambda\tilde{\beta}^2 m_{XY} - \tilde{\beta}(\lambda m_{YY} - m_{XX}) - m_{XY} = 0 \tag{6-14}$$

with solutions

$$\tilde{\beta}_1 = \theta + \sqrt{\theta^2 + \frac{1}{\lambda}} \qquad \tilde{\beta}_2 = \theta - \sqrt{\theta^2 + \frac{1}{\lambda}} \tag{6-15}$$

where

$$\theta = \frac{m_{YY} - (1/\lambda)m_{XX}}{2m_{XY}} \tag{6-16}$$

θ can be computed from the observed X, Y values and the assumed values for λ. On substitution in (6-15) we have two possible values for $\tilde{\beta}$. It is clear from inspection of (6-15) that irrespective of whether θ is positive or negative, $\tilde{\beta}_1$ is always positive and $\tilde{\beta}_2$ is always negative. Since β measures the slope of the relation between the true values ψ and χ, it seems intuitively correct that we should take the positive root $\tilde{\beta}_1$ as our estimate if the sample covariance between the observed values m_{XY} is positive, and take the negative root $\tilde{\beta}_2$ if m_{XY} is negative.[1] An estimate of β is thus obtained from (6-15), with the choice of sign determined by the covariance of X

[1] This is in contradiction to the advice given by Kendall, who merely writes the positive root $\tilde{\beta}_1$ and states, "We take the positive root to maximize the

and Y. Finally, an estimate of α has to be obtained. From (6-12) we have

$$\tilde{\alpha} = \bar{Y} - \tilde{\beta}\bar{\tilde{\chi}}$$

and from (6-11),

$$\tilde{\chi}_i = \frac{X_i + \lambda\tilde{\beta}Y_i - \lambda\tilde{\alpha}\tilde{\beta}}{1 + \lambda\tilde{\beta}^2}$$

Thus

$$\bar{\tilde{\chi}} = \frac{\bar{X} + \lambda\tilde{\beta}\bar{Y} - \lambda\tilde{\beta}(\bar{Y} - \tilde{\beta}\bar{\tilde{\chi}})}{1 + \lambda\tilde{\beta}^2}$$

giving

$$\bar{\tilde{\chi}} = \bar{X}$$

Thus the maximum-likelihood estimate of α is

$$\tilde{\alpha} = \bar{Y} - \tilde{\beta}\bar{X} \tag{6-17}$$

There are two interesting special cases of this model. Suppose $\lambda = 0$. Then $\sigma_u^2 = 0$; that is, there is no error of measurement in X ($= \chi$), and (6-14) reduces to

$$\tilde{\beta} = \frac{m_{XY}}{m_{XX}}$$

which is the slope of the least-squares regression of Y on X. Alter-

---

likelihood." See M. G. Kendall, *A Course in Multivariate Analysis*, Hafner, New York, 1957, p. 64.

From (6-6) it is clear that the likelihood will be maximized if the sum of squares

$$S = \sum_{i=1}^{n} (X_i - \chi_i)^2 + \lambda \sum_{i=1}^{n} (Y_i - \alpha - \beta\chi_i)^2$$

is minimized. It may be shown that

$$S = \frac{\lambda(\beta^2 m_{XX} - 2\beta m_{XY} + m_{YY})}{1 + \lambda\beta^2}$$

Substituting $\tilde{\beta}_1$ and $\tilde{\beta}_2$ from (6-15) successively in S gives terms which we may define as S_1 and S_2. By algebraic manipulation we may show

$$S_1 - S_2 = \frac{-8\lambda\sqrt{\theta^2 + 1/\lambda}\, m_{XY}(1 + \lambda\theta^2)}{4(1 + \lambda\theta^2)}$$

$$= -2\lambda m_{XY}\sqrt{\theta^2 + \frac{1}{\lambda}}$$

Since λ and θ^2 are both positive, the sign of $S_1 - S_2$ depends solely on that of m_{XY}.

If $m_{XY} > 0$, $S_1 - S_2 < 0$, so that S_1 gives the smaller value for the sum of squares, and hence $\tilde{\beta}_1$ is the appropriate estimate. If $m_{XY} < 0$, then S_2 gives the smaller sum of squares, and $\tilde{\beta}_2$ is the appropriate estimate.

natively, suppose $\lambda \to \infty$, so that $1/\lambda \to 0$, then $\sigma_v^2 \to 0$ and there is no error of measurement in Y $(= \psi)$. Equation (6-14) then gives

$$\tilde{\beta} = \frac{m_{YY}}{m_{XY}}$$

which is the reciprocal of the slope of the least-squares regression of X on Y.

These last two results show that conventional least squares may be regarded as two extreme limiting cases of the general errors-in-variables model. If the X measurement contains no error, then the maximum-likelihood estimate of the parameter β in the relation

$$\psi = \alpha + \beta\chi$$

between the true values is given by the least-squares regression of Y on X, while if Y contains no errors of measurement, the maximum-likelihood estimate of β is provided by the reciprocal of the slope of the regression of X on Y.

Before considering the second case in the classical approach, let us consider if this first case might be extended to include the assumption of a stochastic relation between the true values. The model would then be

$$X_i = \chi_i + u_i \tag{6-1}$$
$$Y_i = \psi_i + v_i \tag{6-2}$$
$$\psi_i = \alpha + \beta\chi_i + \epsilon_i \tag{6-3a}$$

The first two relations are the same as before, with u and v indicating the errors of observation. The ϵ term in (6-3a) is a stochastic disturbance term. These three relations might be expressed more simply as

$$X_i = \chi_i + u_i$$
$$Y_i = \alpha + \beta\chi_i + \epsilon_i + v_i$$

If u, v, and ϵ are all assumed to be normally and independently distributed with zero expectations and variances σ_u^2, σ_v^2, and σ_ϵ^2, then there is an exact formal correspondence between this and the previous model, provided we regard the composite term $\epsilon + v$ in this one as the equivalent of the error of observation in Y in the previous one. It is clear that the term $\epsilon + v$ has a normal distribution with zero expectation and variance equal to $\sigma_\epsilon^2 + \sigma_v^2$. If one could now obtain an a priori or independent estimate of λ, where

$$\lambda = \frac{\sigma_u^2}{\sigma_\epsilon^2 + \sigma_v^2}$$

then our earlier formulas (6-15) and (6-17) would still be appropriate. This, however, is a much more formidable requirement than estimating the ratio of the error variances as in (6-10) above, for we should now require to know *in advance* of our estimation procedure the variance of the stochastic term in the relation connecting the true values. But this is usually one of the most important statistics on which we hope to obtain information from our calculations, and it is difficult to see how a priori information on its magnitude might be obtained.

A less formidable requirement in practice might be to assume that the error variances σ_u^2 and σ_v^2 are known in absolute value (and not just their ratio) and then to follow through on the maximum-likelihood approach. The logarithm of the likelihood function would be

$$L^* = \text{const} - \frac{n}{2}\log(\sigma_\epsilon^2 + \sigma_v^2) - \frac{1}{2\sigma_u^2}\sum_{i=1}^{n}(X_i - \chi_i)^2 - \frac{1}{2(\sigma_\epsilon^2 + \sigma_v^2)}\sum_{i=1}^{n}(Y_i - \alpha - \beta\chi_i)^2 \qquad (6\text{-}18)$$

Differentiating partially with respect to σ_ϵ^2, χ_i, α, and β gives the estimating equations

$$\begin{aligned}
\tilde{\sigma}_\epsilon^2 &= \frac{1}{n}\sum_{i=1}^{n}(Y_i - \tilde{\alpha} - \tilde{\beta}\tilde{\chi}_i)^2 - \sigma_v^2 \\
\frac{1}{\sigma_u^2}(X_i - \tilde{\chi}_i) &+ \frac{\tilde{\beta}}{\tilde{\sigma}_\epsilon^2 + \sigma_v^2}(Y_i - \tilde{\alpha} - \tilde{\beta}\tilde{\chi}_i) = 0 \qquad i = 1, 2, \ldots, n \qquad (6\text{-}19) \\
&\sum_{i=1}^{n}(Y_i - \tilde{\alpha} - \tilde{\beta}\tilde{\chi}_i) = 0 \\
&\sum_{i=1}^{n}\tilde{\chi}_i(Y_i - \tilde{\alpha} - \tilde{\beta}\tilde{\chi}_i) = 0
\end{aligned}$$

To simplify, let us define

$$\sigma^2 = \sigma_\epsilon^2 + \sigma_v^2$$

and let us assume that we know σ_u^2, but not necessarily σ_v^2 (for we can estimate the combined variance σ^2). If σ_v^2 were known in addition, one could obtain a separate estimate of σ_ϵ^2 as $\tilde{\sigma}^2 - \sigma_v^2$.

From the second equation of (6-19),

$$\tilde{\sigma}^2(X_i - \tilde{\chi}_i) + \tilde{\beta}\sigma_u^2(Y_i - \tilde{\alpha} - \tilde{\beta}\tilde{\chi}_i) = 0$$

Averaging this relation over the sample observations gives

$$\tilde{\sigma}^2(\bar{X} - \bar{\tilde{\chi}}) + \tilde{\beta}\sigma_u^2(\bar{Y} - \tilde{\alpha} - \tilde{\beta}\bar{\tilde{\chi}}) = 0$$

and by subtraction we obtain

$$\tilde{\chi}_i - \bar{\tilde{\chi}} = \frac{\tilde{\sigma}^2 x_i + \tilde{\beta}\sigma_u^2 y_i}{\tilde{\sigma}^2 + \tilde{\beta}^2\sigma_u^2} \tag{6-20}$$

where x_i and y_i denote deviations from sample means.

The maximum-likelihood estimate of β from (6-19) is

$$\tilde{\beta} = \frac{\Sigma y_i(\tilde{\chi}_i - \bar{\tilde{\chi}})}{\Sigma(\tilde{\chi}_i - \bar{\tilde{\chi}})^2}$$

Using (6-20) we can then obtain

$$\tilde{\beta} = \frac{(\tilde{\sigma}^2\Sigma x_i y_i + \tilde{\beta}\sigma_u^2\Sigma y_i^2)(\tilde{\sigma}^2 + \tilde{\beta}^2\sigma_u^2)}{\tilde{\sigma}^4\Sigma x_i^2 + \tilde{\beta}^2\sigma_u^4\Sigma y_i^2 + 2\tilde{\beta}\tilde{\sigma}^2\sigma_u^2\Sigma x_i y_i}$$

which gives

$$\tilde{\beta}^2\sigma_u^2 m_{XY} - \tilde{\beta}(\sigma_u^2 m_{YY} - \tilde{\sigma}^2 m_{XX}) - \tilde{\sigma}^2 m_{XY} = 0 \tag{6-21}$$

The maximum-likelihood estimate of σ^2 is

$$\begin{aligned}\tilde{\sigma}^2 &= \frac{1}{n}\sum_{i=1}^{n}(Y_i - \tilde{\alpha} - \tilde{\beta}\tilde{\chi}_i)^2 \\ &= \frac{1}{n}\left[\sum y_i^2 - \tilde{\beta}\sum y_i(\tilde{\chi}_i - \bar{\tilde{\chi}})\right] \\ &= m_{YY} - \frac{\tilde{\beta}(\tilde{\sigma}^2 m_{XY} + \tilde{\beta}\sigma_u^2 m_{YY})}{\tilde{\sigma}^2 + \tilde{\beta}^2\sigma_u^2}\end{aligned}$$

giving

$$\tilde{\sigma}^2 = m_{YY} - \tilde{\beta}m_{XY} - \tilde{\beta}^2\sigma_u^2 \tag{6-22}$$

Substituting (6-22) in (6-21) and simplifying gives a cubic equation in $\tilde{\beta}$, namely,

$$a_0\tilde{\beta}^3 + a_1\tilde{\beta}^2 + a_2\tilde{\beta} + a_3 = 0 \tag{6-23}$$

where

$$\begin{aligned} a_0 &= -\sigma_u^2 m_{XX} \\ a_1 &= m_{XY}(2\sigma_u^2 - m_{XX}) \\ a_2 &= m_{XY}^2 + m_{YY}(m_{XX} - \sigma_u^2) \\ a_3 &= -m_{XY}m_{YY} \end{aligned} \tag{6-24}$$

Notice that if we consider the special case where $\sigma_u^2 = 0$, that is, there is no error in X, then (6-21) reduces to

$$\tilde{\beta} = \frac{m_{XY}}{m_{XX}}$$

which is the slope of the least-squares regression of Y on X, and from (6-22) we also obtain the familiar least-squares estimate of the error variance

$$\hat{\sigma}^2 = m_{YY} - \tilde{\beta} m_{XY}$$

These results provide some check on (6-21) and (6-22) since, if $\sigma_u^2 = 0$, the assumptions of this model give an identity between least-squares estimates and maximum-likelihood estimates.

To solve the cubic (6-23), we note that the coefficients a_0, a_1, a_2, a_3 depend only on second-order moments to be computed from the sample observations on X and Y and on the variance of the error component in X, which is assumed to be known. If the cubic yields more than one real root in any specific application, one would have to check which root maximizes the likelihood function (6-18). Substitution of the solution of (6-23) in (6-22) finally gives the maximum-likelihood estimate of the error variance.

Simpler, alternative estimates which have the property of consistency may be developed as follows. From (6-1), (6-2), and (6-3a) we have

$$\frac{1}{n}\sum_{i=1}^{n}(X_i - \bar{X})^2 = \frac{1}{n}\sum_{i=1}^{n}(\chi_i - \bar{\chi})^2 + \frac{1}{n}\sum_{i=1}^{n}(u_i - \bar{u})^2 + \frac{2}{n}\sum_{i=1}^{n}(\chi_i - \bar{\chi})(u_i - \bar{u})$$

$$\frac{1}{n}\sum_{i=1}^{n}(Y_i - \bar{Y})^2 = \beta^2\frac{1}{n}\sum_{i=1}^{n}(\chi_i - \bar{\chi})^2 + \frac{1}{n}\sum_{i=1}^{n}(\epsilon_i - \bar{\epsilon})^2 + \frac{1}{n}\sum_{i=1}^{n}(v_i - \bar{v})^2 + \text{cross-product terms}$$

$$\frac{1}{n}\sum_{i=1}^{n}(Y_i - \bar{Y})(X_i - \bar{X}) = \beta\frac{1}{n}\sum_{i=1}^{n}(\chi_i - \bar{\chi})^2 + \text{cross-product terms}$$

Taking expected values of both sides in all three relations gives

$$E\left[\frac{1}{n}\sum(X_i - \bar{X})^2\right] = \frac{1}{n}\sum(\chi_i - \bar{\chi})^2 + \frac{n-1}{n}\sigma_u^2 \qquad (6\text{-}25)$$

$$E\left[\frac{1}{n}\sum(Y_i - \bar{Y})^2\right] = \beta^2\frac{1}{n}\sum(\chi_i - \bar{\chi})^2 + \frac{n-1}{n}(\sigma_\epsilon^2 + \sigma_v^2) \qquad (6\text{-}26)$$

$$E\left[\frac{1}{n}\sum(Y_i - \bar{Y})(X_i - \bar{X})\right] = \beta\frac{1}{n}\sum(\chi_i - \bar{\chi})^2 \qquad (6\text{-}27)$$

since the expected value of all cross-product terms is zero, on the assumption that errors are mutually independent and also independent of the true values.

Replace the expected values on the left-hand side of these equations by the sample second-order moments m_{XX}, m_{YY}, and m_{XY}, and then solve for the unknown parameters. On the assumption that σ_u^2 is known, (6-25) and (6-27) then give

$$\tilde{\tilde{\beta}} = \frac{m_{XY}}{m_{XX} - \frac{n-1}{n}\sigma_u^2} \tag{6-28}$$

If we treat σ_v^2 as unknown, the best that can then be done is to obtain an estimate of the combined variance $\sigma^2 = \sigma_\epsilon^2 + \sigma_v^2$, namely,

$$\tilde{\tilde{\sigma}}^2 = \frac{n}{n-1}\left(m_{YY} - \frac{m_{XY}^2}{m_{XX} - \frac{n-1}{n}\sigma_u^2} \right) \tag{6-29}$$

The estimates (6-28) and (6-29) will be consistent, for the second-order moments m_{XX}, m_{YY}, and m_{XY} will converge in probability to the limit of their expectations. Finally, α would be estimated as usual by

$$\tilde{\tilde{\alpha}} = \bar{Y} - \tilde{\tilde{\beta}}\bar{X}$$

If σ_v^2 were also known, the estimate of β in (6-28) would remain unaffected, but it would now be possible to obtain an estimate of σ_ϵ^2 alone, namely,

$$\tilde{\tilde{\sigma}}_\epsilon^2 = \frac{n}{n-1}\left[m_{YY} - \frac{m_{XY}^2}{m_{XX} - \frac{n-1}{n}\sigma_u^2} \right] - \sigma_v^2 \tag{6-30}$$

The second subcase in the classical approach treats the true value χ as a random variable. The likelihood function (6-6) above for the first subcase contains no term involving the probabilities of $\chi_1 \quad \chi_2 \quad \cdots \quad \chi_n$, and in that case there are two possible interpretations. One is that χ is a random variable, so that the complete likelihood function would read

$$P(\mathbf{X},\mathbf{Y}) = P(\boldsymbol{\chi})P(\mathbf{uv}|\boldsymbol{\chi})$$

where the boldface letters indicate vectors. Concentrating solely on the conditional probability $P(\mathbf{uv}|\boldsymbol{\chi})$, as we have done in the first subcase, is then equivalent to assuming that, even though the χ values may have been generated by some probability process, we are deriving statistical estimators appropriate to the situation where the initial set of χ values can be exactly duplicated in successive trials, though the **u,v** values will of course vary from trial to trial. The second interpretation is that the χ's follow no probability law and the *initial* χ values can be set quite arbitrarily at any specified values $\chi_1 \quad \chi_2 \quad \ldots \quad \chi_n$, which can then be exactly duplicated in successive trials. Both situations seem unrealistic, for if the true values are in principle unobservable, how are we able to control their values in successive trials?

Let us now assume

$$X = \chi + u \tag{6-1}$$
$$Y = \psi + v \tag{6-2}$$
$$\psi = \alpha + \beta\chi \tag{6-3}$$

where χ, u, and v have independent normal distributions with variances σ_χ^2, σ_u^2, and σ_v^2. Since X and Y are linear functions of normal variables, X, Y will have a bivariate normal distribution. It is clear from the above three relations that

$$\begin{aligned} \sigma_X^2 &= \sigma_\chi^2 + \sigma_u^2 \\ \sigma_Y^2 &= \beta^2\sigma_\chi^2 + \sigma_v^2 \\ \sigma_{XY} &= \beta\sigma_\chi^2 \end{aligned}$$

where σ_{XY} denotes the covariance of X and Y, namely, $E\{[X - E(X)][Y - E(Y)]\}$. Since X, Y have a bivariate normal distribution, the sample moments m_{XX}, m_{YY}, m_{XY} will be maximum-likelihood estimates of σ_X^2, σ_Y^2, and σ_{XY}. If we also repeat assumption (6-10) that

$$\frac{\sigma_u^2}{\sigma_v^2} = \lambda$$

we obtain the three equations

$$\begin{aligned} m_{XX} &= \tilde{\sigma}_\chi^2 + \lambda\tilde{\sigma}_v^2 \\ m_{YY} &= \tilde{\beta}^2\tilde{\sigma}_\chi^2 + \tilde{\sigma}_v^2 \\ m_{XY} &= \tilde{\beta}\tilde{\sigma}_\chi^2 \end{aligned} \tag{6-31}$$

which can be solved for the three unknowns $\tilde{\sigma}_\chi^2$, $\tilde{\sigma}_v^2$, and $\tilde{\beta}$. These estimators, being functions of maximum-likelihood estimates, will themselves be maximum-likelihood estimators.

Solving (6-31) for $\tilde{\beta}$ gives

$$\lambda\tilde{\beta}^2 m_{XY} - \tilde{\beta}(\lambda m_{YY} - m_{XX}) - m_{XY} = 0$$

This is exactly the same quadratic in $\tilde{\beta}$ as was obtained in (6-14) above for the fixed-variate, nonstochastic case, and so the solution outlined in (6-15) to (6-17) applies here.

Finally, let us examine the case where the relationship between the true values is a stochastic one. We have

$$\begin{aligned} X &= \chi + u \\ Y &= \psi + v \\ \psi &= \alpha + \beta\chi + \epsilon \end{aligned}$$

If we assume that χ, u, v, and ϵ all have independent, normal distributions, then ψ, χ will have a bivariate normal distribution, and so will Y, X. We have

$$\begin{aligned} \sigma_X^2 &= \sigma_\chi^2 + \sigma_u^2 \\ \sigma_Y^2 &= \beta^2\sigma_\chi^2 + \sigma_\epsilon^2 + \sigma_v^2 \\ \sigma_{XY} &= \beta\sigma_\chi^2 \end{aligned} \tag{6-32}$$

where σ_{XY} denotes the covariance of X and Y. If we replace the elements on the left-hand side of (6-32) by their maximum-likelihood estimates m_{XX}, m_{YY}, and m_{XY} and if we assume σ_u^2 to be known and also let $\sigma^2 = \sigma_\epsilon^2 + \sigma_v^2$, we have

$$\begin{aligned} m_{XX} &= \tilde{\sigma}_\chi^2 + \sigma_u^2 \\ m_{YY} &= \tilde{\beta}^2\tilde{\sigma}_\chi^2 + \tilde{\sigma}^2 \\ m_{XY} &= \tilde{\beta}\tilde{\sigma}_\chi^2 \end{aligned} \tag{6-33}$$

This yields as the maximum-likelihood estimate of β,

$$\tilde{\beta} = \frac{m_{XY}}{m_{XX} - \sigma_u^2} \tag{6-34}$$

which is almost an exact parallel of the consistent estimate in the fixed-variate case in (6-28).

6-3. Prediction Problems

In the models discussed above, the emphasis has been on the estimation of the parameters of the relationship between the true values. Suppose instead that the problem is that of predicting Y for a given value of X, or equivalently, that of predicting ψ for a given value of X. For example, suppose Y denotes measured consumption expenditure and X denotes measured income and the assumed relation between the true values has a one-period lag, that is,

$$\psi_t = \alpha + \beta\chi_{t-1} + \epsilon_t$$

For period n, say, we have a measured income X_n, but we do not know χ_n and our problem is to predict Y_{n+1} (or ψ_{n+1}). Should we use estimates of α and β obtained by one of the methods outlined above and obtain the prediction

$$\tilde{Y}_{n+1} = \tilde{\alpha} + \tilde{\beta} X_n \tag{6-35}$$

or should we in fact apply least squares directly to the measured X, Y values and predict from the least-squares relation? From the relationship assumed above,

$$\begin{aligned} E(Y_{n+1}|X_n) &= E(\alpha + \beta\chi_n + \epsilon_{n+1} + v_{n+1}|X_n) \\ &= \alpha + \beta E(\chi_n|X_n) \end{aligned}$$

Thus we require to evaluate $E(\chi_n|X_n)$.

Remembering $X = \chi + u$, and assuming that χ and u are independently and normally distributed with means μ_χ and zero and variances $\sigma_\chi{}^2$ and $\sigma_u{}^2$, we can then show that[1]

$$E(\chi_n|X_n) = \frac{\sigma_u{}^2\mu_\chi + \sigma_\chi{}^2 X_n}{\sigma_\chi{}^2 + \sigma_u{}^2}$$

Thus

$$E(Y_{n+1}|X_n) = \alpha + \frac{\beta\sigma_u{}^2\mu_\chi}{\sigma_\chi{}^2 + \sigma_u{}^2} + \frac{\beta\sigma_\chi{}^2 X_n}{\sigma_\chi{}^2 + \sigma_u{}^2} \tag{6-36}$$

Comparison of (6-35) and (6-36) shows that, apart from sampling fluctuations in $\tilde{\alpha}$ and $\tilde{\beta}$, (6-35) will be an unbiased estimator of (6-36) only for $X_n = \mu_\chi$. If $X_n > \mu_\chi$, (6-35) will have a persistent upward bias, while if $X_n < \mu_\chi$, it will be biased downward.

We have already shown that the direct application of least squares to X, Y gives an estimated regression slope b, which converges in probability to

$$\operatorname{plim} b_n = \frac{\beta}{1 + \sigma_u{}^2/\sigma_\chi{}^2}$$

Denote the least-squares prediction by

$$\hat{Y}_{n+1} = \bar{Y} + b_n(X_n - \bar{X})$$

This prediction converges in probability to

$$\begin{aligned} \operatorname{plim} \hat{Y}_{n+1} &= \alpha + \beta\mu_\chi + \frac{\beta}{1 + \sigma_u{}^2/\sigma_\chi{}^2}(X_n - \mu_\chi) \\ &= \alpha + \frac{\beta\sigma_u{}^2\mu_\chi}{\sigma_\chi{}^2 + \sigma_u{}^2} + \frac{\beta\sigma_{\chi^2}}{\sigma_\chi{}^2 + \sigma_u{}^2} X_n \\ &= E(Y_{n+1}|X_n) \end{aligned}$$

[1] See Exercise 6-1.

Thus, where this type of prediction is required, least squares is appropriate, even though it would not be used to obtain estimates of the structural parameters.

6-4. Grouping of Observations

The two main contributions here are those of Wald and Bartlett.[1] Wald postulated

$$X = \chi + u$$
$$Y = \psi + v$$
$$\psi = \alpha + \beta\chi$$

where the errors u, v are assumed to be serially and mutually independent. Assuming an even number of observations, $n = 2m$, the practical procedure is very simple. The X values are to be ordered in ascending magnitude. Assuming that the X subscripts actually indicate the order of magnitude, we have an ordered array

$$X_1 \quad X_2 \quad \cdots \quad X_m \quad X_{m+1} \quad \cdots \quad X_n$$

and the corresponding Y values

$$Y_1 \quad Y_2 \quad \cdots \quad Y_m \quad Y_{m+1} \quad \cdots \quad Y_n$$

Defining the subgroup means

$$\bar{X}_1 = \frac{1}{m}\sum_{i=1}^{m} X_i \qquad \bar{X}_2 = \frac{1}{m}\sum_{i=m+1}^{n} X_i$$
$$\bar{Y}_1 = \frac{1}{m}\sum_{i=1}^{m} Y_i \qquad \bar{Y}_2 = \frac{1}{m}\sum_{i=m+1}^{n} X_i$$

Wald's suggested estimates are

$$\text{est of } \beta = b = \frac{\bar{Y}_1 - \bar{Y}_2}{\bar{X}_1 - \bar{X}_2} \tag{6-37}$$

$$\text{est of } \alpha = a = \bar{Y} - b\bar{X} \tag{6-38}$$

On the assumption that

$$\liminf_{n\to\infty} \left| \frac{1}{m}\sum_{i=1}^{m} \chi_i - \frac{1}{m}\sum_{i=m+1}^{n} \chi_i \right| > 0 \tag{6-39}$$

[1] A. Wald, "The Fitting of Straight Lines If Both Variables Are Subject to Error," *Ann. Math. Statist.*, vol. 11, pp. 284–300, 1940. M. S. Bartlett, "The Fitting of Straight Lines If Both Variables Are Subject to Error," *Biometrics*, vol. 5, pp. 207–242, 1949.

these estimates are shown to be consistent, and Wald also shows how confidence intervals for α and β may be determined. Unfortunately, the crucial assumption (6-39) is not valid for normally distributed variables.

Bartlett's modification is to define subgroup means based on k observations at each end of the array. Denote these means by

$$\bar{X}_1 = \frac{1}{k}\sum_{i=1}^{k} X_i \qquad \bar{X}_3 = \frac{1}{k}\sum_{i=n-k+1}^{n} X_i$$

$$\bar{Y}_1 = \frac{1}{k}\sum_{i=1}^{k} Y_i \qquad \bar{Y}_3 = \frac{1}{k}\sum_{i=n-k+1}^{n} Y_i$$

Bartlett's suggested estimates are then

$$b' = \frac{\bar{Y}_3 - \bar{Y}_1}{\bar{X}_3 - \bar{X}_1} \tag{6-40}$$

$$a' = \bar{Y} - b'\bar{X} \tag{6-41}$$

where it remains to determine the number of observations that should be used to compute the subgroup means. For the special case of *equally spaced* X values, Bartlett shows that the sampling variance of b' will be minimized, for given error variances, if $k = n/3$.

The main difference between these grouping methods and the classical ones is the simplicity of the calculations and the dropping of the assumption of normality. The grouping methods have also been extended to handle more than two variables.[1]

6-5. Use of Instrumental Variables

Suppose we repeat again assumptions (6-1) to (6-3) to obtain

$$Y = \alpha + \beta X + w \tag{6-4}$$

where $\quad w = v - \beta u$

As has been shown, the application of least squares to (6-4) would not give best linear unbiased estimates—nor would it even give consistent estimates.

If it is possible to find another variable Z which is independent

[1] J. W. Hooper and H. Theil, "The Extension of Wald's Method of Fitting Straight Lines to Multiple Regression," *Rev. Intern. Statist. Inst.*, 1958. See also H. Theil and J. van Ijzeren, "On the Efficiency of Wald's Method of Fitting Straight Lines," *Rev. Intern. Statist. Inst.*, 1956.

of both errors u and v, we may consider the estimate

$$\hat{\beta} = \frac{\sum_{i=1}^{n} y_i z_i}{\sum_{i=1}^{n} x_i z_i} \tag{6-42}$$

using lowercase letters to denote deviations from sample means. Thus

$$\hat{\beta} = \frac{\beta \sum_{i=1}^{n} x_i z_i + \sum_{i=1}^{n} z_i(w_i - \bar{w})}{\sum_{i=1}^{n} x_i z_i}$$

Since Z is presumed to be independent of the errors u and v, the term $\sum_{i=1}^{n} z_i(w_i - \bar{w})$ converges in probability to zero as n becomes very large, so that (6-42) provides a *consistent* estimate of β. Z is termed an instrumental variable, and to obtain consistent estimates of the parameters of a relation embracing more than two variables, sufficient additional instrumental variables may be introduced. It is clear from (6-42) that Z should be chosen so as to have a fairly high correlation with X, for if our sample gives $\Sigma x_i z_i = 0$, the method of instrumental variables breaks down.

There are three major difficulties with this suggested use of instrumental variables for errors-in-variables problems. First, there is the arbitrary nature of the variables chosen as instrumental and the possibility of very large variations in the resultant estimates according to the instrumental set selected. Second, there is the great difficulty of checking on the assumption that each instrumental variable is independent of each and all the errors of observation. Third, the approach elevates consistency to a position of extreme importance, which is unwarranted in a case involving the possibility of very large sampling variances.

Example. To illustrate some of these calculations consider the data on road casualties and licensed vehicles in the United Kingdom given in Table 1-1. For these data we have

$$n = 11 \qquad \bar{X} = 519.182 \qquad \bar{Y} = 217.818$$
$$\Sigma x^2 = 169{,}495.64 \qquad \Sigma y^2 = 17{,}619.64 \qquad \Sigma xy = 52{,}876.36$$

Let us assume that both variables are subject to measurement error and that the ratio of the error variances is unity ($\lambda = 1$). Notice that in specifying the value of λ one must pay close attention to the *units* in which the variables are measured. For example, if it is thought the variance error is the same for each variable, and then for purposes of calculation one variable is divided by 100 and the other by 1,000, the proper value of λ to insert in the calculations will not be unity, but either $1/100$ or 100, according to which variable has been labeled X and which Y.

Assuming $\lambda = 1$, substitution in (6-16) gives

$$\begin{aligned}\theta &= \frac{m_{YY} - \frac{1}{\lambda} m_{XX}}{2m_{XY}} = \frac{17{,}619.64 - 169{,}495.64}{2(52{,}876.36)} \\ &= -1.43614\end{aligned}$$

Since $m_{XY} > 0$, we take the positive root from (6-15); that is,

$$\begin{aligned}\tilde{\beta} &= \theta + \sqrt{\theta^2 + 1/\lambda} \\ &= 0.31386\end{aligned}$$

and finally compute $\tilde{\alpha}$ from (6-17) as

$$\begin{aligned}\tilde{\alpha} &= \bar{Y} - \tilde{\beta}\bar{X} \\ &= 54.8675\end{aligned}$$

Similar calculations may be made for other postulated values of λ.

To apply the Wald or Bartlett method requires the reordering of the data to put the X values in ascending order of magnitude. For the Wald method a simple application of (6-37) and (6-38) gives

$$\begin{aligned}b &= \frac{\bar{Y}_1 - \bar{Y}_2}{\bar{X}_1 - \bar{X}_2} = \frac{182.6 - 255.0}{407.8 - 636.4} = 0.3167 \\ a &= 53.3933\end{aligned}$$

Bartlett's method gives

$$\begin{aligned}b' &= \frac{\bar{Y}_3 - \bar{Y}_1}{\bar{X}_3 - \bar{X}_1} \\ &= \frac{262.00 - 174.25}{663.25 - 394.25} \\ &= 0.3262 \\ a' &= 48.4608\end{aligned}$$

The following table assembles some of these estimates for purposes of comparison.

TABLE 6-1. PARAMETER ESTIMATES UNDER VARIOUS ASSUMPTIONS ABOUT THE ERROR VARIANCES

Estimate of	$\lambda = 0$	$\lambda = \frac{1}{2}$	$\lambda = 1$	$\lambda = 2$	$\lambda \to \infty$	Wald	Bartlett
α	55.85	55.78	54.87	54.10	44.83	53.39	48.46
β	0.3120	0.3130	0.3139	0.3154	0.3332	0.3167	0.3262

The $\lambda = 0$ case corresponds to the least-squares regression of Y on X, and the $\lambda = \infty$ case to that of X on Y. The various estimates are remarkably close together in this example, but this is a reflection of the very high correlation (0.97) between the two sample series. As this correlation diminishes, the two extreme regression values diverge more widely and other values of λ give intermediate estimates.

6-6. Extensions to More than Two Variables

Finally, let us look at extensions to a relation involving more than two variables. Once again the treatment subdivides according to whether we postulate an exact or a stochastic relation between the true values. We shall first of all assume a stochastic relation and develop the three-variable model, which then extends easily to the general case of k variables.

Assume

$$\begin{aligned} X_{1t} &= \chi_{1t} + u_{1t} \\ X_{2t} &= \chi_{2t} + u_{2t} \\ Y_t &= \psi_t + v_t \end{aligned} \tag{6-43}$$

and

$$\psi_t = \beta_0 + \beta_1\chi_{1t} + \beta_2\chi_{2t} + \epsilon_t \tag{6-44}$$

where u_1, u_2, and v indicate errors of observation and ϵ a stochastic disturbance term. Assume that u_1, u_2, and v are normally distributed about zero means with variances var (u_1), var (u_2), var (v) and covariances cov (u_1u_2), cov (u_1v), and cov (u_2v). Assume also that ϵ has a normal distribution with zero mean and variance, var (ϵ), but we take it to be distributed independently of the errors of measurement u_1, u_2, and v. All four error terms are assumed independent of the distribution of χ_1 and χ_2. From (6-43) and (6-44) we have

$$\begin{aligned} \text{var}(X_1) &= \text{var}(\chi_1) + \text{var}(u_1) \\ \text{var}(X_2) &= \text{var}(\chi_2) + \text{var}(u_2) \\ \text{var}(Y) &= \text{var}(\psi) + \text{var}(v) \\ &= \beta_1^2\,\text{var}(\chi_1) + \beta_2^2\,\text{var}(\chi_2) + 2\beta_1\beta_2\,\text{cov}(\chi_1\chi_2) \\ &\qquad + \text{var}(\epsilon) + \text{var}(v) \end{aligned} \tag{6-45}$$

$$\begin{aligned} \text{cov}(X_1X_2) &= \text{cov}(\chi_1\chi_2) + \text{cov}(u_1u_2) \\ \text{cov}(YX_1) &= \beta_1\,\text{var}(\chi_1) + \beta_2\,\text{cov}(\chi_1\chi_2) + \text{cov}(u_1v) \\ \text{cov}(YX_2) &= \beta_1\,\text{cov}(\chi_1\chi_2) + \beta_2\,\text{var}(\chi_2) + \text{cov}(u_2v) \end{aligned}$$

If χ_1 and χ_2 follow a bivariate normal distribution, then Y, X_1, and X_2 will have a multivariate normal distribution, so that the second-order sample moments

$$m_{X_1X_2} = \frac{1}{n}\sum_{t=1}^{n}(X_{1t} - \bar{X}_1)(X_{2t} - \bar{X}_2)$$

etc., will be maximum-likelihood estimates of the variance-covariance terms on the left-hand side of (6-45). Assuming the variance-covariance matrix of the measurement errors to be known, we can then substitute from the first, second, and fourth equations of (6-45) into the last two to obtain the following simultaneous equations for $\tilde{\beta}_1$ and $\tilde{\beta}_2$:

$$\begin{aligned}\tilde{\beta}_1[m_{X_1X_1} - \text{var}\,(u_1)] + \tilde{\beta}_2[m_{X_1X_2} - \text{cov}\,(u_1u_2)] &= m_{YX_1} - \text{cov}\,(u_1v)\\ \tilde{\beta}_1[m_{X_1X_2} - \text{cov}\,(u_1u_2)] + \tilde{\beta}_2[m_{X_2X_2} - \text{var}\,(u_2)] &= m_{YX_2} - \text{cov}\,(u_2v)\end{aligned} \tag{6-46}$$

Notice that (6-46) is very similar to the least-squares estimating equations for the linear normal case,

$$(\mathbf{X'X})\mathbf{b} = \mathbf{X'Y}$$

for if we use the deviation form for three variables, this becomes

$$\begin{aligned}b_1m_{X_1X_1} + b_2m_{X_1X_2} &= m_{X_1Y}\\ b_1m_{X_1X_2} + b_2m_{X_2X_2} &= m_{X_2Y}\end{aligned}$$

The only difference between this and (6-46) is that the sample second-order moments have to be corrected by using the variance-covariance error terms.

The general case may then be easily written down. Let there be k explanatory variates $X_1, X_2, \ldots, X_k$, expressed in deviation form as

$$\mathbf{X} = \begin{bmatrix} x_{11} & x_{21} & \cdots & x_{k1}\\ x_{12} & x_{22} & \cdots & x_{k2}\\ \cdot & & & \cdot\\ \cdot & & & \cdot\\ \cdot & & & \cdot\\ x_{1n} & x_{2n} & \cdots & x_{kn}\end{bmatrix}$$

Also write

$$\mathbf{Y} = \begin{bmatrix} y_1\\ y_2\\ \cdot\\ \cdot\\ \cdot\\ y_n\end{bmatrix} \qquad \mathbf{U} = \begin{bmatrix} \text{var}\,(u_1) & \text{cov}\,(u_1u_2) & \cdots & \text{cov}\,(u_1u_k)\\ \text{cov}\,(u_1u_2) & \text{var}\,(u_2) & \cdots & \text{cov}\,(u_2u_k)\\ \cdot & & & \cdot\\ \cdot & & & \cdot\\ \text{cov}\,(u_1u_k) & \text{cov}\,(u_2u_k) & \cdots & \text{var}\,(u_k)\end{bmatrix}$$

and

$$\mathbf{V} = \begin{bmatrix} \text{cov}\,(u_1v)\\ \text{cov}\,(u_2v)\\ \cdot\\ \cdot\\ \cdot\\ \text{cov}\,(u_kv)\end{bmatrix}$$

Then the general estimating equation for $\tilde{\boldsymbol{\beta}} = \{\tilde{\beta}_1 \quad \tilde{\beta}_2 \quad \cdots \quad \tilde{\beta}_k\}$ is

$$(\mathbf{X}'\mathbf{X} - \mathbf{U})\tilde{\boldsymbol{\beta}} = \mathbf{X}'\mathbf{Y} - \mathbf{V} \tag{6-47}$$

The intercept term $\tilde{\beta}_0$ would be estimated as usual by passing the plane through the sample means.

The simplest way of understanding the generalization of the classical case of an exact relation between the true variables is to rework the two-variable case in a slightly different fashion. Let us define

$$\left.\begin{aligned} X_{1i} &= \chi_{1i} + u_{1i} \\ X_{2i} &= \chi_{2i} + u_{2i} \end{aligned}\right\} \qquad i = 1, \ldots, n \tag{6-48}$$

and

$$\alpha_0 + \alpha_1\chi_{1i} + \alpha_2\chi_{2i} = 0 \qquad i = 1, \ldots, n \tag{6-49}$$

where X's denote observed values, χ's true values, and u's observation errors as before. Equation (6-49) specifies the exact linear relation between the true values, apart from an arbitrary constant. For example, the coefficient of χ_1 may be set equal to unity by dividing through the relation by α_1, but writing it as in (6-49) preserves a symmetry and simplifies subsequent developments.

If we assume the errors to be mutually and serially independent with variances σ_1^2 and σ_2^2, we may define the estimation problem as that of minimizing the sum of squares

$$S = \frac{1}{\sigma_1^2}\sum_{i=1}^{n}(X_{1i} - \chi_{1i})^2 + \frac{1}{\sigma_2^2}\sum_{i=1}^{n}(X_{2i} - \chi_{2i})^2 \tag{6-50}$$

subject to (6-49). A justification of this sum of squares in which each error is weighted by the reciprocal of its variance is that if the errors are normally distributed, the expression (6-50) appears in the exponent of the likelihood, so that maximizing the likelihood involves minimizing S. Making the further assumption

$$\sigma_2^2 = \lambda\sigma_1^2 \tag{6-51}$$

where λ is a known constant, we have to minimize

$$S = \frac{1}{\sigma_1^2}\sum_{i=1}^{n}(X_{1i} - \chi_{1i})^2 + \frac{1}{\lambda\sigma_1^2}\sum_{i=1}^{n}(X_{2i} - \chi_{2i})^2 \tag{6-52}$$

subject to

$$\alpha_0 + \alpha_1\chi_{1i} + \alpha_2\chi_{2i} = 0 \qquad i = 1, \ldots, n$$

This constrained minimum problem may be solved by first of all introducing n Lagrange multipliers μ_i $(i = 1, \ldots, n)$ and defining

$$S^* = S + \sum_{i=1}^{n} \mu_i(\alpha_0 + \alpha_1\chi_{1i} + \alpha_2\chi_{2i}) \tag{6-53}$$

Taking partial derivatives of S^* with respect to χ_{1i}, χ_{2i} $(i = 1, \ldots, n)$, and α_0 and equating to zero gives

$$\begin{aligned}
\frac{\partial S^*}{\partial \chi_{1i}} &= \frac{-2}{\sigma_1^2}(X_{1i} - \hat{\chi}_{1i}) + \mu_i\alpha_1 = 0 \qquad i = 1, \ldots, n \\
\frac{\partial S^*}{\partial \chi_{2i}} &= \frac{-2}{\lambda\sigma_1^2}(X_{2i} - \hat{\chi}_{2i}) + \mu_i\alpha_2 = 0 \qquad i = 1, \ldots, n \\
\frac{\partial S^*}{\partial \alpha_0} &= \sum_{i=1}^{n} \mu_i = 0
\end{aligned} \tag{6-54}$$

These give estimators of χ_{1i}, χ_{2i} as

$$\left.\begin{aligned}
\hat{\chi}_{1i} &= X_{1i} - \frac{\mu_i\alpha_1\sigma_1^2}{2} \\
\hat{\chi}_{2i} &= X_{2i} - \frac{\mu_i\alpha_2\lambda\sigma_1^2}{2}
\end{aligned}\right\} \qquad i = 1, \ldots, n \tag{6-55}$$

Substituting these estimators in (6-49), the αs have to be such that

$$\alpha_0 + \alpha_1\hat{\chi}_{1i} + \alpha_2\hat{\chi}_{2i} = 0 \qquad i = 1, \ldots, n \tag{6-56}$$

Averaging over the n estimates gives

$$\alpha_0 + \alpha_1\bar{\hat{\chi}}_1 + \alpha_2\bar{\hat{\chi}}_2 = 0 \tag{6-57}$$

where $\bar{\hat{\chi}}_1$ and $\bar{\hat{\chi}}_2$ denote the means of the n estimated values of $\hat{\chi}_{1i}$ and $\hat{\chi}_{2i}$. But Eqs. (6-54) imply that

$$\bar{\hat{\chi}}_1 = \bar{X}_1 \qquad \text{and} \qquad \bar{\hat{\chi}}_2 = \bar{X}_2 \tag{6-58}$$

which enables us to write (6-56) as

$$\alpha_0 + \alpha_1\bar{X}_1 + \alpha_2\bar{X}_2 = 0 \tag{6-59}$$

from which α_0 may be estimated when estimates of α_1 and α_2 have been obtained. Subtracting (6-57) from (6-56) gives

$$\alpha_1(\hat{\chi}_{1i} - \bar{\hat{\chi}}_1) + \alpha_2(\hat{\chi}_{2i} - \bar{\hat{\chi}}_2) = 0 \qquad i = 1, \ldots, n \tag{6-60}$$

that is, the relationship (6-49) may be written in terms of deviations from means and the intercept term disappears.

Thus the problem may be formulated as the minimization of

$$S = \frac{1}{\sigma_1^2} \sum_{i=1}^{n} (X_{1i} - \chi_{1i})^2 + \frac{1}{\lambda\sigma_1^2} \sum_{i=1}^{n} (X_{2i} - \chi_{2i})^2$$

subject to

$$\alpha_1\chi_{1i} + \alpha_2\chi_{2i} = 0 \qquad i = 1, \ . \ . \ . \ , n$$

where the X and χ symbols now represent *deviations* from means. The equations in (6-55) still hold in deviation form, and by multiplying the first by α_1 and the second by α_2, summing, and using $\alpha_1\chi_{1i} + \alpha_2\chi_{2i} = 0$, we obtain

$$\alpha_1X_{1i} + \alpha_2X_{2i} = \frac{\mu_i\sigma_1^2(\alpha_1^2 + \lambda\alpha_2^2)}{2}$$

But we may also write from (6-55)

$$\frac{(X_{1i} - \tilde{\chi}_{1i})^2}{\sigma_1^2} + \frac{(X_{2i} - \tilde{\chi}_{2i})^2}{\lambda\sigma_1^2} = \frac{\mu_i^2\sigma_1^2(\alpha_1^2 + \lambda\alpha_2^2)}{4}$$
$$= \frac{(\alpha_1X_{1i} + \alpha_2X_{2i})^2}{\sigma_1^2(\alpha_1^2 + \lambda\alpha_2^2)}$$

Hence the sum of squares defined in (6-52) may be written

$$S = \frac{\sum_{i=1}^{n} (\alpha_1X_{1i} + \alpha_2X_{2i})^2}{\sigma_1^2(\alpha_1^2 + \lambda\alpha_2^2)} \tag{6-61}$$

where the sum now appears as a function of the two parameters α_1 and α_2 and deviations of the observed X values from their sample means.

We see that S is homogeneous of degree zero in α_1 and α_2. Thus if $\tilde{\alpha}_1$ and $\tilde{\alpha}_2$ minimize S, then so will $c\tilde{\alpha}_1$ and $c\tilde{\alpha}_2$, where c is any positive constant. In other words, we can determine only the ratio $\tilde{\alpha}_1/\tilde{\alpha}_2$, but that is all we need since the coefficient of one of the two variables can be set arbitrarily at unity. The values of α_1 and α_2 which minimize S will be the same, except for an arbitrary multiplying constant, as those which minimize

$$\sum_{i=1}^{n} (\alpha_1X_{1i} + \alpha_2X_{2i})^2$$

subject to the constraint

$$\sigma_1^2(\alpha_1^2 + \lambda\alpha_2^2) = k$$

where k is an arbitrary nonzero constant.[1] We thus define

$$S^* = \sum_{i=1}^{n} (\alpha_1 X_{1i} + \alpha_2 X_{2i})^2 - \mu[\sigma_1^2(\alpha_1^2 + \lambda\alpha_2^2) - k] \qquad (6\text{-}62)$$

Then

$$\begin{aligned} \frac{\partial S^*}{\partial \alpha_1} &= 2 \sum X_{1i}(\alpha_1 X_{1i} + \alpha_2 X_{2i}) - 2\mu\sigma_1^2\alpha_1 = 0 \\ \frac{\partial S^*}{\partial \alpha_2} &= 2 \sum X_{2i}(\alpha_1 X_{1i} + \alpha_2 X_{2i}) - 2\lambda\mu\sigma_1^2\alpha_2 = 0 \end{aligned} \qquad (6\text{-}63)$$

Remembering that the X symbols represent deviations from sample means, these equations simplify to

$$\begin{aligned} (m_{11} - \mu\sigma_1^2/n)\alpha_1 + m_{12}\alpha_2 &= 0 \\ \frac{1}{\lambda} m_{12}\alpha_1 + \left(\frac{1}{\lambda} m_{22} - \mu\sigma_1^2/n\right)\alpha_2 &= 0 \end{aligned} \qquad (6\text{-}64)$$

where the m_{ij} denote sample moments

$$m_{ij} = \frac{1}{n} \sum_{t=1}^{n} (X_{it} - \bar{X}_i)(X_{jt} - \bar{X}_j)$$

Defining $r = \mu\sigma_1^2/n$ and $k_2 = 1/\lambda$, which from (6-51) is equivalent to defining

$$k_2\sigma_2^2 = \sigma_1^2 \qquad (6\text{-}65)$$

[1] In general let

$$S = \frac{f(\alpha_1,\alpha_2)}{g(\alpha_1,\alpha_2)}$$

$$\frac{\partial S}{\partial \alpha_1} = \frac{g\dfrac{\partial f}{\partial \alpha_1} - f\dfrac{\partial g}{\partial \alpha_1}}{g^2} = 0$$

$$\frac{\partial S}{\partial \alpha_2} = \frac{g\dfrac{\partial f}{\partial \alpha_2} - f\dfrac{\partial g}{\partial \alpha_2}}{g^2} = 0$$

Since, by assumption, $g \neq 0$, we have

$$g\frac{\partial f}{\partial \alpha_1} - f\frac{\partial g}{\partial \alpha_1} = 0 = g\frac{\partial f}{\partial \alpha_2} - f\frac{\partial g}{\partial \alpha_2}$$

which gives

$$\frac{f}{g} = \boxed{\frac{\partial f/\partial \alpha_1}{\partial g/\partial \alpha_1} = \frac{\partial f/\partial \alpha_2}{\partial g/\partial \alpha_2}}$$

and $S^* = f(\alpha_1,\alpha_2) - \mu g(\alpha_1,\alpha_2)$

where μ is a Lagrange multiplier.

$$\frac{\partial S^*}{\partial \alpha_1} = \frac{\partial f}{\partial \alpha_1} - \mu\frac{\partial g}{\partial \alpha_1}$$

$$\frac{\partial S^*}{\partial \alpha_2} = \frac{\partial f}{\partial \alpha_2} - \mu\frac{\partial g}{\partial \alpha_2}$$

Eliminating μ gives

$$\boxed{\frac{\partial f/\partial \alpha_1}{\partial g/\partial \alpha_1} = \frac{\partial f/\partial \alpha_2}{\partial g/\partial \alpha_2}}$$

these equations become

$$\begin{aligned}(m_{11} - r)\alpha_1 + m_{12}\alpha_2 &= 0 \\ k_2 m_{12}\alpha_1 + (k_2 m_{22} - r)\alpha_2 &= 0\end{aligned} \tag{6-66}$$

They have a nontrivial solution for α_1 and α_2 only if

$$\begin{vmatrix} m_{11} - r & m_{12} \\ k_2 m_{12} & k_2 m_{22} - r \end{vmatrix} = 0 \tag{6-67}$$

This gives a quadratic equation in r. We take the smaller root to minimize the sum of squares.[1] Substituting this root back in (6-66) we solve for the ratio $\tilde{\alpha}_2/\alpha_1$. Substitution of this back in (6-59) gives

$$\frac{\tilde{\alpha}_0}{\alpha_1} = -\bar{X}_1 - \frac{\tilde{\alpha}_2}{\alpha_1}\bar{X}_2$$

and thus estimates of the structural parameters in (6-49) have been obtained.

A straightforward application of these same methods will handle the general case. The details are left to the reader as an exercise, but from (6-65) and (6-66) it is intuitively clear that if we postulate

$$\alpha_0 + \alpha_1\chi_{1i} + \cdots + \alpha_p\chi_{pi} = 0 \qquad i = 1, \ldots, n$$

and

$$k_j\sigma_j^2 = \sigma_1^2 \qquad j = 2, \ldots, p$$

and assume the errors $X_{ij} - \chi_{ij}$ to be mutually and serially independent, the estimating equations are

$$\begin{aligned}(m_{11} - r)\alpha_1 + m_{12}\alpha_2 + \cdots + m_{1p}\alpha_p &= 0 \\ k_2 m_{12}\alpha_1 + (k_2 m_{22} - r)\alpha_2 + \cdots + k_2 m_{2p}\alpha_p &= 0 \\ &\vdots \\ k_p m_{1p}\alpha_1 + k_p m_{2p}\alpha_2 + \cdots + (k_p m_{pp} - r)\alpha_p &= 0\end{aligned} \tag{6-68}$$

[1] Multiplying the first equation in (6-63) by α_1, the second by α_2, and summing gives

$$\alpha_1^2\Sigma X_{1i}^2 + 2\alpha_1\alpha_2\Sigma X_{1i}X_{2i} + \alpha_2^2\Sigma X_{2i}^2 = \mu\sigma_1^2(\alpha_1^2 + \lambda\alpha_2^2)$$

that is,

$$\sum_{i=1}^{n} (\alpha_1 X_{1i} + \alpha_2 X_{2i})^2 = \mu k$$

so that the sum of squares is minimized by taking the smallest value of μ.

which have a nontrivial solution only if the determinantal equation

$$\begin{vmatrix} m_{11} - r & m_{12} & \cdots & m_{1p} \\ k_2 m_{12} & k_2 m_{22} - r & \cdots & k_2 m_{2p} \\ \cdot & & & \cdot \\ \cdot & & & \cdot \\ \cdot & & & \cdot \\ k_p m_{1p} & k_p m_{2p} & \cdots & k_p m_{pp} - r \end{vmatrix} = 0 \qquad (6\text{-}69)$$

holds. The smallest root of (6-69) is found, and substitution in (6-68) determines the ratios

$$\frac{\tilde{\alpha}_2}{\alpha_1} \cdots \frac{\tilde{\alpha}_p}{\alpha_1}$$

Finally, $\tilde{\alpha}_0/\alpha_1$ is obtained from

$$\frac{\tilde{\alpha}_0}{\alpha_1} = -\bar{X}_1 - \frac{\tilde{\alpha}_2}{\alpha_1}\bar{X}_2 - \cdots - \frac{\tilde{\alpha}_p}{\alpha_1}\bar{X}_p \qquad (6\text{-}70)$$

References

The best single reference on this topic is

1. M. G. Kendall and A. Stuart: *The Advanced Theory of Statistics*, Griffin, London, vol. 2, chap. 29, 1961,

which contains many further references.

One important recent reference which is not contained therein is

2. M. Halperin: "Fitting of Straight Lines and Prediction When Both Variables Are Subject to Error," *J. Am. Statist. Assoc.*, vol. 56, no. 295, pp. 657–669, September, 1961.

Exercises

6-1. Let x and y have independent normal distributions with means μ_x, μ_y and standard deviations σ_x, σ_y, and define $z = x + y$. Derive the conditional distribution of x given z, $f(x|z)$, and hence show that

$$E(x|z) = \frac{\mu_x \sigma_y^2 + \sigma_x^2 z}{\sigma_x^2 + \sigma_y^2}$$

6-2. Solve

$$\begin{vmatrix} m_{11} - r & m_{12} \\ k_2 m_{12} & k_2 m_{22} - r \end{vmatrix} = 0$$

for the data on road casualties and licensed vehicles in Table 1-1 for $k_2 = 1/\lambda = 1$. Hence estimate the coefficients of the linear relationship between casualties and vehicles. Check your answer with the example on page 167.

6-3. Reestimate the parameters of the relationship between Y and X from the data of Exercise 1-6 on the assumptions

(i) $\lambda = \frac{1}{4}$

(ii) $\lambda = 4$

and compare with the original estimates. Check your estimates by using the determinantal-equation approach of (6-65) to (6-67).

6-4. Reestimate the parameters of the linear relation between the three variables of Exercise 4-9 on selected assumptions about the ratios of the error variances.

7

Autocorrelation

7-1. The Two-variable Case

One of the crucial assumptions of the linear model of Part 1 is the *serial* independence of the disturbance term implied in

$$E(\mathbf{uu'}) = \sigma^2\mathbf{I}$$

which gives

$$E(u_t u_{t+s}) = 0 \qquad \text{for all } t \text{ and for all } s \neq 0$$

In particular, it implies that successive disturbances are drawn independently of previous values, though of course finite samples would show nonzero correlations between successive values, if it were possible to measure the disturbances.

There are, however, circumstances in which the assumption of a serially independent disturbance term may not be very plausible. For example, one may make an incorrect specification of the *form* of the relationship between the variables. Suppose we specify a linear relation between Y and X when the true relation is, say, a quadratic. Even though the disturbance term in the true relation may be nonautocorrelated, the quasi-disturbance term associated with the linear relation will contain a term in X^2. If there is any serial correlation in the X values, then we shall have serial correlation in the composite disturbance term. This example is a special case of the problem of omitted variables. In general, we include only certain important variables in the specified relation, and the disturbance term must then represent the influence of omitted variables. Serial correlation in individual omitted variables need not necessarily imply a serially correlated disturbance term, for individual components may cancel one another out. However, if the serial correlation in the omitted variables is pervasive and if the omitted variables tend to move in phase, then there is a real possibility of an autocorrelated disturbance term. A disturbance term may also contain a component due to measurement error in the "explained" variable. This too may be a source of serial correlation in the composite disturbance.

Before embarking on a treatment of the general case, we shall consider a simple two-variable relation. Let us postulate

$$Y_t = \alpha + \beta X_t + u_t \tag{7-1}$$

where we assume that the disturbance u_t follows a first-order autoregressive scheme

$$u_t = \rho u_{t-1} + \epsilon_t \tag{7-2}$$

where $|\rho| < 1$ and ϵ_t satisfies the assumptions

$$\left.\begin{aligned} E(\epsilon_t) &= 0 & & \\ E(\epsilon_t \epsilon_{t+s}) &= \sigma_\epsilon^2 & s &= 0 \\ &= 0 & s &\neq 0 \end{aligned}\right\} \text{for all } t \tag{7-3}$$

We then have

$$\begin{aligned} u_t &= \rho u_{t-1} + \epsilon_t \\ &= \rho(\rho u_{t-2} + \epsilon_{t-1}) + \epsilon_t \\ &= \cdots \\ &= \epsilon_t + \rho\epsilon_{t-1} + \rho^2\epsilon_{t-2} + \cdots \end{aligned}$$

that is,

$$u_t = \sum_{\tau=0}^{\infty} \rho^\tau \epsilon_{t-\tau} \tag{7-4}$$

Therefore $\quad E(u_t) = 0$

since $\quad E(\epsilon_t) = 0 \quad$ for all t

Furthermore,

$$E(u_t^2) = E(\epsilon_t^2) + \rho^2 E(\epsilon_{t-1}^2) + \rho^4 E(\epsilon_{t-2}^2) + \cdots$$

since the ϵ are serially independent, and so

$$E(u_t^2) = (1 + \rho^2 + \rho^4 + \cdots)\sigma_\epsilon^2$$

Thus

$$\sigma_u^2 = \frac{\sigma_\epsilon^2}{1 - \rho^2} \qquad \text{for all } t \tag{7-5}$$

$$\begin{aligned} E(u_t u_{t-1}) &= E[(\epsilon_t + \rho\epsilon_{t-1} + \rho^2\epsilon_{t-2} + \cdots) \\ &\qquad\qquad (\epsilon_{t-1} + \rho\epsilon_{t-2} + \rho^2\epsilon_{t-3} + \cdots)] \\ &= E\{[\epsilon_t + \rho(\epsilon_{t-1} + \rho\epsilon_{t-2} + \cdots)](\epsilon_{t-1} + \rho\epsilon_{t-2} + \cdots)\} \\ &= \rho E[(\epsilon_{t-1} + \rho\epsilon_{t-2} + \cdots)^2] \\ &= \rho\sigma_u^2 \end{aligned}$$

Similarly, $\quad E(u_t u_{t-2}) = \rho^2\sigma_u^2$

and in general,

$$E(u_t u_{t-s}) = \rho^s \sigma_u^2 \qquad s \neq 0 \tag{7-6}$$

so that relation (7-1) does not satisfy the assumption of a serially independent disturbance term. Scheme (7-2) is the simplest possible type of autoregressive scheme; more complicated types will of course still fail to satisfy the assumption of serial independence

Relation (7-6) may be rewritten to give

$$\frac{E(u_t u_{t-s})}{\sigma_u{}^2} = \rho^s$$

The left-hand side of this expression defines the sth autocorrelation coefficient of the u series. The autocorrelation coefficient of zero order for any series is simply unity, and for a *random* series all coefficients of higher order will be zero.

7-2. Consequences of Autocorrelated Disturbances

If the straightforward least-squares formulas of Part 1 are applied directly to the observations Y_t, X_t, there are three main consequences.

First, we shall obtain unbiased estimates of α and β, but the sampling variances of these estimates may be unduly large compared with those achievable by a slightly different method of estimation. Second, if we apply the usual least-squares formulas for the sampling variances of the regression coefficients, we are likely to obtain a serious underestimate of these variances. In any case these formulas are no longer valid, nor are the precise forms of the t and F tests derived for the linear model of Part 1. Third, we shall obtain *inefficient* predictions, that is, predictions with needlessly large sampling variances.

7-3. Generalized Least Squares

For a general treatment of this problem let us revert to matrix notation and write

$$\mathbf{Y} = \mathbf{X}\boldsymbol{\beta} + \mathbf{u} \tag{7-7}$$

where

$$\mathbf{Y} = \begin{bmatrix} Y_1 \\ Y_2 \\ \cdot \\ \cdot \\ \cdot \\ Y_n \end{bmatrix} \quad \mathbf{X} = \begin{bmatrix} X_{11} & X_{21} & \cdots & X_{k1} \\ X_{12} & X_{22} & \cdots & X_{k2} \\ \cdot & & & \cdot \\ \cdot & & & \cdot \\ \cdot & & & \cdot \\ X_{1n} & X_{2n} & \cdots & X_{kn} \end{bmatrix} \quad \boldsymbol{\beta} = \begin{bmatrix} \beta_1 \\ \beta_2 \\ \cdot \\ \cdot \\ \cdot \\ \beta_k \end{bmatrix} \quad \mathbf{u} = \begin{bmatrix} u_1 \\ u_2 \\ \cdot \\ \cdot \\ \cdot \\ u_n \end{bmatrix} \tag{7-8}$$

We now assume

$$E(\mathbf{u}) = \mathbf{0} \tag{7-9}$$

and

$$E(\mathbf{uu'}) = \mathbf{V} \tag{7-10}$$

where **V**, the variance-covariance matrix of the disturbance term, is a nonsingular matrix of order $n \times n$. For example, if the disturbance term follows a first-order Markov scheme as in (7-2) above,

$$\mathbf{V} = \sigma_u^2 \begin{bmatrix} 1 & \rho & \rho^2 & \cdots & \rho^{n-1} \\ \rho & 1 & \rho & \cdots & \rho^{n-2} \\ \cdot & & & & \cdot \\ \cdot & & & & \cdot \\ \cdot & & & & \\ \rho^{n-1} & \rho^{n-2} & \rho^{n-3} & \cdots & 1 \end{bmatrix}$$

Define

$$\boldsymbol{\beta}^* = \mathbf{AY} \tag{7-11}$$

where **A** is a matrix of order $k \times n$, as a linear estimator of $\boldsymbol{\beta}$ (that is, linear in the Y values). For this to be an unbiased estimator we require

$$E(\mathbf{AY}) = \boldsymbol{\beta}$$

But

$$\begin{aligned} E(\mathbf{AY}) &= E[\mathbf{A}(\mathbf{X}\boldsymbol{\beta} + \mathbf{u})] \\ &= \mathbf{AX}\boldsymbol{\beta} \qquad \text{using } E(\mathbf{u}) = \mathbf{0} \\ &= \boldsymbol{\beta} \end{aligned}$$

if and only if

$$\mathbf{AX} = \mathbf{I} \tag{7-12}$$

The variance-covariance matrix of the estimators β_i^* is given by $E[(\boldsymbol{\beta}^* - \boldsymbol{\beta})(\boldsymbol{\beta}^* - \boldsymbol{\beta})']$, where the terms in the principal diagonal give the variances. If we sum these sampling variances, we obtain

$$E[(\boldsymbol{\beta}^* - \boldsymbol{\beta})'(\boldsymbol{\beta}^* - \boldsymbol{\beta})] = E[(\mathbf{Au})'(\mathbf{Au})]$$

since $\boldsymbol{\beta}^* = \mathbf{AY} = \mathbf{AX}\boldsymbol{\beta} + \mathbf{Au} = \boldsymbol{\beta} + \mathbf{Au}$. Thus[1]

$$\begin{aligned} E(\boldsymbol{\beta}^* - \boldsymbol{\beta})'(\boldsymbol{\beta}^* - \boldsymbol{\beta}) &= E(\mathbf{u'A'Au}) \\ &= \operatorname{tr}(\mathbf{A'AV}) \end{aligned} \tag{7-13}$$

It might then seem plausible to find a linear unbiased estimator **A** such that the sum of the variances of the estimators is minimized. Formally, the problem becomes:

Find **A** such that tr $(\mathbf{A'AV})$ is minimized subject to the condition $\mathbf{AX} = \mathbf{I}$. Introducing k^2 Lagrange multipliers μ_{ij} $(i, j = 1, \ldots, k)$, the problem may be described as the minimization of

[1] The proof of the last step in this derivation is as follows. Since **A** is of order $k \times n$, $\mathbf{A'A}$ is a symmetric matrix of order $n \times n$ with element, say, w_{ij}.

$$\phi = \text{tr}\,(\mathbf{A'AV}) - \mu_{11}\left(\sum_{i=1}^{n} a_{1i}X_{1i} - 1\right) - \mu_{12}\left(\sum_{i=1}^{n} a_{1i}X_{2i}\right) \cdots - \mu_{1k}\left(\sum_{i=1}^{n} a_{1i}X_{ki}\right)$$
$$- \mu_{21}\left(\sum_{i=1}^{n} a_{2i}X_{1i}\right) - \mu_{22}\left(\sum_{i=1}^{n} a_{2i}X_{2i} - 1\right) \cdots - \mu_{2k}\left(\sum_{i=1}^{n} a_{2i}X_{ki}\right)$$
$$\vdots$$
$$- \mu_{k1}\left(\sum_{i=1}^{n} a_{ki}X_{1i}\right) - \mu_{k2}\left(\sum_{i=1}^{n} a_{ki}X_{2i}\right) \cdots - \mu_{kk}\left(\sum_{i=1}^{n} a_{ki}X_{ki} - 1\right)$$

Thus

$$\mathbf{u'A'Au} = [u_1 \quad u_2 \quad \cdots \quad u_n] \begin{bmatrix} w_{11} & w_{12} & \cdots & w_{1n} \\ \cdot & & & \cdot \\ \cdot & & & \cdot \\ \cdot & & & \cdot \\ w_{n1} & w_{n2} & \cdots & w_{nn} \end{bmatrix} \begin{bmatrix} u_1 \\ u_2 \\ \cdot \\ \cdot \\ \cdot \\ u_n \end{bmatrix}$$
$$= w_{11}u_1^2 + w_{22}u_2^2 + \cdots + w_{nn}u_n^2 + 2w_{12}u_1u_2 + \cdots + 2w_{1n}u_1u_n \; \cdots \; + 2w_{n-1,n}u_{n-1}u_n$$

$$\mathbf{A'Auu'} = \begin{bmatrix} w_{11} & w_{12} & \cdots & w_{1n} \\ \cdot & & & \cdot \\ \cdot & & & \cdot \\ \cdot & & & \cdot \\ w_{n1} & w_{n2} & \cdots & w_{nn} \end{bmatrix} \begin{bmatrix} u_1^2 & u_1u_2 & \cdots & u_1u_n \\ u_2u_1 & u_2^2 & \cdots & u_2u_n \\ \cdot & & & \cdot \\ \cdot & & & \cdot \\ \cdot & & & \cdot \\ u_nu_1 & u_nu_2 & \cdots & u_n^2 \end{bmatrix}$$

Therefore $\text{tr}\,(\mathbf{A'Auu'}) = w_{11}u_1^2 + w_{22}u_2^2 + \cdots + w_{nn}u_n^2 + 2w_{12}u_1u_2 + \cdots + 2w_{1n}u_1u_n \; \cdots \; + 2w_{n-1,n}u_{n-1}u_n$

$$= \mathbf{u'A'Au}$$

Therefore
$$E(\mathbf{u'A'Au}) = E\text{tr}\,[(\mathbf{A'Auu'})]$$
$$= \text{tr}\,[\mathbf{A'A}E(\mathbf{uu'})]$$
$$= \text{tr}\,(\mathbf{A'AV}) \qquad \text{using (7-10)}$$

that is,
$$\phi = \text{tr}\,(\mathbf{A'AV}) - \text{tr}\,[\mathbf{M'}(\mathbf{AX} - \mathbf{I})] \tag{7-14}$$

where
$$\mathbf{M} = \begin{bmatrix} \mu_{11} & \mu_{12} & \cdots & \mu_{1k} \\ \mu_{21} & \mu_{22} & \cdots & \mu_{2k} \\ \cdot & & & \cdot \\ \cdot & & & \cdot \\ \cdot & & & \cdot \\ \mu_{k1} & \mu_{k2} & \cdots & \mu_{kk} \end{bmatrix}$$

Differentiating (7-14) partially with respect to the elements of **A** and equating the partial derivatives to zero gives the matrix equation[1]

$$2\mathbf{AV} = \mathbf{MX'} \tag{7-15}$$

[1] The proof of this result is as follows:

$$\begin{aligned} \text{tr}\,(\mathbf{A'AV}) = v_{11} \sum_{i=1}^{k} a_{i1}^2 + v_{22} \sum_{i=1}^{k} a_{i2}^2 + \cdots + v_{nn} \sum_{i=1}^{k} a_{in}^2 \\ + 2v_{12} \sum_{i=1}^{k} a_{i1}a_{i2} + \cdots + 2v_{1n} \sum_{i=1}^{k} a_{i1}a_{in} \\ \cdot \qquad \qquad \cdot \\ \cdot \qquad \qquad \cdot \\ + 2v_{n-1,n} \sum_{i=1}^{k} a_{i,n-1}a_{in} \end{aligned}$$

since **V** is a symmetric matrix.

Therefore

$$\frac{\partial \phi}{\partial a_{11}} = 2(v_{11}a_{11} + v_{12}a_{12} + \cdots + v_{1n}a_{1n}) - (\mu_{11}X_{11} + \mu_{12}X_{21} + \cdots + \mu_{1k}X_{k1})$$

$$\frac{\partial \phi}{\partial a_{21}} = 2(v_{11}a_{21} + v_{12}a_{22} + \cdots + v_{1n}a_{2n}) - (\mu_{21}X_{11} + \mu_{22}X_{21} + \cdots + \mu_{2k}X_{k1})$$

and in general

$$\frac{\partial \phi}{\partial a_{ij}} = 2(v_{j1}a_{i1} + v_{j2}a_{i2} + \cdots + v_{jn}a_{in}) - (\mu_{i1}X_{1j} + \mu_{i2}X_{2j} + \cdots + \mu_{ik}X_{kj}) \qquad \begin{matrix} i = 1, \ldots, k \\ j = 1, \ldots, n \end{matrix}$$

that it,

$$\frac{\partial \phi}{\partial a_{ij}} = 2(i\text{th row of } \mathbf{A} \text{ into } j\text{th column of } \mathbf{V}) - (i\text{th row of } \mathbf{M} \text{ into } j\text{th row of } \mathbf{X})$$

Equating these kn derivatives to zero gives

$$2\mathbf{AV} = \mathbf{MX'}$$

Postmultiplying (7-15) by $\mathbf{V}^{-1}\mathbf{X}$,

$$\begin{aligned}
& & 2\mathbf{AVV}^{-1}\mathbf{X} &= \mathbf{MX'V}^{-1}\mathbf{X} \\
&\text{therefore} & 2\mathbf{I} &= \mathbf{M}(\mathbf{X'V}^{-1}\mathbf{X}) \qquad \text{since } \mathbf{AX} = \mathbf{I} \\
&\text{therefore} & \mathbf{M} &= 2(\mathbf{X'V}^{-1}\mathbf{X})^{-1} \\
&\text{therefore} & 2\mathbf{AV} &= 2(\mathbf{X'V}^{-1}\mathbf{X})^{-1}\mathbf{X'} \\
&\text{therefore} & \mathbf{A} &= (\mathbf{X'V}^{-1}\mathbf{X})^{-1}\mathbf{X'V}^{-1} \qquad (7\text{-}16)
\end{aligned}$$

Thus an extreme value for the sum of sampling variances occurs at the values indicated in (7-16). To show that the extreme is a minimum, define an arbitrary linear unbiased estimator as

$$\mathbf{b} = (\mathbf{A} + \mathbf{B})\mathbf{Y}$$

where $\mathbf{B}$ is a matrix of order $k \times n$ and is not the null matrix. If this new estimator is unbiased, then

$$\begin{aligned}
E(\mathbf{b}) &= E[(\mathbf{X'V}^{-1}\mathbf{X})^{-1}\mathbf{X'V}^{-1} + \mathbf{B}][\mathbf{X}\boldsymbol{\beta} + \mathbf{u}] \\
&= \boldsymbol{\beta} + \mathbf{BX}\boldsymbol{\beta}
\end{aligned}$$

Thus if this new estimator is to be unbiased, we must have

$$\mathbf{BX} = \mathbf{0}$$

where $\mathbf{0}$ denotes the null matrix of order $k \times k$.

The sum of the sampling variances for this new estimator is

$$\begin{aligned}
E[(\mathbf{b} - \boldsymbol{\beta})'(\mathbf{b} - \boldsymbol{\beta})] &= E\{\mathbf{u}'[(\mathbf{X'V}^{-1}\mathbf{X})^{-1}\mathbf{X'V}^{-1} + \mathbf{B}]' \\
&\qquad [(\mathbf{X'V}^{-1}\mathbf{X})^{-1}\mathbf{X'V}^{-1} + \mathbf{B}]\mathbf{u}\} \\
&= E\{\mathbf{u}'[\mathbf{V}^{-1}\mathbf{X}(\mathbf{X'V}^{-1}\mathbf{X})^{-1} + \mathbf{B}'] \\
&\qquad [(\mathbf{X'V}^{-1}\mathbf{X})^{-1}\mathbf{X'V}^{-1} + \mathbf{B}]\mathbf{u}\} \\
&= E(\mathbf{u'A'Au}) + E\{\mathbf{u}'[\mathbf{V}^{-1}\mathbf{X}(\mathbf{X'V}^{-1}\mathbf{X})^{-1}]\mathbf{Bu}\} \\
&\qquad + E[\mathbf{u'B'}(\mathbf{X'V}^{-1}\mathbf{X})^{-1}\mathbf{X'V}^{-1}\mathbf{u}] + E(\mathbf{u'B'Bu})
\end{aligned}$$

By a similar argument to that used above in the footnote on page 180,

$$\begin{aligned}
& & E\{\mathbf{u}'[\mathbf{V}^{-1}\mathbf{X}(\mathbf{X'V}^{-1}\mathbf{X})^{-1}]\mathbf{Bu}\} &= \operatorname{tr}[\mathbf{V}^{-1}\mathbf{X}(\mathbf{X'V}^{-1}\mathbf{X})^{-1}\mathbf{BV}] \\
&\text{and} & E[\mathbf{u'B'}(\mathbf{X'V}^{-1}\mathbf{X})^{-1}\mathbf{X'V}^{-1}\mathbf{u}] &= \operatorname{tr}[\mathbf{B'}(\mathbf{X'V}^{-1}\mathbf{X})^{-1}\mathbf{X'}] \\
&\text{but} & \operatorname{tr}[\mathbf{V}^{-1}\mathbf{X}(\mathbf{X'V}^{-1}\mathbf{X})^{-1}\mathbf{BV}] &= \operatorname{tr}[\mathbf{X}(\mathbf{X'V}^{-1}\mathbf{X})^{-1}\mathbf{BVV}^{-1}]
\end{aligned}$$

since tr $(\mathbf{ABCD})$ = tr $(\mathbf{BCDA})$, etc., provided the matrices are suitably conformable for multiplication. Thus

$$\begin{aligned}
\operatorname{tr}[\mathbf{V}^{-1}\mathbf{X}(\mathbf{X'V}^{-1}\mathbf{X})^{-1}\mathbf{BV}] &= \operatorname{tr}[(\mathbf{X'V}^{-1}\mathbf{X})^{-1}\mathbf{BX}] \\
&= 0 \qquad \text{since } \mathbf{BX} = \mathbf{0}
\end{aligned}$$

Thus $\quad E[(\mathbf{b} - \boldsymbol{\beta})'(\mathbf{b} - \boldsymbol{\beta})] = E(\mathbf{u'A'Au}) + E(\mathbf{u'B'Bu}) \qquad (7\text{-}17)$

The first term on the right-hand side of (7-17) is the sum of the sampling variances for the estimator **A** defined in (7-16). For any real matrix **B**, the quadratic form $\mathbf{u'B'Bu}$ is positive definite or positive semidefinite.[1] It will be positive definite if the rank of B is k. Thus the sum of the sampling variances for **A** is at least as small as that achievable by any linear unbiased estimator. Notice that in the nonautocorrelated case, $\mathbf{V}^{-1} = (1/\sigma_u^2)\mathbf{I}$ and (7-16) reduces to the straightforward least-squares estimator $(\mathbf{X'X})^{-1}\mathbf{X'}$, derived in Chap. 4.

Formula (7-16) may also be derived by defining the problem as that of choosing an estimator to minimize the sum of squares[2]

$$(\mathbf{Y} - \mathbf{Xb})'\mathbf{V}^{-1}(\mathbf{Y} - \mathbf{Xb})$$

for

$$\begin{aligned}(\mathbf{Y} - \mathbf{Xb})'\mathbf{V}^{-1}(\mathbf{Y} - \mathbf{Xb}) &= (\mathbf{Y}' - \mathbf{b}'\mathbf{X}')\mathbf{V}^{-1}(\mathbf{Y} - \mathbf{Xb}) \\ &= \mathbf{Y}'\mathbf{V}^{-1}\mathbf{Y} - 2\mathbf{b}'\mathbf{X}'\mathbf{V}^{-1}\mathbf{Y} + \mathbf{b}'\mathbf{X}'\mathbf{V}^{-1}\mathbf{Xb}\end{aligned}$$

Differentiating with respect to the components of **b** and equating to zero gives

$$2\mathbf{X}'\mathbf{V}^{-1}\mathbf{Y} = 2\mathbf{X}'\mathbf{V}^{-1}\mathbf{Xb}$$

Hence

$$\mathbf{b} = (\mathbf{X}'\mathbf{V}^{-1}\mathbf{X})^{-1}\mathbf{X}'\mathbf{V}^{-1}\mathbf{Y}$$

The above method of proof may be employed to demonstrate a further property of the estimator $\boldsymbol{\beta}^* = \mathbf{AY}$.

$$\begin{aligned}\boldsymbol{\beta}^* = \mathbf{AY} &= (\mathbf{X}'\mathbf{V}^{-1}\mathbf{X})^{-1}\mathbf{X}'\mathbf{V}^{-1}(\mathbf{X}\boldsymbol{\beta} + \mathbf{u}) \\ &= \boldsymbol{\beta} + (\mathbf{X}'\mathbf{V}^{-1}\mathbf{X})^{-1}\mathbf{X}'\mathbf{V}^{-1}\mathbf{u}\end{aligned}$$

Hence the variance-covariance matrix of the estimates is

$$\begin{aligned}E[(\boldsymbol{\beta}^* - \boldsymbol{\beta})(\boldsymbol{\beta}^* - \boldsymbol{\beta})'] &= E(\mathbf{Auu'A'}) \\ &= (\mathbf{X}'\mathbf{V}^{-1}\mathbf{X})^{-1} \qquad (7\text{-}18)\end{aligned}$$

Once again, define an arbitrary linear unbiased estimator

$$\mathbf{b} = (\mathbf{A} + \mathbf{B})\mathbf{Y} \qquad (7\text{-}19)$$

where, as before, $\mathbf{A} = (\mathbf{X}'\mathbf{V}^{-1}\mathbf{X})^{-1}\mathbf{X}'\mathbf{V}^{-1}$ and **B** is a matrix of order $k \times n$ and is not the null matrix. As shown above, (7-19) is unbiased if and only if $\mathbf{BX} = \mathbf{0}$. The variance-covariance matrix

[1] See Franz E. Hohn, *Elementary Matrix Algebra,* Macmillan, New York, 1958, pp. 264–265. A quadratic form $\mathbf{u'Au}$ is positive definite if $\mathbf{u'Au} > 0$ for all **u**, and positive semidefinite if $\mathbf{u'Au} \geq 0$.

[2] If one assumed the disturbances to be normally distributed, this is the sum of squares that would appear in the exponent of the likelihood function, and it would have to be minimized in order to maximize the likelihood function.

for (7-19) is

$$\begin{aligned} E[(\mathbf{b} - \boldsymbol{\beta})(\mathbf{b} - \boldsymbol{\beta})'] &= E[(\mathbf{A} + \mathbf{B})\mathbf{uu}'(\mathbf{A}' + \mathbf{B}')] \\ &= \mathbf{AVA}' + \mathbf{BVA}' + \mathbf{AVB}' + \mathbf{BVB}' \\ &= (\mathbf{X}'\mathbf{V}^{-1}\mathbf{X})^{-1} + \mathbf{BVB}' \end{aligned} \tag{7-20}$$

for

$$\begin{aligned} \mathbf{BVA}' &= \mathbf{BVV}^{-1}\mathbf{X}(\mathbf{X}'\mathbf{V}^{-1}\mathbf{X})^{-1} \\ &= \mathbf{0} \end{aligned}$$

since

$$\mathbf{BX} = \mathbf{0}$$

and likewise

$$\mathbf{AVB}' = \mathbf{0} \qquad \text{for } \mathbf{X}'\mathbf{B}' = \mathbf{0}$$

The elements in the principal diagonal in (7-18) and (7-20) give the sampling variances of the estimators β_i^* and b_i $(i = 1, \ldots, k)$. Since the elements in the principal diagonal of $\mathbf{BVB}'$ are positive definite quadratic forms,[1]

$$\text{var } \beta_i^* < \text{var } b_i \qquad i = 1, \ldots, k$$

that is, the sampling variance of each separate estimate is smaller than that of any other linear unbiased estimate.

It is interesting to develop more fully the implications of the generalized-least-squares estimator (7-16) for a very simple case of autocorrelated disturbances. Consider the scheme set out in (7-1) to (7-3), namely,

$$Y_t = \alpha + \beta X_t + u_t$$

where

$$u_t = \rho u_{t-1} + \epsilon_t \qquad |\rho| < 1$$

From results (7-5) and (7-6),

$$E(\mathbf{uu}') = \mathbf{V} = \frac{\sigma_\epsilon^2}{1 - \rho^2} \begin{bmatrix} 1 & \rho & \rho^2 & \cdots & \rho^{n-1} \\ \rho & 1 & \rho & \cdots & \rho^{n-2} \\ \cdot & & & & \cdot \\ \cdot & & & & \cdot \\ \cdot & & & & \cdot \\ \rho^{n-1} & \rho^{n-2} & \rho^{n-3} & \cdots & 1 \end{bmatrix} \tag{7-21}$$

Then

$$\mathbf{V}^{-1} = \frac{1}{\sigma_\epsilon^2} \begin{bmatrix} 1 & -\rho & 0 & \cdots & 0 & 0 \\ -\rho & 1 + \rho^2 & -\rho & \cdots & 0 & 0 \\ 0 & -\rho & 1 + \rho^2 & \cdots & 0 & 0 \\ \cdot & & & & & \cdot \\ \cdot & & & & & \cdot \\ \cdot & & & & & \cdot \\ 0 & 0 & 0 & \cdots & -\rho & 1 \end{bmatrix} \tag{7-22}$$

[1] See R. L. Plackett, "A Historical Note on the Method of Least Squares," *Biometrika*, vol. 36, pp. 458–460, 1949.

It can then be shown that the generalized-least-squares estimator is equivalent to a two-step procedure, namely, (1) transform the original variables according to the autoregressive structure of the disturbance term and then (2) apply *simple* least squares to the transformed variables.

Suppose we apply a transformation matrix $\mathbf{T}$ to the relation

$$\mathbf{Y} = \mathbf{X}\boldsymbol{\beta} + \mathbf{u}$$

to give

$$\mathbf{TY} = \mathbf{TX}\boldsymbol{\beta} + \mathbf{Tu} \tag{7-23}$$

The simple-least-squares estimator of $\boldsymbol{\beta}$ in (7-23) is

$$\begin{aligned}\boldsymbol{\beta}^* &= [(\mathbf{TX})'(\mathbf{TX})]^{-1}(\mathbf{TX})'(\mathbf{TY}) \\ &= (\mathbf{X'T'TX})^{-1}\mathbf{X'T'TY}\end{aligned} \tag{7-24}$$

Comparing (7-24) and (7-16) it is seen that the two estimators are identical if

$$\mathbf{T'T} = \mathbf{V}^{-1} \tag{7-25}$$

If, for the sake of simplicity, we take σ_ϵ^2 in (7-22) as unity, a matrix $\mathbf{T}$ which almost completely satisfies (7-25) is the $(n-1) \times n$ matrix

$$\mathbf{T} = \begin{bmatrix} -\rho & 1 & 0 & \cdots & 0 \\ 0 & -\rho & 1 & \cdots & 0 \\ \cdot & & & & \cdot \\ \cdot & & & & \cdot \\ \cdot & & & & \cdot \\ 0 & 0 & 0 & \cdots & 1 \end{bmatrix}$$

for $\mathbf{T'T}$ is the $n \times n$ matrix

$$\mathbf{T'T} = \begin{bmatrix} \rho^2 & -\rho & 0 & \cdots & 0 \\ -\rho & 1+\rho^2 & -\rho & \cdots & 0 \\ \cdot & & & & \cdot \\ \cdot & & & & \cdot \\ \cdot & & & & \cdot \\ 0 & 0 & 0 & \cdots & 1 \end{bmatrix} \tag{7-26}$$

Comparison with (7-22) shows that the only element in which the $\mathbf{T'T}$ and $\mathbf{V}^{-1}$ differ is that in the first row and first column, which is ρ^2 in $\mathbf{T'T}$ and is 1 in $\mathbf{V}^{-1}$.

The transformed variables indicated by **T** are

$$\begin{bmatrix} Y_2 - \rho Y_1 \\ Y_3 - \rho Y_2 \\ \cdot \\ \cdot \\ \cdot \\ Y_n - \rho Y_{n-1} \end{bmatrix} \quad \text{and} \quad \begin{bmatrix} X_2 - \rho X_1 \\ X_3 - \rho X_2 \\ \cdot \\ \cdot \\ \cdot \\ X_n - \rho X_{n-1} \end{bmatrix} \tag{7-27}$$

This transformation produces variables which are in a form suitable for the direct application of simple least squares, for the variance-covariance matrix of the transformed disturbances is

$$E[(\mathbf{Tu})(\mathbf{Tu})'] = \mathbf{TVT}'$$
$$= \sigma_\epsilon^2 \begin{bmatrix} 1 & 0 & \cdots & 0 \\ 0 & 1 & \cdots & 0 \\ \cdot & & & \cdot \\ \cdot & & & \cdot \\ \cdot & & & \cdot \\ 0 & 0 & \cdots & 1 \end{bmatrix}$$

and the simple-least-squares estimator is chosen to minimize

$$(\mathbf{Y} - \mathbf{Xb})'\mathbf{T}'\mathbf{T}(\mathbf{Y} - \mathbf{Xb})$$

which, apart from the slight end effect, is the same as

$$(\mathbf{Y} - \mathbf{Xb})'\mathbf{V}^{-1}(\mathbf{Y} - \mathbf{Xb})$$

which is minimized by the generalized-least-squares estimator.

If one knows or suspects that the disturbance follows a simple Markov scheme with known parameter ρ, then a simple practical estimation procedure is to transform the original variables as in (7-27) and apply simple least squares to the transformed variables. In the absence of any information about ρ, some econometricians have taken it as approximately unity, in which case the appropriate transformation is to take first differences of the variables.[1]

If one applies simple least squares unwittingly to estimate the parameters of a relationship with autocorrelated errors, then one

[1] See, for example, J. R. N. Stone, *The Measurement of Consumers' Expenditure and Behaviour in the United Kingdom*, 1920–1938, vol. I, Cambridge University Press, London, 1954, where Stone takes first differences of all his variables (except time) before proceeding with the regression analysis.

will obtain unbiased estimators, but one is likely to obtain a serious underestimate of their sampling variances and these sampling variances are in any case not minimal.

Consider again the scheme set out in (7-7) to (7-10):

$$\mathbf{Y} = \mathbf{X}\boldsymbol{\beta} + \mathbf{u}$$

The simple-least-squares estimator of $\boldsymbol{\beta}$ where the disturbance is autocorrelated is

$$\begin{aligned} \hat{\boldsymbol{\beta}} &= (\mathbf{X}'\mathbf{X})^{-1}\mathbf{X}'\mathbf{Y} \\ E(\hat{\boldsymbol{\beta}}) &= E[(\mathbf{X}'\mathbf{X})^{-1}\mathbf{X}'(\mathbf{X}\boldsymbol{\beta} + \mathbf{u})] \\ &= \boldsymbol{\beta} \end{aligned}$$

since $E(\mathbf{u}) = \mathbf{0}$

even in the autocorrelated case. Thus simple-least-squares estimates are still unbiased.

The variance-covariance matrix for $\hat{\boldsymbol{\beta}}$ is

$$E[(\hat{\boldsymbol{\beta}} - \boldsymbol{\beta})(\hat{\boldsymbol{\beta}} - \boldsymbol{\beta})'] = (\mathbf{X}'\mathbf{X})^{-1}\mathbf{X}'\mathbf{V}\mathbf{X}(\mathbf{X}'\mathbf{X})^{-1} \tag{7-28}$$

In the nonautocorrelated case, $\mathbf{V} = \sigma_u^2\mathbf{I}$ and (7-28) reduces to $\sigma_u^2(\mathbf{X}'\mathbf{X})^{-1}$ as in (4-11). The use of the conventional formula (4-11) to calculate standard errors can be seriously misleading in the case of autocorrelated disturbances, for two reasons. First, it ignores a string of terms. For example, in the case of one explanatory variable and a disturbance term which follows a first-order Markov scheme, (7-28) gives

$$\operatorname{var}(\hat{\beta}) = \frac{\sigma_u^2}{\sum_{i=1}^{n} x_i^2}\left(1 + 2\rho\frac{\sum_{i=1}^{n-1} x_i x_{i+1}}{\sum_{i=1}^{n} x_i^2} + 2\rho^2\frac{\sum_{i=1}^{n-2} x_i x_{i+2}}{\sum_{i=1}^{n} x_i^2} + \cdots + 2\rho^{n-1}x_1x_n\right) \tag{7-29}$$

where $x_i = X_i - \bar{X}$. The simple-least-squares formula (4-11) is of course

$$\operatorname{var}(\hat{\beta}) = \frac{\sigma_u^2}{\sum_{i=1}^{n} x_i^2} \tag{7-30}$$

The conventional formula thus ignores the sum of terms enclosed in parentheses in (7-29). If ρ is positive and if the explanatory variable X is positively autocorrelated, then this sum of terms will probably exceed unity and (7-30) will yield an underestimate of the true variance. Second, the estimate of σ_u^2 from an autocorrelated series is likely to be biased downward. This point is illustrated in Fig. 7-1. The line $\alpha + \beta X$ indicates the true relation. Suppose both

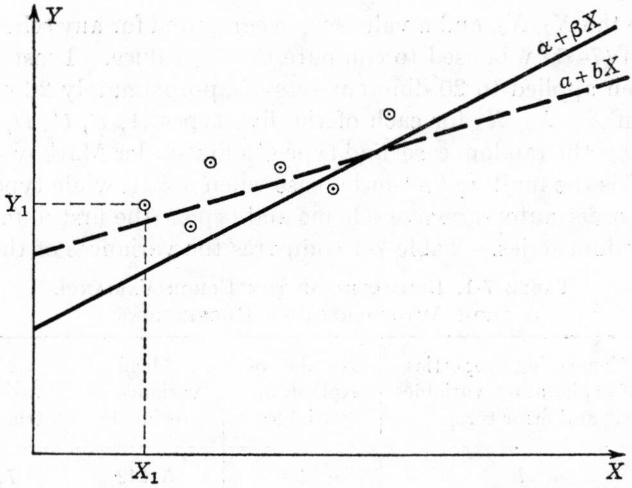

FIG. 7-1

X and u are serially correlated. If the first point (X_1, Y_1) has, say, a large positive u value, then it is quite possible for a series of points to follow, most of which will lie above the true relation. Measuring the scatter of these points about a fitted-least-squares line $a + bX$ will provide an underestimate of σ_u^2, which refers to the scatter about the true relation $\alpha + \beta X$.

This point is confirmed by some sampling experiments of Cochrane and Orcutt.[1] They assumed a relation of the form

$$X_1 = 2X_2 + X_3 + u \tag{7-31}$$

[1] D. Cochrane and G. H. Orcutt, "Application of Least Squares Regressions to Relationships Containing Auto-correlated Error Terms," *J. Am. Statist. Assoc.*, vol. 44, pp. 32–61, 1949.

where X_2, X_3, and u were constructed from the following schemes:

$$(A) \qquad Z_{t+1} = Z_t + 0.3(Z_t - Z_{t-1}) + \epsilon_{t+1}$$
$$(B) \qquad Z_{t+1} = Z_t + \epsilon_{t+1}$$
$$(C) \qquad Z_{t+1} = 0.3Z_t + \epsilon_{t+1}$$
$$(D) \qquad Z_{t+1} = \epsilon_{t+1}$$
$$(E) \qquad Z_{t+1} = \epsilon_{t+1} - \epsilon_t$$

the ϵs being serially independent with zero mean and constant variance.

Once the X_2, X_3, and u values were computed for any scheme, the relation (7-31) was used to compute the X_1 values. Least squares was then applied to 20 different sets of approximately 20 observations on X_1, X_2, X_3 for each of the five types A, B, C, D, and E. Type D is the random case, and type C a first-order Markov scheme. Type B is the limiting first-order case when $\rho = 1$, while type A is a second-order autoregressive scheme and type E the first differencing of a random series. Table 7-1 compares the variances of the resid-

TABLE 7-1. ESTIMATES OF THE ERROR VARIANCE FROM AUTOCORRELATED RERRESSIONS

No.	Generating properties of explanatory variables and error terms	Number of explanatory variables	Mean variance of residuals	Mean variance of true errors
1	*B*	1	5,142	7,725
2	*D*	1	1,375	1,466
3	*B*	2 and time	784	4,386
4	*B*	2	1,690	4,386
5	*D*	2	634	749

SOURCE: D. Cochrane and G. H. Orcutt, "Application of Least Squares Regressions to Relationships Containing Auto-correlated Error Terms," *J. Am. Statist. Assoc.*, vol. 44, p. 52, table VII, 1949.

uals about the fitted regressions with the variances of the true errors. Even in the case of the random series, lines 2 and 5, there is a slight underestimate of the true error variance, but this becomes very serious in the autocorrelated case. For example, line 4 shows that the mean value of the residual variance of 20 separate regressions is only about 40 per cent of the true value. When time is included as an explanatory variable (line 3), the mean of the estimated values is only about 18 per cent of the true value.

Formulas (7-18) and (7-28) may be used to give some idea of the relative variances of simple least squares and generalized least squares in the illustrative case of one explanatory variable and a first-order autoregressive disturbance. Collecting results, we have

$$\hat{\boldsymbol{\beta}} = (\mathbf{X}'\mathbf{X})^{-1}\mathbf{X}'\mathbf{Y} \qquad \boldsymbol{\beta}^* = (\mathbf{X}'\mathbf{V}^{-1}\mathbf{X})^{-1}\mathbf{X}'\mathbf{V}^{-1}\mathbf{Y}$$

$$\text{var}\,(\hat{\boldsymbol{\beta}}) = (\mathbf{X}'\mathbf{X})^{-1}\mathbf{X}'\mathbf{V}\mathbf{X}(\mathbf{X}'\mathbf{X})^{-1} \qquad \text{var}\,(\boldsymbol{\beta}^*) = (\mathbf{X}'\mathbf{V}^{-1}\mathbf{X})^{-1}$$

For the above illustrative case,

$$\text{var}\,(\hat{\beta}) = \frac{\sigma_u^2}{\sum_{i=1}^{n} x_i^2}\left(1 + 2\rho\frac{\sum_{i=1}^{n-1} x_i x_{i+1}}{\sum_{i=1}^{n} x_i^2} + 2\rho^2\frac{\sum_{i=1}^{n-2} x_i x_{i+2}}{\sum_{i=1}^{n} x_i^2} + \cdots + 2\rho^{n-1}x_1x_n\right)$$

and

$$\text{var}\,(\beta^*) = \frac{\sigma_u^2(1-\rho^2)}{(1+\rho^2)\sum_{i=1}^{n} x_i^2 - \rho^2(x_1^2 + x_n^2) - 2\rho\sum_{i=1}^{n-1} x_i x_{i+1}}$$

From (7-5) above we have $\sigma_u^2(1-\rho^2) = \sigma_\epsilon^2$. Hence

$$\text{var}\,(\hat{\beta}) = \frac{\sigma_\epsilon^2}{(1-\rho^2)\sum_{i=1}^{n} x_i^2} \times \left(1 + 2\rho\frac{\sum_{i=1}^{n-1} x_i x_{i+1}}{\sum_{i=1}^{n} x_i^2} + 2\rho^2\frac{\sum_{i=1}^{n-2} x_i x_{i+2}}{\sum_{i=1}^{n} x_i^2} + \cdots + 2\rho^{n-1}x_1x_n\right)$$

and

$$\text{var}\,(\beta^*) = \frac{\sigma_\epsilon^2}{(1+\rho^2)\sum_{i=1}^{n} x_i^2 - \rho^2(x_1^2 + x_n^2) - 2\rho\sum_{1=1}^{n-1} x_i x_{i+1}}$$

If the X variable were serially independent, then we could neglect the serial covariances in these expressions and we should have approximately that

$$\frac{\text{var}\,(\beta^*)}{\text{var}\,(\hat{\beta})} = \frac{1-\rho^2}{1+\rho^2}$$

If $\rho = 0.5$, the efficiency of simple least squares compared with generalized least squares is about 60 per cent, while if $\rho = 0.9$, the efficiency of simple least squares falls to only 10 per cent. If the X's are serially correlated and we neglect autocorrelation coefficients of more than the second degree, the above result will still be approximately true, and it is clear that, if we have knowledge of the autocorrelation structure of the disturbance term, generalized least squares will yield a much more efficient estimate than simple least squares.

7-4. The Durbin-Watson *d* Statistic

We have shown above the possibly serious consequences of unwittingly applying least squares to relationships containing autocorrelated terms. It is very important, therefore, to be able to test for the presence of autocorrelated disturbances and, if necessary, to adopt alternative estimating procedures.

A suitable test is available in the Durbin-Watson *d* statistic.[1]

Let z_t $(t = 1, \ldots, n)$ denote the residuals from a fitted-least-squares regression. We then define

$$d = \frac{\sum_{t=2}^{n} (z_t - z_{t-1})^2}{\sum_{t=1}^{n} z_t^2}$$

Exact significance levels for d are not available, but Durbin and Watson have tabulated lower and upper bounds d_L and d_U for various values of n and k (= number of *explanatory* variables). To conduct a one-sided test of *positive* autocorrelation, compute d.

If $d < d_L$, reject the hypothesis of random disturbances in favor of that of positive autocorrelation. If $d > d_U$, do not reject the hypothesis.

If $d_L < d < d_U$, the test is inconclusive and further observations would ideally be required.[2]

7-5. Estimation Methods

If it appears from the Durbin-Watson test or otherwise that we have to deal with a case of autocorrelated disturbances, three main estimation methods are available.

i. Knowledge of V. An ideal and usually unattainable position is exact knowledge of the variance-covariance matrix **V** of the disturbance term. Generalized-least-squares estimators are then pro-

[1] J. Durbin and G. S. Watson, "Testing for Serial Correlation in Least-squares Regression," pts. I and II, *Biometrika*, 1950 and 1951.

[2] An alternative test of the *d* statistic has recently been obtained by H. Theil and A. L. Nagar, "Testing the Independence of Regression Disturbances," *J. Am. Statist. Assoc.*, vol. 56, pp. 793–806, 1961.

vided by

$$\boldsymbol{\beta}^* = (\mathbf{X'V^{-1}X})^{-1}\mathbf{X'V^{-1}Y}$$

with

$$\text{var}(\boldsymbol{\beta}^*) = (\mathbf{X'V^{-1}X})^{-1}$$

An approximation to this position is sometimes available when the investigator has an estimate of $\mathbf{V}$, say, $\mathbf{V}_1$, which can then be substituted in the above formulas. The resultant estimators will be unbiased, but there will be an inaccuracy in computing the variance-covariance matrix as

$$(\mathbf{X'V_1^{-1}X})^{-1}$$

It should in fact be

$$(\mathbf{X'V_1^{-1}X})^{-1}\mathbf{X'V_1^{-1}VV_1^{-1}X}(\mathbf{X'V_1^{-1}X})^{-1}$$

The multiplicative factor $\mathbf{X'V_1^{-1}VV_1^{-1}X}(\mathbf{X'V_1^{-1}X})^{-1}$ would have to be applied to the estimated variance matrix. Unfortunately, this factor involves the unknown $\mathbf{V}$, but it is clear that the closer our $\mathbf{V}_1$ approaches $\mathbf{V}$, the closer does this multiplicative factor approach the unit matrix. However, an imperfect estimate of $\mathbf{V}$ is better than assuming the problem away by applying simple least squares.

ii. Iterative Procedure. An iterative procedure which does *not* work is to apply simple least squares, that is, computing

$$\mathbf{b} = (\mathbf{X'X})^{-1}\mathbf{X'Y}$$

and, from the computed residuals $\hat{\mathbf{u}} = \mathbf{Y} - \mathbf{Xb}$, estimating the variance-covariance matrix of the disturbance by calculating

$$\mathbf{V}_2 = \hat{\mathbf{u}}\hat{\mathbf{u}}'$$

and using $\mathbf{V}_2$ in the formula,

$$\mathbf{b} = (\mathbf{X'V_2^{-1}X})^{-1}\mathbf{X'V_2^{-1}Y}$$

The difficulty here is that $\mathbf{V}_2$ is singular, so that $\mathbf{V}_2^{-1}$ does not exist. This may be seen by examining the determinant of $\mathbf{V}_2$.

$$|\mathbf{V}_2| = \begin{vmatrix} \hat{u}_1^2 & \hat{u}_1\hat{u}_2 & \cdots & \hat{u}_1\hat{u}_n \\ \hat{u}_2\hat{u}_1 & \hat{u}_2^2 & \cdots & \hat{u}_2\hat{u}_n \\ \vdots & & & \vdots \\ \hat{u}_n\hat{u}_1 & \hat{u}_n\hat{u}_2 & \cdots & \hat{u}_n^2 \end{vmatrix}$$

$$= \hat{u}_1\hat{u}_2\cdots\hat{u}_n \begin{vmatrix} \hat{u}_1 & \hat{u}_1 & \cdots & \hat{u}_1 \\ \hat{u}_2 & \hat{u}_2 & \cdots & \hat{u}_2 \\ \vdots & & & \vdots \\ \hat{u}_n & \hat{u}_n & \cdots & \hat{u}_n \end{vmatrix} = 0$$

An iterative procedure which does work, however, is to compute the simple-least-squares residuals $\hat{u}_1 \quad \hat{u}_2 \quad \cdots \quad \hat{u}_n$ as above and then to use these along with some assumption about the *form* of the autoregressive structure of the disturbance. For example, if it is assumed that the autoregressive scheme is a first-order one,

$$u_t = \rho u_{t-1} + \epsilon_t$$

one could estimate ρ by computing the least-squares regression

$$\hat{u}_t = r\hat{u}_{t-1} + e_t$$

The coefficient r is then used to compute the transformed variables $(Y_t - rY_{t-1})$, $(X_{2t} - rX_{2,t-1})$, $(X_{3t} - rX_{3,t-1})$, etc., and simple least squares again applied to estimate the relation between these transformed variables. If the residuals from this second relationship are not significantly autocorrelated, the estimation procedure can stop at the second round; if they are significantly autocorrelated, they are used to provide a new estimate of ρ, and this in turn is used to compute a new set of transformed variables from Y_t, X_{2t}, X_{3t}, etc., until a random set of residuals results.

iii. Estimation of All Parameters, Including Those of the Autoregressive Structure. Assume, as before,

$$\mathbf{Y} = \mathbf{X}\boldsymbol{\beta} + \mathbf{u}$$

If $\mathbf{u}$ has an autoregressive structure, then a transformation matrix $\mathbf{T}$ can be found such that

$$\mathbf{T}\mathbf{u} = \boldsymbol{\varepsilon}$$

where $\epsilon_1 \quad \epsilon_2 \quad \cdots \quad \epsilon_n$ are independently distributed with zero mean and constant variance. If the ϵ are, in addition, normally distributed, then maximum-likelihood estimates are provided by minimizing the sum of squares

$$\begin{aligned} \boldsymbol{\varepsilon}'\boldsymbol{\varepsilon} &= (\mathbf{Y}' - \boldsymbol{\beta}'\mathbf{X}')\mathbf{T}'\mathbf{T}(\mathbf{Y} - \mathbf{X}\boldsymbol{\beta}) \\ &= \mathbf{Y}'\mathbf{T}'\mathbf{T}\mathbf{Y} - 2\boldsymbol{\beta}'\mathbf{X}'\mathbf{T}'\mathbf{T}\mathbf{Y} + \boldsymbol{\beta}'\mathbf{X}'\mathbf{T}'\mathbf{T}\mathbf{X}\boldsymbol{\beta} \end{aligned} \tag{7-32}$$

Differentiating this sum of squares partially with respect to the unknown elements of $\mathbf{T}$ and $\boldsymbol{\beta}$ and setting the results equal to zero would give the maximum-likelihood estimating equations. These, however, will be nonlinear in the unknowns, and their solution will be lengthy and tedious, though not in general impossible. The rapid development of computing equipment and techniques should facilitate the solution of equations such as this.

A simpler two-stage estimating procedure has recently been suggested by Durbin that gives estimates which will have *asymptotically* the same mean vector and variance matrix as the least-squares estimates that would be obtained by the direct minimization of (7-32).[1] Durbin postulates the general model

$$Y_t = \beta_1 X_{1t} + \cdots + \beta_q X_{qt} + u_t \qquad t = 1, \ldots, n \tag{7-33}$$

where $\{u_t\}$ is a stationary autoregressive series generated by

$$u_t + \alpha_1 u_{t-1} + \cdots + \alpha_p u_{t-p} = \epsilon_t \qquad t = \cdots, -1, 0, 1, \ldots \tag{7-34}$$

and where each series $X_{i1}, X_{i2}, \ldots$ $(i = 1, \ldots, q)$ is a given series of constants. The ϵ_ts are assumed independently and identically distributed with zero mean and constant variance. Equations (7-33) and (7-34) may be used to give

$$Y_t + \alpha_1 Y_{t-1} + \cdots + \alpha_p Y_{t-p} = \beta_1 X_{1t} + \cdots + \beta_q X_{qt} + \alpha_1\beta_1 X_{1,t-1} + \cdots + \alpha_p\beta_q X_{q,t-p} + \epsilon_t \tag{7-35}$$

Let $-a_1, \ldots, -a_p$ be the coefficients of $Y_{t-1}, \ldots, Y_{t-p}$ in the fitted-least-squares regression of Y_t on $Y_{t-1}, \ldots, Y_{t-p}, X_{1t}, \ldots, X_{qt}, X_{1,t-1}, \ldots, X_{q,t-1}, \ldots, X_{1,t-p}, \ldots, X_{q,t-p}$. Let

$$v_t = Y_t + a_1 Y_{t-1} + \cdots + a_p Y_{t-p}$$

and $w_{it} = X_{it} + a_1 X_{i,t-1} + \cdots + a_p X_{i,t-p}$ $(i = 1, \ldots, q)$. Then $b_1 \cdots b_q$ are the coefficients of $w_{1t}, \ldots, w_{qt}$ in the fitted-least-squares regression of v_t on $w_{1t}, \ldots, w_{qt}$.

Example. Suppose we wished to apply this procedure to the very simple case

$$Y_t = \beta X_t + u_t \tag{7-36}$$

$$u_t + \alpha_1 u_{t-1} = \epsilon_t \tag{7-36a}$$

In the first step we should compute the least-squares regression of Y_t on Y_{t-1}, X_t, and X_{t-1}, denoting the resultant coefficient of Y_{t-1} by $-a$. In the second step we compute the series

$$v_t = Y_t + aY_{t-1}$$
$$w_t = X_t + aX_{t-1}$$

and regress v_t on w_t, which provides the estimate of β.

7-6. Prediction Problems

Autocorrelated disturbances arise most frequently in the estimation of relationships from *time-series data.* We have already seen

[1] J. Durbin, "Estimation of Parameters in Time-series Regression Models," *J. Royal Statist. Soc.*, ser. B, vol. 22, no. 1, pp. 139–153, 1960.

that knowledge of the autoregressive structure of the disturbances improves the efficiency of our estimation process as compared with the estimators yielded by simple least squares. A similar result holds for prediction problems: it pays to incorporate knowledge of the autoregressive structure into the making of the prediction.

Suppose we have time-series observations on X_t, Y_t $(t = 1, \ldots, n)$, where we postulate a linear relation

$$Y_t = \alpha + \beta X_t + u_t \tag{7-1}$$

with a disturbance following a first-order scheme

$$u_t = \rho u_{t-1} + \epsilon_t \tag{7-2}$$

where ϵ conforms to assumptions (7-3). Let the prediction problem be defined as that of predicting Y_{n+1} for some given value of X_{n+1} in the period immediately succeeding the last sample observation. The expected value of Y_{n+1}, *given* the values $u_1, \ldots, u_n$ that have generated the sample, is

$$\begin{aligned} E(Y_{n+1}|u_1, \ldots, u_n) &= \alpha + \beta X_{n+1} + E(u_{n+1}|u_1, \ldots, u_n) \\ &= \alpha + \beta X_{n+1} + \rho u_n \qquad \text{using (7-2) and (7-3)} \end{aligned} \tag{7-37}$$

Substituting for u_n in this from (7-1) gives the alternative expression

$$E(Y_{n+1}|u_1, \ldots, u_n) = \alpha(1 - \rho) + \beta(X_{n+1} - \rho X_n) + \rho Y_n \tag{7-38}$$

that is,

$$\begin{aligned} &E[(Y_{n+1} - \rho Y_n)|u_1, \ldots, u_n] \\ &\qquad = \alpha(1 - \rho) + \beta(X_{n+1} - \rho X_n) \end{aligned} \tag{7-39}$$

Knowledge of ρ, if available, enables us to write (7-1) in the form

$$Y_t - \rho Y_{t-1} = \alpha(1 - \rho) + \beta(X_t - \rho X_{t-1}) + \epsilon_t \tag{7-40}$$

which satisfies in full the assumptions of the simple linear model. The results derived in Sec. 1-6 on prediction thus apply to (7-40), namely, that the direct application of least squares to the transformed variables $(Y_t - \rho Y_{t-1})$, $(X_t - \rho X_{t-1})$ will yield best linear predictors. Thus the best linear predictor of $(Y_{n+1} - \rho Y_n)$ is

$$\alpha^*(1 - \rho) + \beta^*(X_{n+1} - \rho X_n)$$

where α^* and β^* indicate the least-squares estimators of the parameters in (7-40). This is the same as saying that the best linear predictor of Y_{n+1}, *conditional* on the observed sample values Y_n, Y_{n-1}, etc., is

$$\alpha^*(1 - \rho) + \beta^*(X_{n+1} - \rho X_n) + \rho Y_n \tag{7-41}$$

which is equivalent to

$$\alpha^* + \beta^* X_{n+1} + \rho[Y_n - (\alpha^* + \beta^* X_n)] \tag{7-42}$$

From (7-42) it is seen that the best linear predictor of Y_{n+1} incorporates two important points. First, the parameters are estimated by utilizing knowledge of the autoregressive structure, if possible, and second, to the term $(\alpha^* + \beta^* X_{n+1})$ we add a term which is the product of ρ and the *estimated* disturbance in the previous period.

If one had applied simple least squares to (7-1), obtaining estimators $\hat{\alpha}$ and $\hat{\beta}$, and made a prediction

$$\hat{Y}_{n+1} = \hat{\alpha} + \hat{\beta} X_{n+1} \tag{7-43}$$

this would be inferior to (7-42) on two counts. It would, first, be biased, since it takes no account of recent disturbances, and second, it would be less efficient, since the simple-least-squares estimators on which the prediction is based are less efficient than the generalized-least-squares estimators. The above results obviously extend directly to the case of more than one explanatory variable.

Example. Consider the data on personal disposable income and personal consumption in the United States given in Exercise 1-5 and repeated in the first three columns of the accompanying table. By the methods of Chap. 1, we determine the least-squares regression of Y on X to be

$$\hat{Y} = 7.0 + 0.9025X$$

Applying this equation to the income data in column 3 gives the $\hat{Y}$ values shown in column 4. The computed residuals are determined from

$$\hat{u} = Y - \hat{Y}$$

and shown in column 5, and their first differences are given in column 6. From columns 5 and 6 we then compute the Durbin-Watson statistic

$$d = \frac{\Sigma(\Delta\hat{u})^2}{\Sigma\hat{u}^2} = 1.07$$

TABLE 7-2. PERSONAL DISPOSABLE INCOME AND PERSONAL CONSUMPTION IN THE UNITED STATES, 1948–1957
(Billions, constant 1954 dollars)

Year (1)	Consumption Y (2)	Income X (3)	$\hat{Y}$ (4)	$\hat{u}$ (5)	$\Delta\hat{u}$ (6)
1948	199	212	198.3	0.7	
1949	204	214	200.1	3.9	3.2
1950	216	231	215.5	0.5	−3.4
1951	218	237	220.9	−2.9	−3.4
1952	224	244	227.2	−3.2	−0.3
1953	235	255	237.1	−2.1	1.1
1954	238	257	238.9	−0.9	1.2
1955	256	273	253.4	2.6	3.5
1956	264	284	263.3	0.7	−1.9
1957	270	290	268.7	1.3	0.6

The Durbin-Watson tables do not extend as low as 10 observations, but this d value is rather low and indicative of positive serial correlation.

To illustrate the calculations, however, we proceed to estimate the coefficient r of a first-order autoregressive scheme for the residuals

$$\hat{u}_t = r\hat{u}_{t-1} + e_t$$

that is,

$$r = \frac{\sum_{t=2}^{n} \hat{u}_t\hat{u}_{t-1}}{\sum_{t=2}^{n} \hat{u}_{t-1}^2}$$

From the data in column 5, r is estimated as 0.457, which leads us to define transformed variables as

$$Y'_t = Y_t - 0.457Y_{t-1}$$
$$X'_t = X_t - 0.457X_{t-1}$$

These transformed variables are computed from columns 2 and 3 and shown in Table 7-3.

Applying least squares to these data gives

$$\hat{Y}'_t = 2.6 + 0.9114X'_t \tag{7-44}$$

The constant 2.6 is an estimate of $\alpha(1 - r)$, so that relation (7-44) may be stated in terms of the original variables as

$$\hat{Y}_t = 4.8 + 0.9114X_t$$

TABLE 7-3

Year	$Y'_t = Y_t - 0.457Y_{t-1}$	$X'_t = X_t - 0.457X_{t-1}$	$\hat{Y}'_t$	$\hat{u}'_t$	$\Delta\hat{u}'_t$
1949	113.1	117.1	109.3	3.8	
1950	122.8	133.2	124.0	−1.2	−5.0
1951	119.3	131.4	122.4	−3.1	−1.9
1952	124.4	135.7	126.3	−1.9	1.2
1953	132.6	143.5	133.4	−0.8	1.1
1954	130.6	140.5	130.7	−0.1	0.7
1955	147.2	155.6	144.4	2.8	2.9
1956	147.0	159.2	147.7	−0.7	−3.5
1957	149.4	160.2	148.6	0.8	1.5

Applying (7-44) to the X'_t values leads to the completion of Table 7-3 on the same lines as Table 7-2. The d value for the transformed variables is 1.41, which is less indicative of positive serial correlation than the residuals from the original variables, so that it would be safer to compute standard errors and confidence intervals for β from the transformed than from the original data.

References

The seminal article on autocorrelated disturbances and their effect on estimated sampling errors is

1. D. Cochrane and G. H. Orcutt: "Application of Least Squares Regressions to Relationships Containing Auto-correlated Error Terms," *J. Am. Statist. Assoc.*, vol. 44, pp. 32–61, 1949.

The Durbin-Watson d test is described in

2. J. Durbin and G. S. Watson: "Testing for Serial Correlation in Least-squares Regression," pts. I and II, *Biometrika*, 1950 and 1951.

For Durbin's suggested two-stage procedure, see

3. J. Durbin: "Estimation of Parameters in Time-series Regression Models," *J. Royal Statist. Soc.*, ser. B, vol. 22, no. 1, pp. 139–153, 1960.

The alternative d test, with a table of significance points, is given in

4. H. Theil and A. L. Nagar: "Testing the Independence of Regression Disturbances," *J. Am. Statist. Assoc.*, vol. 56, pp. 793–806, 1961.

Exercises

7-1. If

$$\mathbf{V} = \frac{1}{1-\rho^2}\begin{bmatrix} 1 & \rho & \rho^2 & \cdots & \rho^{n-1} \\ \rho & 1 & \rho & \cdots & \rho^{n-2} \\ \cdot & & & & \cdot \\ \cdot & & & & \cdot \\ \cdot & & & & \cdot \\ \rho^{n-1} & \rho^{n-2} & \rho^{n-3} & \cdots & 1 \end{bmatrix}$$

show that

$$V^{-1} = \begin{bmatrix} 1 & -\rho & 0 & \cdots & 0 & 0 \\ -\rho & 1+\rho^2 & -\rho & \cdots & 0 & 0 \\ 0 & -\rho & 1+\rho^2 & \cdots & 0 & 0 \\ \cdot & & & & & \cdot \\ \cdot & & & & & \cdot \\ \cdot & & & & & \cdot \\ 0 & 0 & 0 & \cdots & -\rho & 1 \end{bmatrix}$$

7-2. Compute the generalized-least-squares estimator (7-16) for the data of Exercise 1-5, on the assumption that the disturbance follows a first-order autoregressive scheme with $\rho = 0.457$, and compare your results with those obtained in the example at the end of this chapter.

7-3. Apply (7-41) to the data of Exercise 1-5 in order to forecast real consumption for 1958 on the assumption of an income figure of 300 billion.

7-4. Develop formulas for confidence-interval predictions based on (7-41).

8

Miscellaneous Single-equation Problems

This chapter is devoted to various other problems that may arise in the content of a single-equation model. Topics covered include multicollinearity, heteroscedasticity, lagged variables, pooling of time series and cross-section data, and the use of dummy variables.

8-1. Multicollinearity

This is the name given to the general problem which arises when some or all of the explanatory variables in a relation are so highly correlated one with another that it becomes very difficult, if not impossible, to disentangle their separate influences and obtain a reasonably precise estimate of their relative effects. It is convenient to consider several distinct cases.

Case I. Suppose theory leads us to expect a linear relation between Y, X_2, and X_3.

$$Y_t = \beta_1 + \beta_2 X_{2t} + \beta_3 X_{3t} + \epsilon_t \tag{8-1}$$

By means of n observations on the X's we attempt to estimate the parameters of (8-1). We know already that, if we write

$$\mathbf{Y} = \begin{bmatrix} y_1 \\ y_2 \\ \cdot \\ \cdot \\ \cdot \\ y_n \end{bmatrix} \qquad \mathbf{X} = \begin{bmatrix} x_{21} & x_{31} \\ x_{22} & x_{32} \\ \cdot & \cdot \\ \cdot & \cdot \\ \cdot & \cdot \\ x_{2n} & x_{3n} \end{bmatrix} \qquad \hat{\boldsymbol{\beta}} = \begin{bmatrix} \hat{\beta}_2 \\ \hat{\beta}_3 \end{bmatrix}$$

where the variables are expressed in deviation form, the least-squares estimates are

$$\hat{\boldsymbol{\beta}} = (\mathbf{X'X})^{-1}\mathbf{X'Y}$$

with

$$\text{var}\,(\hat{\boldsymbol{\beta}}) = \sigma^2(\mathbf{X'X})^{-1}$$

This estimating procedure would break down if it were impossible to form $(\mathbf{X'X})^{-1}$, that is, if $|\mathbf{X'X}| = 0$. Suppose that X_2 and X_3 were connected by an *exact* linear relation

$$X_{2t} = k_2 + k_3X_{3t} \qquad \text{for all } t$$

then

$$x_{2t} = k_3x_{3t}$$

and

$$(\mathbf{X'X}) = \begin{bmatrix} \Sigma x_2^2 & \Sigma x_2x_3 \\ \Sigma x_2x_3 & \Sigma x_3^2 \end{bmatrix}$$

$$= \Sigma x_3^2 \begin{bmatrix} k_3^2 & k_3 \\ k_3 & 1 \end{bmatrix}$$

so that

$$|\mathbf{X'X}| = 0$$

This is the case of perfect multicollinearity where the two explanatory variables are connected by an exact linear relation. It is then impossible to estimate the separate influences of X_2 and X_3, and our estimating method breaks down. The geometrical interpretation of this case is interesting and revealing. The scatter of points in the X_2, X_3 plane must lie exclusively on the straight line $X_2 = k_2 + k_3X_3$; the Y values then give rise merely to a vertical scatter of points (i.e., in the Y direction) above and below a single straight line in three-dimensional space. Attempting to fit (8-1) to the data involves inserting a plane in a three-dimensional scatter of points, but in the case outlined above our scatter is really only two-dimensional, for the complete lack of scatter in the X_2, X_3 plane means that all the sample points lie on a single vertical plane which contains the line $X_2 = k_2 + k_3X_3$.

Even this case is not entirely hopeless. If we can obtain independent estimates of an appropriate number of parameters, then the sample data can be employed to obtain estimates of the remaining parameters. Consider the general case where $\mathbf{X}$ is of order $n \times k$ and $\hat{\boldsymbol{\beta}}$ is a column vector of k elements. Exact relations between some of the explanatory variables will reduce the rank of $\mathbf{X'X}$ below k. If the rank of this matrix is, say, r, we may with any necessary rearrangements regard the last $k - r$ rows of $\mathbf{X'X}$ as linearly dependent on the first r, and instead of writing the complete set of normal equations

$$(\mathbf{X'X})\hat{\boldsymbol{\beta}} = \mathbf{X'Y} \tag{8-2}$$

we may write the abbreviated set

$$\mathbf{S}\hat{\boldsymbol{\beta}} = \mathbf{X}_r'\mathbf{Y} \tag{8-3}$$

where $\mathbf{S}$ is a matrix of order $r \times k$, consisting of the first r rows of $\mathbf{X}'\mathbf{X}$, and $\mathbf{X}_r'$ is a matrix of order $r \times n$, being the observations on the first r explanatory variables. Now at least one minor of order r in $\mathbf{S}$ is nonzero. Suppose, for example, that the first r columns of $\mathbf{S}$ are linearly independent. We may then write (8-3) as

$$\mathbf{S}_1\hat{\boldsymbol{\beta}}_r + \mathbf{S}_2\hat{\boldsymbol{\beta}}_{k-r} = \mathbf{X}_r'\mathbf{Y} \tag{8-4}$$

where the $\mathbf{S}$ matrix has been partitioned into a nonsingular matrix $\mathbf{S}_1$ of order r and a matrix $\mathbf{S}_2$ of order $r \times (k - r)$, and the $\hat{\boldsymbol{\beta}}$ vector has been partitioned conformably. If the $\hat{\boldsymbol{\beta}}_{k-r}$ vector denotes $k - r$ coefficients known independently, then we may solve (8-4) for the unknown r coefficients.

$$\hat{\boldsymbol{\beta}}_r = \mathbf{S}_1^{-1}[\mathbf{X}_r'\mathbf{Y} - \mathbf{S}_2\hat{\boldsymbol{\beta}}_{k-r}] \tag{8-5}$$

A solution similar to (8-5) may be obtained for each set of r linearly independent columns in $\mathbf{S}$. It is possible, however, that even if $k - r$ coefficients are known a priori, the r unknown coefficients may correspond to a linearly dependent set of columns and so no solution can be obtained.

As an illustration of this technique, consider the three-variable case in deviation form. Equation (8-2) then corresponds to

$$\begin{bmatrix} \Sigma x_2^2 & \Sigma x_2x_3 \\ \Sigma x_2x_3 & \Sigma x_3^2 \end{bmatrix} \begin{bmatrix} \hat{\beta}_2 \\ \hat{\beta}_3 \end{bmatrix} = \begin{bmatrix} \Sigma x_2y \\ \Sigma x_3y \end{bmatrix}$$

If $x_3 = kx_2$, the second equation is redundant, and we may write (8-3) in this case as

$$[\Sigma x_2^2 \quad \Sigma x_2x_3] \begin{bmatrix} \hat{\beta}_2 \\ \hat{\beta}_3 \end{bmatrix} = \Sigma x_2y$$

which gives (8-4) as

$$\hat{\beta}_2\Sigma x_2^2 + \hat{\beta}_3\Sigma x_2x_3 = \Sigma x_2y$$

If $\hat{\beta}_3$ is known a priori, the estimate $\hat{\beta}_2$, corresponding to (8-5), is

$$\hat{\beta}_2 = \frac{\Sigma x_2y - \hat{\beta}_3\Sigma x_2x_3}{\Sigma x_2^2} \tag{8-6}$$

which may be written as

$$\hat{\beta}_2 = \frac{\Sigma x_2(y - \hat{\beta}_3 x_3)}{\Sigma x_2{}^2}$$

This is the simple-least-squares estimator of the slope of the regression of $(y - \hat{\beta}_3 x_3)$ on x_2, so that the estimating technique embodied in (8-5) is equivalent to correcting the dependent variable for the influence of those explanatory variables with known coefficients and regressing this residual on the remaining explanatory variables.

As an illustration of how the technique may break down, consider again the three-variable case, written this time in terms of the original variables and with the assumption that $X_3 = kX_2$. Equation (8-3) then becomes

$$\begin{bmatrix} n & \Sigma X_2 & k\Sigma X_2 \\ \Sigma X_2 & \Sigma X_2{}^2 & k\Sigma X_2{}^2 \end{bmatrix} \begin{bmatrix} \hat{\beta}_1 \\ \hat{\beta}_2 \\ \hat{\beta}_3 \end{bmatrix} = \begin{bmatrix} \Sigma Y \\ \Sigma X_2 Y \end{bmatrix}$$

If $\hat{\beta}_2$ or $\hat{\beta}_3$ is known a priori, these equations can be solved for the other two, but if $\hat{\beta}_1$ is the known coefficient, no estimates of β_2 and β_3 are possible since the minor

$$\begin{vmatrix} \Sigma X_2 & k\Sigma X_2 \\ \Sigma X_2{}^2 & k\Sigma X_2{}^2 \end{vmatrix} = 0$$

Case II. A less extreme and much more likely case is that the values of the explanatory variables which appear in our sample are highly correlated but not perfectly correlated. In the three-variable case,

$$\text{var}\,(\hat{\beta}_2) = \frac{\sigma^2}{\Sigma x_{2\cdot 3}^2} \qquad \text{var}\,(\hat{\beta}_3) = \frac{\sigma^2}{\Sigma x_{3\cdot 2}^2}$$

where $x_{2\cdot 3} = x_2 - b_{23}x_3$, etc.

For high correlation between X_2 and X_3, $\Sigma x_{2\cdot 3}^2$ and $\Sigma x_{3\cdot 2}^2$ are both very small and they diminish as the correlation between X_2 and X_3 increases. Thus the standard errors should give ample warning of the imprecision attaching to the estimates of the separate effects of X_2 and X_3 when the two variables are highly correlated. However, σ^2 is usually unknown, and we base an estimate of it upon $\Sigma x_{1\cdot 23}^2$. There is no apparent reason why this estimate should be biased downward by increasing intercorrelation of the explanatory variables. Haavelmo has in fact argued that "the estimate of σ^2 is not impaired by the fact that the independent variables are highly intercorrelated."[1] Stone, however, argues that

$$\text{var}\ (\hat{\beta}_2) \propto \frac{1 - R^2_{1\cdot 23}}{1 - r_{23}{}^2}$$

and both $R_{1.23}$ and r_{23} will be close to unity, so that it may easily happen that var ($\hat{\beta}_2$) is small compared with $\hat{\beta}_2$, in which case the misleading conclusion may be reached that $\hat{\beta}_2$ is relatively well determined.[2] The implicit assumption on Stone's argument is that increasing intercorrelation of the explanatory variables necessarily reduces $\Sigma x^2_{1\cdot 23}$ (increases $R_{1.23}$). This is not plausible a priori, nor is it confirmed in the numerical example given in Table 8-1.

TABLE 8-1. NUMERICAL EXAMPLE ON MULTICOLLINEARITY

X_2	10	20	30	40	50
v	−6	3	−3	12	−12
$X_3 = X_2 + v$	4	23	27	52	38
ϵ	1	0	4	1	2
$X_1 = 2X_2 + X_3 + \epsilon$	25	63	91	133	140

X_3 has been constructed to be correlated with X_2, and X_1 has been calculated as

$$X_1 = 2X_2 + X_3 + \epsilon$$

Applying least squares to these data gives

$$r_{23}{}^2 = 0.74 \qquad R^2_{1\cdot 23} = 0.9991 \qquad \Sigma x^2_{1\cdot 23} = 8.1 \qquad \Sigma x^2_{2\cdot 3} = 261.9$$
$$\hat{\beta}_2 = 2.086 \qquad \text{var}\ (\hat{\beta}_2) = 0.0155$$

Next we wish to examine the effect on these estimates of increasing the correlation between X_2 and X_3, with all else unchanged. To do this we commence with the same X_2 values as before, but change v to −2, 1, −1, 4, −4; that is, we reduce the original v values to one-third of their initial size. We then build up X_3 and finally X_1, retaining exactly the same ϵ values as before. Applying least

[1] See T. Haavelmo, "Remarks on Frisch's Confluence Analysis and Its Use in Econometrics," chap. 5 in T. Koopmans (ed.), *Statistical Inference in Dynamic Economic Models*, Wiley, New York, 1950, p. 260.

[2] See J. R. N. Stone, "The Analysis of Market Demand," *J. Royal Statist. Soc.*, vol. 108, pp. 296–297, 1945.

squares to the new values gives

$$r_{23}{}^2 = 0.96 \qquad R^2_{1\cdot 23} = 0.9985 \qquad \Sigma x^2_{1\cdot 23} = 13.5 \qquad \Sigma x^2_{2\cdot 3} = 36.5$$
$$\hat{\beta}_2 = 2.20 \qquad \text{var}\,(\hat{\beta}_2) = 0.1849$$

The correlation between the explanatory variables has been increased from $r^2 = 0.74$ to $r^2 = 0.96$, but there has been no sign of any corresponding reduction in $\Sigma x^2_{1\cdot 23}$; it has in fact increased from 8.1 to 13.5. The sampling variance of $\hat{\beta}_2$ has been estimated as $\text{var}\,(\hat{\beta}_2) = \Sigma x^2_{1\cdot 23}/[(n-3)\Sigma x^2_{2\cdot 3}]$. This estimated variance has increased from 0.0155 to 0.1849, that is, by a factor of about 12, as the correlation between X_2 and X_3 has increased, and bears ample witness to the greater indeterminancy of estimates as multicollinearity becomes more serious.

Case III. The third case may appropriately be labeled the Frisch case.[1] Suppose we take the view that the variables in our analysis are composed of two parts, a systematic, or "true," part and an "error" component,

$$\underset{\text{observed}}{\underset{\downarrow}{X_{it}}} = \underset{\text{true}}{\underset{\downarrow}{X'_{it}}} + \underset{\text{error}}{\underset{\downarrow}{X''_{it}}}$$

Suppose further that our theory suggests an *exact* linear relation between the systematic parts of the variables, and it is our objective to estimate the parameters of this relation, say,

$$X'_1 = \beta_1 + \beta_2 X'_2 + \beta_3 X'_3$$

If an exact linear relation also holds between X'_2 and X'_3, then by analogy with case I it is impossible to determine the parameters β_2 and β_3. However, this fact may be obscured in practice by the presence of errors of observation, and the application of least squares may well give estimates which stand up to the usual significance tests. While the true values will lie on a single straight *line* in three-dimensional space, the actual observations will be clustered around such a line, and their departures from the line will merely be the result of errors of observation. In this case it is these discrepancies that determine our estimated coefficients and their estimated variances, and the conventional significance test will merely consist in working out the ratio of two functions-of-error terms.

[1] See R. Frisch, *Statistical Confluence Analysis by Means of Complete Regression Systems,* University Economics Institute, Oslo, 1934.

In the case of high, but not perfect, correlation between X_2 and X_3, our estimates will probably be dominated by the error terms. Frisch's bunch-map analysis was designed to indicate this type of dangerous situation, the basic idea being the determination of the regression plane by minimizing the residual sum of squares in various directions. In the pure-error case the points will be distributed at random about some line in space, and the different determinations will give radically different values for any given coefficient. If the scatter of points is not purely random, then the various determinations will give regression estimates closer together.

Case IV. If multicollinearity is serious, in the sense that estimated parameters have an unsatisfactorily low degree of precision, we are in the statistical position of not being able to make bricks without straw. The remedy lies essentially in the acquisition, if possible, of new data which will break the multicollinearity deadlock. Early demand studies, for example, which were based on time-series data, ran into difficulties because of the correlation between the explanatory variables, income and prices, plus the often inadequate variation in the income series. The use of cross-section budget data gave a wide range of income variation, thus enabling a fairly precise determination of the income coefficient, which could then be employed in the time-series analysis. This combined use of time-series and cross-section data is now conventional practice in demand studies.[1] There are, however, difficulties of specification and interpretation.[2]

If forecasting is a primary objective, then intercorrelation of explanatory variables may not be too serious, provided it may reasonably be expected to continue in the future.

8-2. Heteroscedasticity

One of the assumptions of the linear normal regression model was

$$E(\mathbf{uu}') = \sigma^2\mathbf{I}$$

[1] See J. Tobin, "A Statistical Demand Function for Food in the U.S.A.," *J. Royal Statist. Soc.*, ser. A, vol. 113, pp. 113–141, 1950. J. R. N. Stone, *The Measurement of Consumers' Expenditure and Behaviour in the United Kingdom, 1920–1938*, Cambridge, London, 1954. H. Wold and L. Jureen, *Demand Analysis*, Wiley, New York, 1953.

[2] See J. Meyer and E. Kuh, "How Extraneous Are Extraneous Estimates?" *Rev. Economics and Statistics*, vol. 39, pp. 380–393, 1957.

that is, that the disturbances were independently distributed variables with a constant variance σ^2. The condition of a constant variance is referred to as *homoscedasticity*, and its opposite as *heteroscedasticity*.

In the usual matrix notation,

$$\mathbf{Y} = \mathbf{X}\boldsymbol{\beta} + \mathbf{u} \tag{8-7}$$

Suppose now that

$$E(\mathbf{uu}') = \sigma^2 \begin{bmatrix} \frac{1}{\lambda_1} & 0 & \cdots & 0 \\ 0 & \frac{1}{\lambda_2} & \cdots & 0 \\ \cdot & & & \cdot \\ \cdot & & & \cdot \\ \cdot & & & \cdot \\ 0 & 0 & \cdots & \frac{1}{\lambda_n} \end{bmatrix} \tag{8-8}$$

If we now define the diagonal matrix

$$\mathbf{\Lambda} = \begin{bmatrix} \sqrt{\lambda_1} & 0 & \cdots & 0 \\ 0 & \sqrt{\lambda_2} & \cdots & 0 \\ \cdot & & & \cdot \\ \cdot & & & \cdot \\ \cdot & & & \cdot \\ 0 & 0 & \cdots & \sqrt{\lambda_n} \end{bmatrix} \tag{8-9}$$

and premultiply through (8-7), we have

$$\mathbf{\Lambda Y} = \mathbf{\Lambda X}\boldsymbol{\beta} + \mathbf{\Lambda u} \tag{8-10}$$

The variance-covariance matrix for the transformed disturbance $(\mathbf{\Lambda u})$ is

$$E(\mathbf{\Lambda uu}'\mathbf{\Lambda}') = \sigma^2\mathbf{I}$$

so that we may apply simple least squares directly to relation (8-10). The least-squares estimator $\hat{\boldsymbol{\beta}}$ is then

$$\hat{\boldsymbol{\beta}} = (\mathbf{X}'\mathbf{\Lambda}^2\mathbf{X})^{-1}\mathbf{X}'\mathbf{\Lambda}^2\mathbf{Y} \tag{8-11}$$

with variance-covariance matrix

$$\text{var}\,(\hat{\boldsymbol{\beta}}) = \sigma^2(\mathbf{X}'\mathbf{\Lambda}^2\mathbf{X})^{-1} \tag{8-12}$$

For the case of a single explanatory variable,

$$\mathbf{X}'\mathbf{\Lambda}^2\mathbf{X} = \begin{bmatrix} \sum_{i=1}^{n} \lambda_i & \sum_{i=1}^{n} \lambda_i X_i \\ \sum_{i=1}^{n} \lambda_i X_i & \sum_{i=1}^{n} \lambda_i X_i^2 \end{bmatrix}$$

and (8-11) gives the two simultaneous equations

$$\begin{aligned} \hat{\beta}_1 \Sigma\lambda_i + \hat{\beta}_2 \Sigma\lambda_i X_i &= \Sigma\lambda_i Y_i \\ \hat{\beta}_1 \Sigma\lambda_i X_i + \hat{\beta}_2 \Sigma\lambda_i X_i^2 &= \Sigma\lambda_i X_i Y_i \end{aligned} \tag{8-13}$$

and from (8-12) the sampling variance of the regression slope $\hat{\beta}_2$ will be

$$\text{var}\,(\hat{\beta}_2) = \frac{\sigma^2 \Sigma\lambda_i}{(\Sigma\lambda_i)(\Sigma\lambda_i X_i^2) - (\Sigma\lambda_i X_i)^2} \tag{8-14}$$

If we applied simple least squares directly to (8-7), our estimator $\boldsymbol{\beta}^*$ would be

$$\boldsymbol{\beta}^* = (\mathbf{X}'\mathbf{X})^{-1}\mathbf{X}'\mathbf{Y} \tag{8-15}$$

which would be unbiased. Its variance-covariance matrix would be

$$E[(\boldsymbol{\beta}^* - \boldsymbol{\beta})(\boldsymbol{\beta}^* - \boldsymbol{\beta})'] = (\mathbf{X}'\mathbf{X})^{-1}\mathbf{X}'E(\mathbf{uu}')\mathbf{X}(\mathbf{X}'\mathbf{X})^{-1} \tag{8-16}$$

In the case of a single explanatory variable, (8-15) reduces to the usual normal equations

$$\begin{aligned} n\beta_1^* + \beta_2^* \Sigma X &= \Sigma Y \\ \beta_1^* \Sigma X + \beta_2^* \Sigma X^2 &= \Sigma XY \end{aligned} \tag{8-17}$$

while (8-16) gives, for the sampling variance of the regression slope,

$$\text{var}\,(\beta_2^*) = \frac{\sigma^2\left[\left(\sum \frac{1}{\lambda_i}\right)\left(\sum X_i\right)^2 - 2n\left(\sum \frac{1}{\lambda_i} X_i\right)\left(\sum X_i\right) + n^2\left(\sum \frac{1}{\lambda_i} X_i^2\right)\right]}{\left[n\sum X_i^2 - \left(\sum X_i\right)^2\right]^2} \tag{8-18}$$

If the elements of the matrix $\mathbf{\Lambda}$ are known, then the choice of whether to apply least squares to the transformed data as in (8-10) or directly to the original data as in (8-7) depends upon the sampling variances indicated in (8-12) and (8-16). We shall illustrate the comparison in the case of one explanatory variable by making various assumptions about the form of heteroscedasticity.

Suppose, for example, that the standard deviation of the disturbance term is proportional to the value of X; that is,

$$E(u_i^2) = \sigma^2 X_i^2 \qquad i = 1, \ldots, n \tag{8-19}$$

where σ^2 denotes some constant. This situation is pictured in Fig. (8-1), and something of this kind may be expected in budget studies,

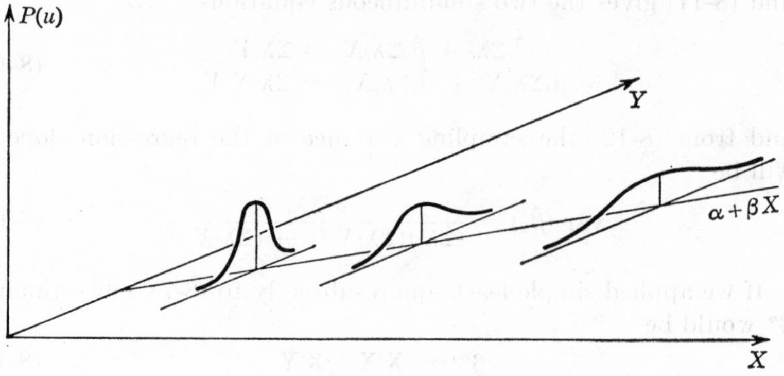

FIG. 8-1

where X denotes income and Y expenditure on a given item or group of items. Comparing (8-8) and (8-19) shows that we may write

$$\sqrt{\lambda_i} = \frac{1}{X_i} \tag{8-20}$$

Making this substitution in formulas (8-14) and (8-18) gives

$$\text{var}\,(\hat{\beta}_2) = \frac{\sigma^2 \Sigma(1/X_i^2)}{n\Sigma(1/X_i^2) - [\Sigma(1/X_i)]^2} \tag{8-21}$$

and

$$\text{var}\,(\beta_2^*) = \sigma^2 \frac{(\Sigma X_i^2)(\Sigma X_i)^2 - 2n(\Sigma X_i^3)(\Sigma X_i) + n^2(\Sigma X_i^4)}{[n\Sigma X_i^2 - (\Sigma X_i)^2]^2} \tag{8-22}$$

For a simple numerical comparison let us assume X takes on the values 1, 2, 3, 4, 5. We then find

$$\frac{\text{var}\,(\hat{\beta}_2)}{\text{var}\,(\beta_2^*)} = \frac{0.69}{1.24} = 0.56$$

so that the efficiency of least squares applied to the original data is only about 56 per cent of least squares applied to the transformed data. Notice that if we apply (8-20) to (8-10), we obtain

$$\frac{Y_i}{X_i} = \beta_1 \frac{1}{X_i} + \beta_2 + v_i \qquad i = 1, \ldots, n$$

where $v_i = u_i/X_i$. Thus our estimate of β_2, the coefficient of X in the original relation, is given by computing the *intercept* in the regression of Y_i/X_i on $1/X_i$, and the formula (8-21) is in fact the sampling variance of the intercept in the linear regression with $1/X_i$ as the explanatory variable.

As a final example, suppose the variance of the disturbance is proportional to X; that is,

$$E(u_i^2) = \sigma^2 X_i$$

Reference to (8-8) shows that we can then write

$$\lambda_i = \frac{1}{X_i}$$

Substitution in (8-14) and (8-18) then gives

$$\text{var}(\hat{\beta}_2) = \sigma^2 \frac{\Sigma(1/X_i)}{\Sigma(1/X_i)\Sigma X_i - n^2}$$

and

$$\text{var}(\beta_2^*) = \sigma^2 \frac{(\Sigma X_i)^3 - 2n(\Sigma X_i^2)(\Sigma X_i) + n^2(\Sigma X_i^3)}{[n\Sigma X_i^2 - (\Sigma X_i)^2]^2}$$

For the above numerical example

$$\frac{\text{var}(\hat{\beta}_2)}{\text{var}(\beta_2^*)} = 0.83$$

which shows the application of simple least squares to the original data to be relatively more efficient than in the previous example, which is to be expected, since the second example assumes a less radical departure from constant variance than does the first. It is still better, however, to apply least squares to the transformed data, as indicated by (8-10), provided the transformation matrix $\mathbf{\Lambda}$ is known.

8-3. Lagged Variables

Suppose theory leads to the formulation of a relationship in which lagged values of the dependent variables appear on the right-hand side of the relation. The simplest possible example would be

$$Y_t = \alpha + \beta Y_{t-1} + \epsilon_t \tag{8-23}$$

where we assume the ϵ values to be serially independent. One of the conditions for the application of simple least squares in the case of a single explanatory variable is

$$E\{\epsilon_t[X_{t+\tau} - E(X_{t+\tau})]\} = 0 \qquad \text{for all } t \qquad \text{for } \tau = \cdots -1, 0, 1, \ldots \tag{8-24}$$

Thus (8-24) implies, for example, that ϵ_t should be independent of future values X_{t+1}, X_{t+2}, etc., as well as of current and past values. In model (8-23), $X_t = Y_{t-1}$, so that ϵ_t influences $Y_t(= X_{t+1})$. Thus while ϵ_t is independent of $X_t, X_{t-1}, \ldots$, it is *not* independent of X_{t+1}, X_{t+2}, etc. What are the consequences of using least-squares estimators when this assumption of independence between disturbance term and explanatory variable is violated?

The answer is that the least-squares estimates will be biased, though if the disturbance term follows a normal distribution, they will tend to have the desirable *asymptotic* properties of consistency and efficiency.

Suppose we have observations $Y_1, Y_2, \ldots, Y_n$, generated by the scheme

$$Y_t = \alpha + \beta Y_{t-1} + \epsilon_t$$

where the ϵ are taken to be normally and independently distributed with zero mean and constant variance σ^2. Let us assume first of all that Y_1 is a fixed number; that is, we are supposing that the sequence of observations always starts at the same number and that the remaining values depend upon the $n - 1$ values $\epsilon_2, \ldots, \epsilon_n$ that come from the postulated probability distribution for ϵ. The likelihood function for the sample is then

$$\begin{aligned}
\Pr(\epsilon_2\epsilon_3 \cdots \epsilon_n) &= \Pr(\epsilon_2)\Pr(\epsilon_3) \cdots \Pr(\epsilon_n) \\
&= \frac{1}{(\sigma\sqrt{2\pi})^{n-1}} \exp\left(-\frac{1}{2\sigma^2}\sum_{i=2}^{n} \epsilon_i^2\right) d\epsilon_2 \cdots d\epsilon_n \\
&= \frac{1}{(\sigma\sqrt{2\pi})^{n-1}} \exp\left[-\frac{1}{2\sigma^2}\sum_{i=2}^{n} (Y_i - \alpha - \beta Y_{i-1})^2\right] d\epsilon_2 \cdots d\epsilon_n
\end{aligned} \tag{8-25}$$

Maximizing this likelihood function with respect to α and β is the same as minimizing

$$\sum_{i=2}^{n} (Y_i - \alpha - \beta Y_{i-1})^2$$

This yields the least-squares estimates $\hat{\alpha}$ and $\hat{\beta}$, obtained by solving

$$\sum_{i=2}^{n} Y_i = (n-1)\hat{\alpha} + \hat{\beta} \sum_{i=2}^{n} Y_{i-1}$$

$$\sum_{i=2}^{n} Y_i Y_{i-1} = \hat{\alpha} \sum_{i=2}^{n} Y_{i-1} + \hat{\beta} \sum_{i=2}^{n} Y_{i-1}^2$$

Thus for the special case of fixed Y_1, the least-squares estimates are maximum-likelihood estimates and so have the desirable large-sample properties of consistency and efficiency.

If Y_1 itself is a random variable, the sequence is started off by a drawing from the Y_1 distribution. By successive backward substitution in (8-23) we obtain

$$Y_t = \frac{\alpha}{1-\beta} + \sum_{\tau=0}^{\infty} \beta^{\tau} \epsilon_{t-\tau} \qquad |\beta| < 1 \tag{8-26}$$

Therefore

$$E(Y_t) = \frac{\alpha}{1-\beta} \tag{8-27}$$

and

$$\operatorname{var}(Y_t) = \frac{\sigma^2}{1-\beta^2} \tag{8-28}$$

Since ϵ is normal, Y_t will have a normal distribution, with the mean and variance specified in (8-27) and (8-28). The probability of obtaining a value Y_1 is then

$$L_1 = \frac{\sqrt{1-\beta^2}}{\sqrt{2\pi}\,\sigma} \exp\left[-\frac{1-\beta^2}{2\sigma^2}\left(Y_1 - \frac{\alpha}{1-\beta}\right)^2\right] dY_1$$

The likelihood function for the sample is then

$$L_1 \left(\frac{1}{\sigma\sqrt{2\pi}}\right)^{n-1} \exp\left[-\frac{1}{2\sigma^2}\sum_{t=2}^{n}(Y_t - \alpha - \beta Y_{t-1})^2\right] dY_2 \cdots dY_n$$

The maximum-likelihood estimates obtained from this will differ from the least-squares estimates, but as n increases, these maximum-likelihood estimates will tend stochastically to the least-squares estimates.[1]

Econometricians, however, can only derive cold comfort from large-sample properties of estimators, and unfortunately the least-squares estimates may be seriously biased in small samples. Hurwicz has demonstrated the existence of this bias.[2] His proof is not an easy one mathematically, and he has worked out the case explicitly only for $n = 3$. The following method is mathematically simpler, but is deficient in that it indicates only the sign of the bias and not the order of magnitude.

Consider again

$$Y_t = \alpha + \beta Y_{t-1} + \epsilon_t \tag{8-23}$$

The least-squares estimate of β is

$$\hat{\beta} = \frac{\sum_{t=2}^{n} (Y_t - \bar{Y})(Y_{t-1} - \bar{\bar{Y}})}{\sum_{t=2}^{n} (Y_{t-1} - \bar{\bar{Y}})^2} \tag{8-29}$$

where $$\bar{Y} = \frac{1}{n-1} (Y_2 + \cdots + Y_n)$$

and $$\bar{\bar{Y}} = \frac{1}{n-1} (Y_1 + \cdots + Y_{n-1})$$

From (8-23),

$$\bar{Y} = \alpha + \beta\bar{\bar{Y}} + \bar{\epsilon}$$

therefore $$Y_t - \bar{Y} = \beta(Y_{t-1} - \bar{\bar{Y}}) + (\epsilon_t - \bar{\epsilon})$$

and $$\hat{\beta} = \beta + \frac{\sum_{t=2}^{n} (Y_{t-1} - \bar{\bar{Y}})\epsilon_t}{\sum_{t=2}^{n} (Y_{t-1} - \bar{\bar{Y}})^2} \tag{8-30}$$

$E(\hat{\beta})$ thus involves the expected value of the last term on the right-hand side of (8-30). The precise evaluation is difficult since the numerator and denominator depend upon the same random variables. However, the *sign* of the whole will depend upon the sign of

[1] See Tjalling C. Koopmans (ed.), *Statistical Inference in Dynamic Economic Models*, Cowles Commission Monograph 10, Wiley, New York, 1950, chap. 7, by L. Hurwicz, "Prediction and Least Squares," p. 298, footnote 3.

[2] *Ibid.*, chap. 15, by L. Hurwicz, "Least Squares Bias in Time Series," pp. 365–383.

the numerator. From (8-23) we have

$$
\begin{aligned}
& Y_1 \\
Y_2 &= \alpha + \beta Y_1 + \epsilon_2 \\
Y_3 &= \alpha + \alpha\beta + \beta^2 Y_1 + \beta\epsilon_2 + \epsilon_3 \\
Y_4 &= \alpha + \alpha\beta + \alpha\beta^2 + \beta^3 Y_1 + \beta^2\epsilon_2 + \beta\epsilon_3 + \epsilon_4 \\
&\cdot \\
&\cdot \\
&\cdot \\
Y_{n-1} &= \alpha + \alpha\beta + \cdots + \alpha\beta^{n-3} + \beta^{n-2} Y_1 + \beta^{n-3}\epsilon_2 + \cdots + \epsilon_{n-1}
\end{aligned}
$$

Thus $\bar{\bar{Y}}$ = terms in α, β, and Y_1 plus $B_2\epsilon_2 + B_3\epsilon_3 + \cdots + B_{n-1}\epsilon_{n-1}$, where the B's are averages of the powers of β. Thus if

TABLE 8-2. BIASES DUE TO LAGGED VARIABLES AND AUTOCORRELATED DISTURBANCES

	True value	Mean of 20 sample determinations	Standard error of mean
Constant term	0	−18.36	4.71
Slope	0.4	0.90	0.02

SOURCE: G. H. Orcutt and D. Cochrane, "A Sampling Study of the Merits of Autoregressive and Reduced Form Transformations in Regression Analysis," *J. Am. Statist. Assoc.*, vol. 44, p. 365, table I, 1949.

$\beta > 0$, all the B's are positive. Assuming independence for the ϵs, it then follows that

$$E\left[\sum_{t=2}^{n} (Y_{t-1} - \bar{\bar{Y}})\epsilon_t\right] = -\sigma^2 \sum_{i=2}^{n-1} B_i$$

which gives a negative bias if $\beta > 0$.

If we combine the two complications of lagged variables and autocorrelated residuals, things get really bad. Orcutt and Cochrane examined the scheme

$$x_t = 0.4x_{t-1} + u_t$$

where the u_t were positively autocorrelated and about three times as large numerically as x.[1] The results are shown in Table 8-2.

[1] See G. H. Orcutt and D. Cochrane, "A Sampling Study of the Merits of Autoregressive and Reduced Form Transformations in Regression Analysis," *J. Am. Statist. Assoc.*, vol. 44, pp. 356–372, 1949.

The standard error of the mean in the last column of the table is computed from the spread of the sample estimates. We see that for the regression slope these are clustered very closely around a value which is more than twice the true value. This is indeed a remarkable result. Autocorrelated disturbances alone do not lead us to expect biased estimates; lagged variables would lead us to expect in this case a *negative* bias; yet the *simultaneous* presence of the two complications produces a substantial *positive* bias. This result highlights once again a striking weakness of the current state of econometrics, in that the joint result of several complications cannot be inferred as the sum of their separate results.

Lagged variables have been employed to an increasing extent in recent econometric work as a consequence of attempts to formulate certain relationships more realistically.[1] Suppose one variable reacts to movements of another variable with a lagged response. A possible representation of such a lagged response is

$$Y_t = \alpha_0 X_t + \alpha_1 X_{t-1} + \alpha_2 X_{t-2} + \cdots + u_t \tag{8-31}$$

Any attempt to estimate the coefficients of (8-31) as it stands will probably founder on the close intercorrelation of successive values of X. It is often presumably realistic to expect more remote values of X to exercise a smaller influence than more recent values. An extremely simple form of this hypothesis is to assume that the α coefficients decline exponentially; that is,

$$\alpha_j = \alpha\lambda^j \qquad \begin{array}{l} j = 1, 2, \ldots \\ 0 \leqq \lambda < 1 \end{array} \tag{8-32}$$

We may then write (8-31) twice over to give

$$\begin{aligned} Y_{t+1} &= \alpha X_{t+1} + \alpha\lambda X_t + \alpha\lambda^2 X_{t-1} + \cdots + u_{t+1} \\ \lambda Y_t &= \qquad\quad\ \ \alpha\lambda X_t + \alpha\lambda^2 X_{t-1} + \cdots + \lambda u_t \end{aligned}$$

and hence

$$Y_{t+1} = \lambda Y_t + \alpha X_{t+1} + (u_{t+1} - \lambda u_t) \tag{8-33}$$

or

$$\Delta Y_t = \alpha X_{t+1} - \gamma Y_t + (u_{t+1} - \lambda u_t) \tag{8-34}$$

where $\Delta Y_t = Y_{t+1} - Y_t$

and $\gamma = 1 - \lambda$

[1] See L. M. Koyck, *Distributed Lags and Investment Analysis*, North-Holland Publishing Company, Amsterdam, 1954. Marc Nerlove, *Distributed Lags and Demand Analysis for Agricultural and Other Commodities*, Agriculture Handbook 141, U.S. Department of Agriculture, 1958.

The great advantage of (8-33) over (8-31) from the point of view of estimation is that the former contains only two explanatory variables, so that the multicollinearity problem is substantially overcome. Serious estimation problems, however, still remain. If u follows a first-order Markov scheme with parameter λ,

$$u_t - \lambda u_{t-1} = \epsilon_t \tag{8-35}$$

where ϵ is assumed to be serially independent and to have a constant variance, then (8-33) has a serially independent disturbance term and, as shown at the beginning of this section, the application of least squares will yield consistent estimates of α and λ, but the estimates will of course be biased for finite sample sizes. It is very unlikely that u should obligingly follow (8-35): if, for example, u is serially independent, $u_t - \lambda u_{t-1}$ is autocorrelated and least-squares estimates of α and λ will not even be consistent; furthermore, as the example of Table 8-2 shows, the biases produced by lagged variables in conjunction with autocorrelated disturbances can be very serious.

Attempts have been made to derive *consistent* estimates of the parameters of (8-33). Assume

$$u_t = \xi u_{t-1} + \epsilon_t \qquad 0 \leqq \xi < 1 \tag{8-36}$$

and assume that least-squares estimates $\hat{\alpha}$ and $\hat{\lambda}$ of the parameters α and λ have been obtained so that we can compute the sum of squared residuals.

$$\sum_{t=1}^{n} z_t^2 = \sum_{t=1}^{n} (Y_t - \hat{\alpha}X_t - \hat{\lambda}Y_{t-1})^2$$

To obtain consistent estimates of α and λ, Koyck proposes the two equations[1]

$$\begin{aligned} \bar{\alpha}\Sigma X_t^2 + \bar{\lambda}\Sigma X_t Y_{t-1} &= \Sigma X_t Y_t \\ \bar{\alpha}\Sigma X_t Y_{t-1} + \bar{\lambda}\Sigma Y_{t-1}^2 &= \Sigma Y_t Y_{t-1} + \frac{(\bar{\lambda} - \xi)\Sigma z_t^2}{1 - \xi\bar{\lambda} + \hat{\lambda}(\bar{\lambda} - \xi)} \end{aligned} \tag{8-37}$$

ξ is unknown, and no method of estimation is proposed. Koyck's suggestion is that various values between zero and unity might be tried for ξ and Eqs. (8-37) solved for each value. This would indicate the range of $\bar{\alpha}$, $\bar{\lambda}$ values corresponding to various values of ξ;

[1] Koyck, *op. cit.*, p. 36.

Koyck's empirical studies show, in fact, remarkably little variation in these estimates over the full range of ξ values.

For the special case where u is serially independent ($\xi = 0$), Klein has shown that the estimates given by Koyck's formula (8-37) may be obtained in a simpler fashion.[1] Equation (8-33) may be rewritten as

$$Y_t - u_t = \alpha X_t + \lambda(Y_{t-1} - u_{t-1}) \tag{8-38}$$

where the u's are regarded as observation errors. As shown in Chap. 6, estimates of the coefficients of a relationship of this kind depend upon the ratio of the error variances. In this case this ratio can be taken as unity, and if the u_t follow a normal distribution, a maximum-likelihood estimate of λ is obtained by solving the following quadratic:

$$\lambda^2\left[\frac{(\Sigma X_tY_{t-1})(\Sigma X_tY_t)}{\Sigma X_t^2} - \Sigma Y_tY_{t-1}\right] + \lambda\left[\Sigma Y_t^2 - \Sigma Y_{t-1}^2 + \frac{(\Sigma X_tY_{t-1})^2 - (\Sigma X_tY_t)^2}{\Sigma X_t^2}\right] + \left[\Sigma Y_tY_{t-1} - \frac{(\Sigma X_tY_{t-1})(\Sigma X_tY_t)}{\Sigma X_t^2}\right] = 0 \tag{8-39}$$

The other coefficient is then given by

$$\text{est } \alpha = \frac{-\text{est } \lambda \Sigma X_tY_{t-1} + \Sigma X_tY_t}{\Sigma X_t^2} \tag{8-40}$$

The estimates are thus obtained in one step instead of two, but they are identical with those obtained from (8-37) after substituting $\xi = 0$. Klein also proposes an iterative procedure for obtaining estimates in the more general case of $\xi \neq 0$.[2] All those methods, however, are likely to produce biased estimates in small samples of the size that is customary in econometric work.

Koyck was led originally to the formulation (8-31) by considering various technological, institutional, and subjective reasons for the reactions of producers or consumers being spread over a certain period of time. Suppose that the X variable has been constant

[1] See L. R. Klein, "The Estimation of Distributed Lags," *Econometrica*, vol. 26, no. 4, pp. 553–565, October, 1958.

[2] *Ibid.*, pp. 557–559. But see also E. Malinvaud, "The Estimation of Distributed Lags: A Comment," *Econometrica*, vol. 29, no. 3, pp. 430–433, July, 1961, where it is shown that these estimates in the general case are not consistent.

at a level X_0 sufficiently long for Y to be fully adjusted to that level at $Y_0 = \alpha X_0$. Let us assume that in period 1, X changes to a level $X_0 + \Delta X$ and remains at this new level indefinitely. Assuming a system of reactions

$$\begin{aligned} Y_1 - Y_0 &= \alpha_0 \, \Delta X \\ Y_2 - Y_1 &= \alpha_1 \, \Delta X \\ Y_3 - Y_2 &= \alpha_2 \, \Delta X \end{aligned}$$

etc., gives

$$Y_t = \left(\alpha - \sum_{i=0}^{t-1} \alpha_i\right) X_0 + \left(\sum_{i=0}^{t-1} \alpha_i\right) (X_0 + \Delta X)$$

If we now assume instead that, after constancy at X_0, the X variable takes a sequence of values $X_1, X_2, X_3, \ldots$, then the Y value at any time will be the sum of a number of separate reactions.

$$\begin{aligned} Y_1 - Y_0 &= \alpha_0(X_1 - X_0) \\ Y_2 - Y_1 &= \alpha_0(X_2 - X_1) + \alpha_1(X_1 - X_0) \\ Y_3 - Y_2 &= \alpha_0(X_3 - X_2) + \alpha_1(X_2 - X_1) + \alpha_2(X_1 - X_0) \end{aligned}$$

giving

$$Y_t = \alpha_0 X_t + \alpha_1 X_{t-1} + \alpha_2 X_{t-2} + \cdots + \left(\alpha - \sum_{i=0}^{t-1} \alpha_i\right) X_0$$

This scheme of reactions is somewhat implausible since it assumes that at time t the change in Y, that is, $Y_t - Y_{t-1}$, is the sum of a reaction to the current change in X, namely, $\alpha_0(X_t - X_{t-1})$, plus a reaction delayed one period to the previous change in X, namely, $\alpha_1(X_{t-1} - X_{t-2})$, plus a reaction delayed two periods to the change in X two periods back, and so on. It may be quite plausible to assume, say, that $X_{t-2} - X_{t-3}$ produces a reaction $\alpha_2(X_{t-2} - X_{t-3})$ on Y in period t if X has since remained constant at the level X_{t-2}, and quite implausible to assume that this same reaction would be forthcoming if X had continued to change after period $t - 2$.

Even though (8-31) may be too rigid and mechanistic, more general and perhaps more realistic assumptions still give rise to distributed lags. Suppose that on the basis of the past history of X, people form an expectation of a likely future level X^* and would like to adjust Y to that level in accordance with the relation

$$Y^* = bX^* \tag{8-41}$$

The formation of X^* may be described by

$$X_t^* - X_{t-1}^* = \beta(X_t - X_{t-1}^*) \tag{8-42}$$

which postulates an adjustment in expectation based on the discrepancy emerging between the current value and the previous expectation. Equation (8-42) is equivalent to

$$X_t^* = \sum_{\lambda=0}^{\infty} \beta(1-\beta)^\lambda X_{t-\lambda} \tag{8-43}$$

There may also exist some lags in the adjustment of Y to Y^*, which we shall write

$$Y_t - Y_{t-1} = \delta(Y_t^* - Y_{t-1}) \tag{8-44}$$

or equivalently,

$$Y_t = \sum_{\lambda=0}^{\infty} \delta(1-\delta)^\lambda Y_{t-\lambda}^* \tag{8-45}$$

Thus the *expected* value of X is an exponentially weighted average of all previous *actual* X values, while the *actual* value of Y is an exponentially weighted average of all previous *desired* values of Y.

The model given by Eqs. (8-41), (8-42), and (8-45) may be written in two alternative forms. By successive substitution we have

$$\begin{aligned} Y_t = b\beta\delta\{X_t &+ [(1-\beta) + (1-\delta)]X_{t-1} + [(1-\beta)^2 \\ &+ (1-\beta)(1-\delta) + (1-\delta)^2]X_{t-2} + [(1-\beta)^3 + (1-\beta)^2(1-\delta) \\ &+ (1-\beta)(1-\delta)^2 + (1-\delta)^3]X_{t-3} + \cdots\} \end{aligned} \tag{8-46}$$

This reduction does not provide a form suitable for statistical estimation.

An alternative reduction is as follows:

$$\begin{aligned} Y_t &= \delta Y_t^* + (1-\delta)Y_{t-1} && \text{from (8-44)} \\ &= b\delta X_t^* + (1-\delta)Y_{t-1} && \text{substituting (8-41)} \\ &= b\delta[\beta X_t + (1-\beta)X_{t-1}^*] + (1-\delta)Y_{t-1} && \text{substituting (8-42)} \\ &= b\delta\left[\beta X_t + (1-\beta)\left(\frac{1}{b\delta}Y_{t-1} - \frac{1-\delta}{b\delta}Y_{t-2}\right)\right] + (1-\delta)Y_{t-1} \end{aligned}$$

substituting for X_{t-1}^* from the second equation above. Thus

$$Y_t = b\beta\delta X_t + [(1-\beta) + (1-\delta)]Y_{t-1} - (1-\beta)(1-\delta)Y_{t-2} \tag{8-47}$$

Estimation of (8-47) is less difficult than of (8-46), though the presence of two lagged Y values in (8-47) will still give rise to biased estimates. Moreover, since β and δ enter the relation symmetrically, it is impossible to obtain separate estimates of their values from the regression coefficients. One can, however, estimate b, $\beta\delta$, and $\beta + \delta$. For an extensive discussion of various models of this type and the associated problems of estimation, the reader should consult Nerlove.[1]

8-4. Dummy Variables[2]

Econometric research in recent years provides many examples of the use of dummy variables in regression analysis. They are used to represent temporal effects such as shifts in relations between wartime and peacetime years, between different seasons, or between different political regimes. They are also used to represent qualitative variables such as sex, marital condition, and occupational or social status, and they are sometimes used to represent quantitative variables such as age, where it is thought that only broad age groupings are relevant.

As an illustration, suppose consumption expenditure is linearly related to income and that in wartime there is a downward shift in the function. Our hypothesis then is

$$C = \alpha_1 + \beta Y \qquad \text{wartime} \tag{8-48a}$$
$$C = \alpha_2 + \beta Y \qquad \text{peacetime} \tag{8-48b}$$

where $\alpha_2 > \alpha_1$.

These relations might be estimated in a straightforward fashion by fitting (8-48*a*) to wartime data and (8-48*b*) to peacetime data. However, since we are making the assumption that the marginal propensity to consume, β, is the same in each period, a more efficient procedure for estimating β would be to pool the data from both periods. This may be achieved by combining (8-48*a*) and (8-48*b*) into a single relation

$$C = \alpha_1 X_1 + \alpha_2 X_2 + \beta Y \tag{8-49}$$

where the X's are dummy variables such that

$$X_1 = \begin{cases} 1 & \text{in each wartime year} \\ 0 & \text{in each peacetime year} \end{cases}$$

and

$$X_2 = \begin{cases} 0 & \text{in each wartime year} \\ 1 & \text{in each peacetime year} \end{cases}$$

The coefficient of X_1 in the regression of C on X_1, X_2, and Y is then

[1] Nerlove, *op. cit.* See also Nerlove, *The Dynamics of Supply: Estimation of Farmers' Response to Price*, Johns Hopkins, Baltimore, 1958.

[2] I have been greatly helped in the preparation of this section by some mimeographed notes of Professor A. S. Goldberger.

the estimate of the wartime intercept, the coefficient of X_2 is the estimated peacetime intercept, and the coefficient of Y is estimated from all the data on C and Y.

Equation (8-49) contains no intercept term. If one attempts to estimate the parameters of that relation by using a conventional computing program, whether for desk or electronic calculator, in which an intercept term is automatically computed, the estimation procedure breaks down since the appropriate matrix cannot be inverted. If we assume m wartime followed by n peacetime years, the matrix of squares and cross products is

$$\begin{bmatrix} m+n & m & n & \sum_{i=1}^{m+n} Y_i \\ m & m & 0 & \sum_{i=1}^{m} Y_i \\ n & 0 & n & \sum_{i=m+1}^{m+n} Y_i \\ \sum_{i=1}^{m+n} Y_i & \sum_{i=1}^{m} Y_i & \sum_{i=m+1}^{m+n} Y_i & \sum_{i=1}^{m+n} Y_i^2 \end{bmatrix}$$

The first column in this matrix is the sum of the second and third, and the matrix is thus singular. A conventional computing program may, however, be used simply by dropping *one* of the dummy variables. For example, we may write an alternative form of (8-49) as

$$C = \gamma_1 + \gamma_2 X_2 + \beta Y \tag{8-50}$$

where $$X_2 = \begin{cases} 0 & \text{in each wartime year} \\ 1 & \text{in each peacetime year} \end{cases}$$

This gives the wartime consumption function as

$$C = \gamma_1 + \beta Y$$

and the peacetime function as

$$C = (\gamma_1 + \gamma_2) + \beta Y$$

Comparison with (8-48*a*) and (8-48*b*) shows that

$$\gamma_1 = \alpha_1 \qquad \text{and} \qquad \gamma_2 = \alpha_2 - \alpha_1 \tag{8-51}$$

If we wish to incorporate an assumption that the marginal propensity to consume also varies with the period, we may write

$$C = \gamma_1 + \gamma_2 X_2 + \beta_1 Y + \beta_2 Z \tag{8-52}$$

where $Z = X_2 Y$

and $$X_2 = \begin{cases} 0 & \text{in each wartime year} \\ 1 & \text{in each peacetime year} \end{cases}$$

This gives the wartime function as

$$C = \gamma_1 + \beta_1 Y$$

and the peacetime function as

$$C = (\gamma_1 + \gamma_2) + (\beta_1 + \beta_2) Y$$

The above relations contain dummy variables and conventional quantitative variables on the right-hand side. It is also quite feasible to have nothing but dummy variables on the right-hand

TABLE 8-3

Educational level	Sex	X_1	X_2	X_3	X_4	X_5	X_6
I	I	1	0	0	0	0	0
I	II	1	0	0	1	0	0
II	I	1	1	0	0	0	0
II	II	1	1	0	1	1	0
III	I	1	0	1	0	0	0
III	II	1	0	1	1	0	1

side. Suppose, for example, that we regard a dependent variable Y, the number of hours in a year spent in reading nonfiction, as dependent on two qualitative variables, namely, sex and educational attainment. Sex is represented by a dummy variable with two levels, and if we postulate three levels of educational attainment, there are then six possible combinations of dummy variables and our postulated relationship is

$$Y = \beta_1 X_1 + \beta_2 X_2 + \cdots + \beta_6 X_6 + u \tag{8-53}$$

where the X's are defined in Table 8-3.

If we use the symbol $E(Y|\text{II}, \text{I})$ to indicate the expected value of Y, given educational level II and sex classification I, we see from

Table 8-3 and relation (8-53) that

$$
\begin{aligned}
E(Y|\mathrm{I,I}) &= \beta_1 \\
E(Y|\mathrm{I,II}) &= \beta_1 + \beta_4 \\
E(Y|\mathrm{II,I}) &= \beta_1 + \beta_2 \\
E(Y|\mathrm{II,II}) &= \beta_1 + \beta_2 + \beta_4 + \beta_5 \\
E(Y|\mathrm{III,I}) &= \beta_1 + \beta_3 \\
E(Y|\mathrm{III,II}) &= \beta_1 + \beta_3 + \beta_4 + \beta_6
\end{aligned}
$$

This scheme allows for interaction effects. Thus the difference between the sexes for people of educational level I is β_4; for people of educational level II, it is $\beta_4 + \beta_5$; and for people at level III, it is $\beta_4 + \beta_6$. Similarly, for people of sex I, the differential effect of educational level II compared with I is β_2; of III compared with I, β_3; and of III compared with II, $\beta_3 - \beta_2$. For people of sex II, these same three differential effects are, respectively, $\beta_2 + \beta_5$, $\beta_3 + \beta_6$, and $\beta_3 + \beta_6 - \beta_2 - \beta_5$.

So far our dummy variables, taking on values of zero and unity, have been confined to the right-hand side of the relationship, but there is no reason why the dependent variable itself might not have this form. For example, a person owns a car or does not, he has a mortgage on his home or he does not, and so forth. In all such cases the dependent variable takes on only two values, so that we may use unity to indicate the occurrence of the event and zero to indicate its nonoccurrence. If we run a multiple regression of such a dependent variable Y on several explanatory variables X, then we may interpret the calculated value of Y, for any given X, as an estimate of the *conditional* probability of Y, given X. The most extensive application of this approach in econometrics is due to Guy H. Orcutt and his associates at the Social Systems Research Institute of the University of Wisconsin.[1] The work of the Institute is concerned with the integration of sociological and other variables with the more orthodox economic variables in the study of the dynamics of socioeconomic systems, and since many of these variables, whether explanatory or dependent, are of qualitative form, the use of dummy variables with conventional regression analysis is a natural development.

In a study of the mortgage-debt holdings of United States spending units, Orcutt and Rivlin have split the problem into two parts.

[1] See Guy H. Orcutt, Martin Greenberger, John Korbel, and Alice M. Rivlin, *Microanalysis of Socioeconomic Systems: A Simulation Study*, Harper & Row, New York, 1961.

First they develop a prediction equation for the *probability* that a spending unit has mortgage debt, and then for spending units with a nonzero mortgage debt they develop a prediction equation for the *amount* of mortgage debt.[1] The first equation, based on data from the Survey of Consumer Finances, is

$$\hat{Y}_1 = -0.08 + F_{1.1} + F_{1.2} + F_{1.3} + F_{1.4}$$

where $\hat{Y}_1$ is the predicted probability that a spending unit will hold mortgage debt, and the values of functions $F_{1.1}$, $F_{1.2}$, etc., are obtained from the following tables.

$F_{1.1}$ (marital status)		$F_{1.2}$ (age of head)	
Marital status	$F_{1.1}$	Age of head	$F_{1.2}$
Unmarried	0	18–20	0
1 year	0.07	21–24	−0.02
2 years	0.15	25–29	0.09
3 years	0.19	30–34	0.16
4 years	0.27	35–39	0.25
5–9 years	0.31	40–44	0.22
10–20 years	0.25	45–49	0.24
Over 20 years	0.14	50–54	0.16
		55–59	0.15
		60–64	0.12
		65+	0.07

$F_{1.3}$ (education)		$F_{1.4}$ (race)	
Education of head	$F_{1.3}$	Race of head	$F_{1.4}$
None	0	White	0
Grammar	0.02	Negro	−0.10
Some high school	0.05	Other	−0.14
High school degree	0.08		
Some college	0.12		
College degree	0.13		

Thus the estimated probability that a spending unit headed by a 32-year-old Negro with some high school education and married for

[1] *Ibid.*, chap. 12.

3 years will have mortgage debt is

$$\hat{Y}_1 = -0.08 + 0.19 + 0.16 + 0.05 - 0.10$$
$$= 0.22$$

For units with a nonzero mortgage debt, the prediction equation for the amount of mortgage debt is

$$\hat{Y}_2 = 3{,}040 + F_{2.1} + F_{2.2} + F_{2.3} + F_{2.4}$$

where the F functions are now obtained from the following tables.

$F_{2\cdot1}$ (marital status)		$F_{2\cdot2}$ (age of head)	
Marital status	$F_{2\cdot1}$	Age of head	$F_{2\cdot2}$
Unmarried	0	18–20	0
1 year	4,550	21–24	526
2 years	1,380	25–29	1,290
3 years	1,530	30–34	1,560
4 years	167	35–39	1,200
5–9 years	49	40–44	964
10–20 years	744	45–49	134
Over 20 years	215	50–54	166
		55–59	−1,270
		60–64	−1,140
		65+	−1,000

$F_{2\cdot3}$ (education)		$F_{2\cdot4}$ (race)	
Education	$F_{2\cdot3}$	Race	$F_{2\cdot4}$
None	0	White	0
Grammar	835	Negro	−1,040
Some high school	1,190	Other	−1,010
High school degree	1,980		
Some college	3,610		
College degree	4,930		

Thus the expected amount of mortgage debt for the same unit as before is

$$\hat{Y}_2 = 3{,}040 + 1{,}530 + 1{,}560 + 1{,}190 - 1{,}040$$
$$= \$6{,}280$$

The basic feature of the second step in this analysis is the absence of any assumption about a precise functional form for the relationship. In both steps the application of least-squares regression corresponds to the estimation of cell means, where the cells are defined by the specified steps in the explanatory variables. For example, for the marital-status variable we use seven dummy variables,

$$X_1 = \begin{cases} 1 & \text{if duration is 1 year} \\ 0 & \text{if duration is not 1 year} \end{cases}$$

$$X_2 = \begin{cases} 1 & \text{if duration is 2 years} \\ 0 & \text{if duration is not 2 years} \end{cases}$$

$$\vdots$$

$$X_7 = \begin{cases} 1 & \text{if duration is over 20 years} \\ 0 & \text{if duration is not over 20 years} \end{cases}$$

Dummy variables are also used to represent the other explanatory variables, and when a regression of Y on all dummy variables is run, the least-squares coefficients of the dummy variables are simply the cell means, which are tabulated in the above functions. The above schemes assume additivity. This is not, of course, necessary, since the dummy-variable approach can be extended to incorporate interaction effects, but the approach does require extensive survey observations if sufficiently fine subdivisions are to be made for the explanatory variables and still leave sufficient observations in each cell to provide reliable estimates of the mean values.

Goldberger has shown that one difficulty with applying classical least squares where Y is dichotomous is that the assumption of homoscedastic disturbances is untenable. Writing the X observations at time t as $\mathbf{X}'$, that is, the tth row of $\mathbf{X}$, we have

$$u_t = Y_t - \mathbf{X}_t'\boldsymbol{\beta} \tag{8-54}$$

Since Y_t is either 0 or 1, u_t must be either $-\mathbf{X}_t'\boldsymbol{\beta}$ or $1 - \mathbf{X}_t'\boldsymbol{\beta}$, and if $E(u_t) = 0$, the distribution of u_t, given $\mathbf{X}_t$, is

u_t	$p(u_t)$
$-\mathbf{X}_t'\boldsymbol{\beta}$	$1 - \mathbf{X}_t'\boldsymbol{\beta}$
$1 - \mathbf{X}_t'\boldsymbol{\beta}$	$\mathbf{X}_t'\boldsymbol{\beta}$

from which it may be seen that the variance of u_t is

$$\text{var}(u_t) = E(u_t^2) = (\mathbf{X}_t'\boldsymbol{\beta})(1 - \mathbf{X}_t'\boldsymbol{\beta}) \tag{8-55}$$

The variance-covariance matrix is easily seen to be

$$E(\mathbf{uu}') = \begin{bmatrix} \mathbf{X}_1'\boldsymbol{\beta}(1 - \mathbf{X}_1'\boldsymbol{\beta}) & 0 & 0 & \cdots & 0 \\ 0 & \mathbf{X}_2'\boldsymbol{\beta}(1 - \mathbf{X}_2'\boldsymbol{\beta}) & 0 & \cdots & 0 \\ \cdot & & & & \cdot \\ \cdot & & & & \cdot \\ \cdot & & & & \cdot \\ 0 & 0 & 0 & \cdots & \mathbf{X}_n'\boldsymbol{\beta}(1 - \mathbf{X}_n'\boldsymbol{\beta}) \end{bmatrix} \tag{8-56}$$

so that best linear unbiased estimators would be obtained by using this matrix in (8-11). Since $\boldsymbol{\beta}$ is unknown, Goldberger has suggested a two-stage procedure, which is to obtain conventional least-squares estimates of $\boldsymbol{\beta}$, insert these in (8-56), and use the resultant matrix to obtain the generalized estimate given by (8-11).

References

On multicollinearity, see

1. T. Haavelmo: "Remarks on Frisch's Confluence Analysis and Its Use in Econometrics," chap. 5, p. 260, in T. Koopmans (ed.), *Statistical Inference in Dynamic Economic Models,* Wiley, New York, 1950.
2. J. R. N. Stone: "The Analysis of Market Demand," *J. Royal Statist. Soc.*, vol. 108, pp. 287–382, 1945.
3. R. Frisch: *Statistical Confluence Analysis by Means of Complete Regression Systems,* University Economics Institute, Oslo, 1934.

On the pooling of time-series and cross-section data, see

4. J. Tobin: "A Statistical Demand Function for Food in the U.S.A.," *J. Royal Statist. Soc.*, ser. A, vol. 113, pp. 113–141, 1950.
5. J. R. N. Stone: *The Measurement of Consumers' Expenditure and Behaviour in the United Kingdom, 1920–1938,* Cambridge, London, 1954.
6. H. Wold and L. Jureen: *Demand Analysis,* Wiley, New York, 1953.

For a critical view, see

7. J. Meyer and E. Kuh: "How Extraneous Are Extraneous Estimates?" *Rev. Economics and Statistics,* vol. 39, pp. 380–393, 1957.
8. E. Kuh: "The Validity of Cross-sectionally Estimated Behavior Equations in Time Series Applications," *Econometrica,* vol. 27, pp. 197–214, 1959.

On lagged variables, see

9. Tjalling C. Koopmans (ed.): *Statistical Inference in Dynamic Economic Models,* Cowles Commission Monograph 10, Wiley, New York, 1950, chap. 7, by L. Hurwicz, "Prediction and Least Squares," pp. 266–300, and chap. 15, by L. Hurwicz, "Least Squares Bias in Time Series," pp. 365–383.

10. G. H. Orcutt and D. Cochrane: "A Sampling Study of the Merits of Autoregressive and Reduced Form Transformations in Regression Analysis," *J. Am. Statist. Assoc.*, vol. 44, pp. 356–372, 1949.
11. L. M. Koyck: *Distributed Lags and Investment Analysis*, North-Holland Publishing Company, Amsterdam, 1954.
12. Marc Nerlove: *Distributed Lags and Demand Analysis for Agricultural and Other Commodities*, Agriculture Handbook 141, U.S. Department of Agriculture, 1958.
13. Marc Nerlove: *The Dynamics of Supply: Estimation of Farmers' Response to Price*, Johns Hopkins, Baltimore, 1958.
14. L. R. Klein: "The Estimation of Distributed Lags," *Econometrica*, vol. 26, no. 4, pp. 553–565, October, 1958.
15. E. Malinvaud: "The Estimation of Distributed Lags: A Comment," *Econometrica*, vol. 29, no. 3, pp. 430–433, July, 1961.
16. Z. Griliches: "A Note on Serial Correlation Bias in Estimates of Distributed Lags," *Econometrica*, vol. 29, pp. 65–73.

On dummy variables, see

17. D. B. Suits: "Use of Dummy Variables in Regression Equations," *J. Am. Statist. Assoc.*, vol. 52, pp. 548–551, 1957.
18. G. H. Orcutt, Martin Greenberger, John Korbel, and Alice M. Rivlin: *Microanalysis of Socioeconomic Systems: A Simulation Study*, Harper & Row, New York, 1961,

and for an application of dummy variables to incorporate seasonal shifts in the relations of an econometric model,

19. L. R. Klein, R. J. Ball, A. Hazelwood, and P. Vandome: *An Econometric Model of the United Kingdom*, Blackwell, Oxford, 1961.

Another possible breakdown of the linear regression model occurs when the dependent variable has a lower or upper limit and takes on this limiting value for a substantial number of the sample observations. At a lower (upper) limit negative (positive) deviations from the expected limiting value are impossible, contrary to the assumptions of the normal model. An estimation procedure for such cases, which is a hybrid of probit and multiple-regression analysis, has been suggested in

20. J. Tobin: "Estimation of Relationships for Limited Dependent Variables," *Econometrica*, vol. 26, pp. 24–36, 1958.

A generalization of Tobin's method is given in

21. R. N. Rosett: "A Statistical Model of Friction in Economics," *Econometrica*, vol. 27, pp. 263–267, 1959.

In a broad sense all the topics discussed in Chaps. 6 to 8 are specification errors, in which one or more of the assumptions of the linear normal regression model are incorrect. The term specification error has come to be used, however, for the situation where the true hypothesis is $\mathbf{Y} = \mathbf{X}\boldsymbol{\beta} + \mathbf{u}$, but we mistakenly work with $\mathbf{Y} = \bar{\mathbf{X}}\bar{\boldsymbol{\beta}} + \bar{\mathbf{u}}$. For example, we may leave out variables which should be included, or vice versa, or we may represent a properly included variable by inaccurate measurements. For a general treatment of such problems see

22. H. Theil: "Specification Errors and the Estimation of Economic Relationships," *Review Intern. Statist. Inst.*, vol. 25, pp. 41–51, 1957.

23. H. Theil: *Economic Forecasts and Policy*, 2d ed., North-Holland Publishing Company, Amsterdam, 1961, pp. 211–216, 326–334.

9

Simultaneous-equation Problems: I

9-1. Simultaneous-equation Systems

So far our interest has centered upon estimation and prediction problems for a single equation. Now we must extend the analysis in two respects. First, our interest may still center upon a single equation, but we now take explicit account of the *system* of relations in which our equation is embedded and ask to what extent the simultaneous nature of economic relations invalidates the single-equation procedures described in earlier chapters. Second, we must recognize that in many instances the problem may be to estimate all the parameters in a model and to make predictions from the complete model. Should we then apply our previous single-equation techniques to each relation in the model seriatim? Are there alternative techniques, whether for single equations or complete systems? These are the questions to which we now turn, but to obtain a simple introduction to the major topics, let us postulate a very simple two-equation model.

Consider an income-determination model consisting of a consumption function and an income identity, namely,

$$C_t = \alpha + \beta Y_t + u_t \tag{9-1}$$

$$Y_t = C_t + Z_t \tag{9-2}$$

where C = consumption expenditure
Y = income
Z = nonconsumption expenditure
u = a stochastic disturbance term
t = time period

In this two-equation model Z is assumed to be a set of numbers determined outside the model. For example, Z may be determined by public authorities in a manner independently of C and Y. We then classify C and Y as *endogenous* variables, that is, variables whose values are determined by the simultaneous interaction of the relations in the model, and Z as an *exogenous* variable, that is, one whose value is determined outside the model.

Alternatively, if we think that nonconsumption expenditure Z is influenced by recent changes in the level of income and by the rate of interest r, we may extend the model to include a third relation,

$$Z_t = \gamma(Y_{t-1} - Y_{t-2}) + \delta r_t + v_t$$

If r_t is regarded as an exogenous variable, we now have a model with three relations in the three endogenous variables C, Y, and Z. In general, one must specify as many relations in a model as one has endogenous variables. The classification into endogenous and exogenous is a relative one, depending upon the nature and extent of the system being studied and the purpose for which the model is being built.

To simplify the statistical exposition, we regard Z as exogenous and return to the two-equation system (9-1) and (9-2). Let us specify the following properties of the disturbance term u.

$$E(u_t) = 0 \qquad \text{for all } t \tag{9-3a}$$

$$E(u_t u_{t+s}) = \begin{cases} 0 & \text{for } s \neq 0 \text{ and for all } t \\ \sigma^2 & \text{for } s = 0 \text{ and for all } t \end{cases} \tag{9-3b}$$

Z and u are independent, which will be satisfied if either Z is a set of fixed numbers or if Z is a random variable distributed independently of u (9-3c)

If our problem is to obtain "good" estimates of the parameters of the consumption function (9-1), we may consider first of all applying least squares to C and Y in (9-1). Assumptions (9-3*a*) and (9-3*b*) have removed the problems of heteroscedasticity and autocorrelation. For the valid application of simple least squares there remains only the question of the independence of u and Y. Substituting (9-1) in (9-2) gives

$$Y_t = \alpha + \beta Y_t + Z_t + u_t$$

that is,

$$Y_t = \frac{\alpha}{1-\beta} + \frac{1}{1-\beta} Z_t + \frac{u_t}{1-\beta}$$

so that Y_t is seen in general to be influenced by u_t.

$$E(Y_t) = \frac{\alpha}{1-\beta} + \frac{1}{1-\beta} Z_t$$

and

$$E\{u_t[Y_t - E(Y_t)]\} = \frac{1}{1-\beta} E(u_t^2) \neq 0$$

The disturbance term and the explanatory variable in the consumption equation are thus correlated, and as in the error-in-variables case in Chap. 6, the direct application of least squares to (9-1) will not yield unbiased estimates of α and β. This is a bias for a finite sample size, but direct-least-squares estimates are also inconsistent; that is, a bias persists even for infinitely large samples.

Defining second-order moments

$$m_{CY} = \frac{1}{n} \sum_{t=1}^{n} (C_t - \bar{C})(Y_t - \bar{Y})$$

the least-squares estimators of α and β in (9-1) are seen in Chap. 1 to be

$$\hat{\beta} = \frac{m_{CY}}{m_{YY}} \qquad \text{and} \qquad \hat{\alpha} = \frac{m_{YY}\bar{C} - m_{CY}\bar{Y}}{m_{YY}}$$

Solving the pair of equations (9-1) and (9-2) for the endogenous variables gives

$$C_t = \frac{\beta}{1-\beta} Z_t + \frac{\alpha}{1-\beta} + \frac{u_t}{1-\beta} \tag{9-4}$$

$$Y_t = \frac{1}{1-\beta} Z_t + \frac{\alpha}{1-\beta} + \frac{u_t}{1-\beta} \tag{9-5}$$

Averaging these equations over the sample observations then yields the following deviations:

$$C_t - \bar{C} = \frac{\beta}{1-\beta}(Z_t - \bar{Z}) + \frac{1}{1-\beta}(u_t - \bar{u})$$

$$Y_t - \bar{Y} = \frac{1}{1-\beta}(Z_t - \bar{Z}) + \frac{1}{1-\beta}(u_t - \bar{u})$$

so that

$$m_{CY} = \frac{\beta}{(1-\beta)^2} m_{ZZ} + \frac{1+\beta}{(1-\beta)^2} m_{Zu} + \frac{1}{(1-\beta)^2} m_{uu}$$

$$m_{YY} = \frac{1}{(1-\beta)^2} m_{ZZ} + \frac{2}{(1-\beta)^2} m_{Zu} + \frac{1}{(1-\beta)^2} m_{uu}$$

which gives

$$\hat{\beta} = \frac{\beta m_{ZZ} + (1+\beta) m_{Zu} + m_{uu}}{m_{ZZ} + 2m_{Zu} + m_{uu}}$$

By assumption as $n \to \infty$, $m_{Zu} \to 0$, $m_{uu} \to \sigma^2$, and we can let m_{ZZ} tend to some constant $\bar{m}_{ZZ}$. Thus[1]

$$\begin{aligned} \underset{n\to\infty}{\text{plim}}\ \hat{\beta} &= \frac{\beta \bar{m}_{ZZ} + \sigma^2}{\bar{m}_{ZZ} + \sigma^2} \\ &= \beta + \frac{(1-\beta)\sigma^2/\bar{m}_{ZZ}}{1 + \sigma^2/\bar{m}_{ZZ}} \end{aligned}$$

So long as $0 < \beta < 1$, the second term on the right-hand side of this expression is positive. Thus

$$\underset{n\to\infty}{\text{plim}}\ \hat{\beta} > \beta \qquad 0 < \beta < 1$$

that is, the least-squares estimate of the slope is biased *upward*, and this bias cannot be eliminated by increasing the sample size.

Since the trouble is due to correlation between u and Y in (9-1), it is natural to look for alternative estimation methods which avoid this difficulty. One such method is based on the relations (9-4) and (9-5). These two equations are an alternative way of expressing the model embodied in (9-1) and (9-2), and are known as the *reduced form* of the model. The basic characteristic of the reduced form is that the original system has been solved to express the current values of the endogenous variables as functions of all the other variables in the system, so that each equation of the reduced form contains only one current endogenous variable.

By the assumptions made in (9-3), least squares may be applied directly to estimate the coefficients of the reduced-form equations (9-4) and (9-5). Thus

$$\frac{m_{CZ}}{m_{ZZ}} = \text{best linear unbiased estimator of } \frac{\beta}{1-\beta} \tag{9-6}$$

$$\frac{m_{YZ}}{m_{ZZ}} = \text{best linear unbiased estimator of } \frac{1}{1-\beta} \tag{9-7}$$

$$\frac{m_{ZZ}\bar{C} - m_{CZ}\bar{Z}}{m_{ZZ}} = \text{best linear unbiased estimator of } \frac{\alpha}{1-\beta} \tag{9-8}$$

$$\frac{m_{ZZ}\bar{Y} - m_{YZ}\bar{Z}}{m_{ZZ}} = \text{best linear unbiased estimator of } \frac{\alpha}{1-\beta} \tag{9-9}$$

Either (9-6) or (9-7) will yield an estimator of β, (β^*), and given

[1] This result uses the theorem that the probability limit of a rational function of random variables is the rational function of the probability limits of the variables. See H. Cramer, *Mathematical Methods of Statistics*, Princeton University Press, Princeton, N.J., 1946, pp. 254–255.

that, (9-8) or (9-9) will yield an estimator of α, (α^*). From (9-6)

$$\beta^* = \frac{m_{CZ}}{m_{ZZ} + m_{CZ}}$$

But since

$$Y = C + Z$$
$$y = c + z$$

where the lowercase letters indicate deviations from means, and so

$$m_{YZ} = m_{CZ} + m_{ZZ}$$

Thus

$$\beta^* = \frac{m_{CZ}}{m_{YZ}} \tag{9-10}$$

Likewise, from (9-7),

$$\beta^* = \frac{m_{YZ} - m_{ZZ}}{m_{YZ}} = \frac{m_{CZ}}{m_{YZ}}$$

so that the two equations yield identical estimators of β. Likewise, (9-8) and (9-9) yield identical estimators of α, namely,

$$\alpha^* = \frac{m_{ZZ}\bar{C} - m_{CZ}\bar{Z}}{m_{YZ}} \tag{9-11}$$

The estimators (9-10) and (9-11), though formed from unbiased estimators of the reduced-form parameters, will not themselves be unbiased estimators of the *structural* parameters α and β.[1] They will, however, be consistent estimators. For example, it can easily be shown from (9-4) and (9-5) that β^*, as defined in (9-10), gives

$$\beta^* = \frac{m_{CZ}}{m_{YZ}} = \frac{\beta m_{ZZ} + m_{Zu}}{m_{ZZ} + m_{Zu}} \tag{9-12}$$

Since $m_{Zu} \to 0$ as $n \to \infty$,

$$\operatorname*{plim}_{n\to\infty} \beta^* = \beta \tag{9-13}$$

To establish the bias for a finite sample size we should have to evaluate

$$E(\beta^*) = E\left(\frac{\beta + m_{Zu}/m_{ZZ}}{1 + m_{Zu}/m_{ZZ}}\right)$$

Let us take Z as a set of constants so that m_{ZZ} is constant. Because of the assumptions about u, $E(m_{Zu}) = 0$, for any given sample size, but this result is not sufficient to make β^* an unbiased estimator. For example, let us assume that the u values are such as to produce

[1] Structural parameters refer to the parameters of the original model (or system) as exemplified by (9-1) and (9-2).

the values of m_{Zu}/m_{ZZ}, with the associated probabilities shown in Table 9-1. These satisfy the condition $E(m_{Zu}) = 0$. Assuming the true value of β to be 0.5 and calculating the estimates β^* from (9-12), we see that $E(\beta^*)$ is 0.4870, which displays a downward bias.

The method employed in the above approach is that of *indirect least squares;* that is, simple least squares is applied to find estimates of the parameters of the reduced form, and from these, in

TABLE 9-1

$\dfrac{m_{Zu}}{m_{ZZ}}$	Probability	β^*
−0.2	0.25	$3/8 = 0.3750$
−0.1	0.25	$4/9 = 0.4444$
0.1	0.25	$6/11 = 0.5454$
0.2	0.25	$7/12 = 0.5833$
		$E(\beta^*) = 0.4870$

turn, estimates of the structural parameters are obtained. As we shall see below, this method can be applied only in certain special circumstances.

Two-stage Least Squares. The fundamental difficulty in this model, as we have seen, is the correlation between the disturbance term u and the explanatory variable Y in the consumption relation (9-1). Indirect least squares provides one method of estimation which is sometimes feasible. Two-stage least squares provides a method of more general applicability. A fuller description of the approach will be given below.[1] The objective here is to provide a simple introduction to the basic idea. This idea is to "purge" the explanatory variable Y of the stochastic component associated with the disturbance term u. This may be attempted by taking the least-squares regression of Y on the only exogenous variable in the system, namely, Z, and then replacing Y in the original relation by its estimated value in terms of Z and applying least squares to this reformulated relation. The first least-squares step is thus to compute

$$Y = \hat{\pi}_1 + \hat{\pi}_2 Z + e \tag{9-14}$$

where

$$\hat{\pi}_2 = \frac{m_{YZ}}{m_{ZZ}}$$

and

$$\hat{\pi}_1 = \bar{Y} - \hat{\pi}_2 \bar{Z} \tag{9-15}$$

[1] See pp. 258–260.

The estimated Y values are given by

$$\hat{Y} = \hat{\pi}_1 + \hat{\pi}_2 Z \tag{9-16}$$

In the second step we now substitute these $\hat{Y}$ values in (9-1) to give

$$C = \alpha + \beta(\hat{Y}) + (u + \beta e) \tag{9-17}$$

In this reformulation of (9-1), $\hat{Y}$ is an exact function of Z, which is uncorrelated with u; it is also a property of the least-squares approach that in (9-14) e is uncorrelated with Z; thus $\hat{Y}$ is uncorrelated with the composite disturbance in (9-17). The second step is now completed by applying least squares directly to (9-17) to obtain estimates of α and β. Thus, for example,

$$\hat{\beta} = \frac{m_{C\hat{Y}}}{m_{\hat{Y}\hat{Y}}}$$

From (9-14) $\hat{y} = \hat{\pi}_2 z$, where the lowercase letters, as usual, indicate deviations from arithmetic means. Hence

$$m_{C\hat{Y}} = \hat{\pi}_2 m_{CZ}$$

and

$$m_{\hat{Y}\hat{Y}} = \hat{\pi}_2{}^2 m_{ZZ}$$

therefore

$$\hat{\beta} = \frac{m_{CZ}}{\hat{\pi}_2 m_{ZZ}}$$

$$= \frac{m_{CZ}}{m_{YZ}} \qquad \text{using (9-15)}$$

which is seen to be identical with the indirect-least-squares estimate in (9-10). It then follows directly that the least-squares estimate of α in (9-17) is identical with the indirect-least-squares estimate in (9-11).

Least-variance Ratio. A third approach to the estimation of the parameters of the consumption relation (9-1) may be obtained by means of the least-variance-ratio principle. The specification of the model implies as in (9-1) that consumption is directly determined by income and that nonconsumption expenditure Z does not enter the consumption relation *in addition to* income Y. Thus if we compare

$$C = \alpha + \beta Y + u \tag{9-18a}$$

$$C = \alpha + \beta Y + \gamma Z + v \tag{9-18b}$$

the force of the specification is that $\gamma = 0$. In any finite sample, however, the inclusion of Z as an explanatory variable in addition to Y will, in general, yield a nonzero coefficient for Z and a smaller residual variance for the second of the above relations compared with the first. The least-variance-ratio principle asserts that the estimators of the parameters α and β should be chosen to minimize the ratio of the residual variance of (9-18*a*) to that of (9-18*b*).

Define

$$C^* = C - (\alpha^* + \beta^* Y) \tag{9-19}$$

where α^* and β^* denote least-variance-ratio estimators. Taking means over the sample observations gives

$$c^* = c - \beta^* y \tag{9-20}$$

The residual sum of squares from (9-18*a*) is then Σc^{*2}. Using the definition of C^*, relation (9-18*b*) may be regarded as a relation between C^* and Z. Since Z is an exogenous variable, least squares is appropriate for this relation and the residual sum of squares from (9-18*b*) is then

$$\Sigma(c^* - \hat{\gamma}z)^2$$

where $\hat{\gamma}$ is the least-squares estimator

$$\hat{\gamma} = \frac{\Sigma c^* z}{\Sigma z^2}$$

Hence

$$\Sigma(c^* - \hat{\gamma}z)^2 = \Sigma c^{*2} - \frac{(\Sigma c^* z)^2}{\Sigma z^2}$$

The variance ratio to be minimized is then

$$l = \frac{\Sigma c^{*2}}{\Sigma c^{*2} - (\Sigma c^* z)^2/\Sigma z^2} \tag{9-21}$$

It is clear that in this case the minimum possible value for this ratio is unity and that it will be achieved only when $\Sigma c^* z = 0$. Substitution from (9-20) gives the condition

$$\Sigma(c - \beta^* y)z = 0$$

that is,

$$\beta^* = \frac{m_{CZ}}{m_{YZ}}$$

so that in this simple example all three principles of estimation, namely, indirect least squares, two-stage least squares, and least-variance ratio, yield identical estimators. As we shall see later, this result is due to a rather special feature of this simple model, but the model has introduced some of the basic ideas needed for handling simultaneous-equation problems.

Relations (9-1) and (9-2) are the structural relations of the model, the first being a behavioristic relation embodying a hypothesis about the determination of consumption expenditures and the second being a definitional identity. The model contains two structural relations and two endogenous variables. The structural relations plus the assumptions about stochastic disturbance terms in (9-3*a*) to (9-3*c*) complete the specification of the model. A set of numerical values for the unknown parameters α, β, and σ^2 gives a specific *structure* within the model. Relations (9-4) and (9-5) constitute the reduced form of the model, showing the current values of the endogenous variables as explicit functions of all other variables in the model. The disturbances in the reduced form are seen to be linear functions of the disturbances in the original structural relations. Three estimation principles have been introduced, apart from simple least squares applied to single structural relations. For the example used here, they are seen to give identical results, but this will not in general be true. We have not yet explicitly touched on problems of *identification* apart from the brief discussion in the indirect-least-squares case of the transformation of estimates of the reduced-form coefficients into estimates of the structural parameters. A discussion of the identification problem will show that in cases of underidentification it is impossible to obtain estimates of some or all parameters, in cases of exact identification all three estimating methods give identical results, while in cases of overidentification indirect least squares is impossible but two-stage least squares and least-variance ratio will yield determinate estimates, which will not, however, be identical. We now proceed to a fuller treatment of simultaneous-equation problems by setting up a general linear model and reverting once again to matrix notation.

Let us assume a linear model containing G structural relations. The ith relation at time t may be written

$$\beta_{i1}y_{1t} + \beta_{i2}y_{2t} + \cdots + \beta_{iG}y_{Gt} + \gamma_{i1}x_{1t} + \cdots + \gamma_{iK}x_{Kt} = u_{it} \qquad t = 1, \ldots, n \qquad (9\text{-}22)$$

where the y_{it} denote endogenous variables at time t and every x_{it} is either an exogenous variable or a lagged value of an endogenous variable. These latter two groups are combined to give the class of *predetermined* variables. The model may then be regarded as a theory explaining the determination of the jointly dependent variables y_{it} $(i = 1, \ldots, G; t = 1, \ldots, n)$ in terms of the predetermined variables x_{it} $(i = 1, \ldots, K; t = 1, \ldots, n)$ and the disturbances u_{it} $(i = 1, \ldots, G; t = 1, \ldots, n)$. The theory will in general specify that some of the β, γ coefficients in (9-22) are zero. If it did not, statistical estimation would be impossible since all relations in the model would look alike statistically and one could not distinguish between them. We are also using lowercase letters now to denote the actual variables, and not to indicate deviations from arithmetic means. A constant term in each relation may be allowed for by setting one of the x variables at unity.

The model may then be written in matrix form as

$$\mathbf{B}\mathbf{y}_t + \mathbf{\Gamma}\mathbf{x}_t = \mathbf{u}_t \tag{9-23}$$

where $\mathbf{B}$ = a $G \times G$ matrix of coefficients of current endogenous variables

$\mathbf{\Gamma}$ = a $G \times K$ matrix of coefficients of predetermined variables

$\mathbf{y}_t, \mathbf{x}_t, \mathbf{u}_t$ = column vectors of G, K, and G elements, respectively

$$\mathbf{y}_t = \begin{bmatrix} y_{1t} \\ y_{2t} \\ \cdot \\ \cdot \\ \cdot \\ y_{Gt} \end{bmatrix} \qquad \mathbf{x}_t = \begin{bmatrix} x_{1t} \\ x_{2t} \\ \cdot \\ \cdot \\ \cdot \\ x_{Kt} \end{bmatrix} \qquad \mathbf{u}_t = \begin{bmatrix} u_{1t} \\ u_{2t} \\ \cdot \\ \cdot \\ \cdot \\ u_{Gt} \end{bmatrix}$$

If we assume that the $\mathbf{B}$ matrix is nonsingular, the reduced form of the model may be written

$$\mathbf{y}_t = \mathbf{\Pi}\mathbf{x}_t + \mathbf{v}_t \tag{9-24}$$

where $\mathbf{\Pi}$ = a $G \times K$ matrix of reduced-form coefficients

$\mathbf{v}_t$ = a column vector of G reduced-form disturbances

$$\mathbf{\Pi} = -\mathbf{B}^{-1}\mathbf{\Gamma} \qquad \mathbf{v}_t = \mathbf{B}^{-1}\mathbf{u}_t \tag{9-25}$$

9-2. Identification

Estimation of the parameters of the model (9-23) can proceed only on the basis of assumptions about the probability distribution of the disturbance terms. Let us assume

$$E(\mathbf{u}_t) = \mathbf{0} \qquad \text{for all } t \tag{9-26}$$

and

$$E(\mathbf{u}_t\mathbf{u}_t') = \mathbf{\Phi} = \begin{bmatrix} \sigma_{11} & \sigma_{12} & \cdots & \sigma_{1G} \\ \sigma_{21} & \sigma_{22} & \cdots & \sigma_{2G} \\ \cdot & & & \cdot \\ \cdot & & & \cdot \\ \cdot & & & \cdot \\ \sigma_{G1} & \sigma_{G2} & \cdots & \sigma_{GG} \end{bmatrix} \tag{9-27}$$

where $\mathbf{\Phi}$ is a $G \times G$ symmetric matrix of the variances and covariances of the u_{it}; that is, $\sigma_{ij} = E(u_{it}u_{jt})$ for all t. The absence of any

t subscripts in $\mathbf{\Phi}$ implies that these variances and covariances are constant through time, and notice also that no special assumptions have been made about the off-diagonal terms in $\mathbf{\Phi}$; in other words, the possibility of correlation between the current values of disturbances in different relations is not ruled out. For each identity that the model contains there will be a corresponding row and column of $\mathbf{\Phi}$ consisting only of zeros. Hence the $\mathbf{\Phi}$ matrix will be singular. If the model has been solved initially to eliminate all identities, then we specify that the resultant $\mathbf{\Phi}$ matrix is nonsingular; that is, no disturbance is assumed to be an exact linear function of any other disturbance(s). Let us also assume

$$p(\mathbf{u}_t\mathbf{u}_{t+s}) = p(\mathbf{u}_t)p(\mathbf{u}_{t+s}) \quad \text{for all } t \text{ and, for } s = \pm 1, \pm 2, \ldots \tag{9-28}$$

where $p(\mathbf{u}_t)$ indicates the probability of obtaining the values $u_{1t}, u_{2t}, \ldots, u_{Gt}$. This assumption postulates zero autocorrelations for the disturbance terms.

Referring now to (9-23),

$$\mathbf{B}\mathbf{y}_t + \mathbf{\Gamma}\mathbf{x}_t = \mathbf{u}_t$$

we see that $\mathbf{u}_t$ will be independent of $\mathbf{x}_t, \mathbf{x}_{t-1}, \mathbf{x}_{t-2}$, etc. This is true by assumption for all exogenous variables contained in $\mathbf{x}$, and in the case of predetermined variables such as $\mathbf{y}_{t-1}$, these depend only on the vector $\mathbf{u}_{t-1}$, which by assumption (9-28) is independent of $\mathbf{u}_t$. Hence from (9-23) we can write the probability of $\mathbf{y}_t$ for given $\mathbf{x}_t$ as

$$\begin{aligned} p(\mathbf{y}_t|\mathbf{x}_t) &= p(\mathbf{u}_t|\mathbf{x}_t)\left|\frac{\partial \mathbf{u}_t}{\partial \mathbf{y}_t}\right| \\ &= p(\mathbf{u}_t)\left|\frac{\partial \mathbf{u}_t}{\partial \mathbf{y}_t}\right| \end{aligned} \tag{9-29}$$

where $|\partial\mathbf{u}_t/\partial\mathbf{y}_t|$ indicates the absolute value of the determinant formed from the matrix of partial derivatives

$$\begin{bmatrix} \dfrac{\partial u_{1t}}{\partial y_{1t}} & \dfrac{\partial u_{1t}}{\partial y_{2t}} & \cdots & \dfrac{\partial u_{1t}}{\partial y_{Gt}} \\ \dfrac{\partial u_{2t}}{\partial y_{1t}} & \dfrac{\partial u_{2t}}{\partial y_{2t}} & \cdots & \dfrac{\partial u_{2t}}{\partial y_{Gt}} \\ \vdots & & & \vdots \\ \dfrac{\partial u_{Gt}}{\partial y_{1t}} & \dfrac{\partial u_{Gt}}{\partial y_{2t}} & \cdots & \dfrac{\partial u_{Gt}}{\partial y_{Gt}} \end{bmatrix} \tag{9-30}$$

It can be seen from inspection of relations such as (9-22) that the matrix of partial derivatives defined by (9-30) is merely the coefficient matrix **B**. Hence (9-29) may be written

$$p(\mathbf{y}_t|\mathbf{x}_t) = |\det \mathbf{B}|p(\mathbf{u}_t) \tag{9-31}$$

Using now the assumption of zero autocorrelations made in (9-28), the likelihood of the sample values of the endogenous variables, conditional upon the values of **x**, is given by

$$p(\mathbf{y}_1 \cdots \mathbf{y}_n|\mathbf{x}_1 \cdots \mathbf{x}_n) = |\det \mathbf{B}|^n p(\mathbf{u}_1)p(\mathbf{u}_2) \cdots p(\mathbf{u}_n) \tag{9-32}$$

Now consider multiplying through the system (9-23) by a $G \times G$ nonsingular matrix **A**. This would involve replacing each equation of the original structure by a linear combination of the relations in that structure. The new structure may be written

$$(\mathbf{AB})\mathbf{y}_t + \mathbf{A\Gamma x}_t = \mathbf{w}_t \tag{9-33}$$

where

$$\mathbf{w}_t = \mathbf{Au}_t \tag{9-34}$$

Since the $\mathbf{u}_t$ vectors are assumed to be serially uncorrelated, the $\mathbf{w}_t$ vectors will likewise be serially uncorrelated. The variance-covariance matrix for $\mathbf{w}_t$ is

$$\begin{aligned} E(\mathbf{w}_t\mathbf{w}_t') &= E(\mathbf{Au}_t\mathbf{u}_t'A') \\ &= \mathbf{A\Phi A}' \end{aligned} \tag{9-35}$$

Notice also that

$$\begin{aligned} p(\mathbf{w}_t) &= p(\mathbf{u}_t)\left|\frac{\partial \mathbf{u}_t}{\partial \mathbf{w}_t}\right| \\ &= |\det \mathbf{A}^{-1}|p(\mathbf{u}_t) \end{aligned} \tag{9-36}$$

Hence the conditional likelihood for the $\mathbf{y}_t$ determined from the structure (9-33) in a similar manner to (9-32) above is

$$\begin{aligned} p(\mathbf{y}_1 \cdots \mathbf{y}_n|\mathbf{x}_1 \cdots \mathbf{x}_n) &= |\det (\mathbf{AB})|^n p(\mathbf{w}_1)p(\mathbf{w}_2) \cdots p(\mathbf{w}_n) \\ &= |\det \mathbf{A}|^n|\det \mathbf{B}|^n|\det \mathbf{A}^{-1}|^n p(\mathbf{u}_1)p(\mathbf{u}_2) \cdots p(\mathbf{u}_n) \end{aligned}$$

using (9-36) and the result that det (**AB**) = det **A** det **B**. Thus

$$p(\mathbf{y}_1 \cdots \mathbf{y}_n|\mathbf{x}_1 \cdots \mathbf{x}_n) = |\det \mathbf{B}|^n p(\mathbf{u}_1)p(\mathbf{u}_2) \cdots p(\mathbf{u}_n)$$

since $\det \mathbf{A}^{-1} = 1/\det \mathbf{A}$. This is exactly the same as the likelihood determined for the original structure in (9-32), so that we may say that the two structures (9-23) and (9-33) are *observationally equivalent.*

A special case of (9-33) occurs when we set

$$\mathbf{A} = \mathbf{B}^{-1}$$

so that the transformed structure (9-33) becomes

$$\mathbf{y}_t + \mathbf{B}^{-1}\mathbf{\Gamma x}_t = \mathbf{B}^{-1}\mathbf{u}_t$$

which is the reduced form of the original structure, already defined in (9-24) and (9-25). Now if, in general, we solve the structure (9-33) for its reduced form, we obtain

$$(\mathbf{AB})^{-1}(\mathbf{AB})\mathbf{y}_t + (\mathbf{AB})^{-1}\mathbf{A\Gamma x}_t = (\mathbf{AB})^{-1}\mathbf{Au}_t$$

that is,

$$\mathbf{y}_t + \mathbf{B}^{-1}\mathbf{\Gamma x}_t = \mathbf{B}^{-1}\mathbf{u}_t$$

which is the reduced form of the original structure (9-23). Thus if we postulate a set of structural relations $\mathbf{By}_t + \mathbf{\Gamma x}_t = \mathbf{u}_t$ with reduced form $\mathbf{y}_t + \mathbf{B}^{-1}\mathbf{\Gamma x}_t = \mathbf{B}^{-1}\mathbf{u}_t$, then all structures obtained by premultiplying the original structure by an arbitrary nonsingular matrix of order G will have this same reduced form, and moreover all these structures and the reduced form will be observationally equivalent, in the sense of yielding an identical likelihood function for the endogenous variables.

Identification is defined as the problem of computing the parameters of the structure, which is presumed to have generated the observations on the endogenous variables, from the parameters of the likelihood function. Thus the problem of identification exists quite apart from the sampling problem of obtaining reasonably good estimates of the parameters of the likelihood function. It is logically prior to the estimation problem and would still exist even if our samples were infinitely large. As we have seen above, the likelihood function may be written down in terms of any observationally equivalent structure. In particular, it may be written in terms of the reduced form. Thus

$$p(\mathbf{y}_1, \ldots, \mathbf{y}_n|\mathbf{x}) = p(\mathbf{v}_1)p(\mathbf{v}_2) \cdots p(\mathbf{v}_n)$$

Since $\mathbf{v}_t = \mathbf{y}_t - \mathbf{\Pi x}_t$, the parameters of the likelihood function are simply the elements of the matrix of reduced-form coefficients $\mathbf{\Pi}$ and the elements of the variance-covariance matrix of the reduced-form disturbances $\mathbf{B}^{-1}\mathbf{\Phi}(\mathbf{B}^{-1})'$. Thus the identification problem may be stated as that of deducing the values of the parameters of the structural relations from a knowledge of the reduced-form parameters.

The identification problem for the model as described so far is clearly insoluble. If no restrictions are placed on the **B** and **Γ** matrices, the reduced-form parameters **Π** represent an infinitely large set of structures obtained from the original structure on pre-multiplication by an arbitrary nonsingular matrix **A**. Thus identification may become possible only if certain a priori restrictions are placed on the matrices **B**, **Γ**, and **Φ**. The simplest such restrictions are of a zero-nonzero form, simply specifying that certain elements in **B** and **Γ** are zero. In other words, the specification of the model must needs imply that certain variables do not appear in certain relations. A model in which *all* variables are present in *all* relations is statistically a hopeless proposition. The a priori exclusion of variables, however, is a necessary but, as the following examples will show, not a sufficient condition for identification.

Example i. Consider the model

$$y_{1t} + \beta_{12}y_{2t} + \gamma_{11}x_{1t} = u_{1t} \tag{9-37}$$
$$\beta_{21}y_{1t} + y_{2t} + \gamma_{22}x_{2t} = u_{2t} \tag{9-38}$$

where

$$\mathbf{B} = \begin{bmatrix} 1 & \beta_{12} \\ \beta_{21} & 1 \end{bmatrix} \quad \mathbf{\Gamma} = \begin{bmatrix} \gamma_{11} & 0 \\ 0 & \gamma_{22} \end{bmatrix} \quad \mathbf{\Phi} = \begin{bmatrix} \sigma_{11} & \sigma_{12} \\ \sigma_{12} & \sigma_{22} \end{bmatrix}$$

The reduced form may be written

$$y_{1t} = \pi_{11}x_{1t} + \pi_{12}x_{2t} + v_{1t} \tag{9-39}$$
$$y_{2t} = \pi_{21}x_{1t} + \pi_{22}x_{2t} + v_{2t} \tag{9-40}$$

If we multiply the second equation in the reduced form by β_{12} and add it to the first, we obtain

$$y_{1t} + \beta_{12}y_{2t} = (\pi_{11} + \beta_{12}\pi_{21})x_{1t} + (\pi_{12} + \beta_{12}\pi_{22})x_{2t} + (v_{1t} + \beta_{12}v_{2t}) \tag{9-41}$$

These steps are merely algebraic manipulations of the original system, so if we compare (9-41) with (9-37), the coefficients of all variables must be equal. Thus

$$-\gamma_{11} = \pi_{11} + \beta_{12}\pi_{21} \tag{9-42}$$

and

$$0 = \pi_{12} + \beta_{12}\pi_{22} \tag{9-43}$$

since x_2 does not appear in (9-37). It can also easily be shown, using (9-25), that $v_{1t} + \beta_{12}v_{2t} = u_{1t}$. From (9-43)

$$\beta_{12} = -\frac{\pi_{12}}{\pi_{22}} \tag{9-44}$$

and hence

$$\gamma_{11} = \frac{\pi_{12}\pi_{21} - \pi_{11}\pi_{22}}{\pi_{22}} \tag{9-45}$$

so that the two parameters of (9-37) are obtained uniquely in terms of the elements of **Π**. The parameters of (9-38) may be represented in a similar fashion in terms of the elements of $\mathbf{\Pi}$. Likewise, too, the elements of the variance-covariance matrix of the structural disturbances may be expressed in terms of the variance-covariance matrix of reduced-form disturbances. In general,

$$\mathbf{v}_t = \mathbf{B}^{-1}\mathbf{u}_t$$

Hence $$E(\mathbf{v}_t\mathbf{v}_t') = \mathbf{\Psi} = \mathbf{B}^{-1}\mathbf{\Phi}(\mathbf{B}^{-1})' \tag{9-46}$$

Therefore $$\mathbf{\Phi} = \mathbf{B\Psi B}' \tag{9-47}$$

Now consider premultiplying the pair of equations (9-37), (9-38) by a nonsingular matrix **A** of order 2 to obtain another structure, which is also compatible with the model. In saying that another structure is compatible with, or contained within, the model, we mean that it must not violate any of the assumptions of the model; in this case, x_2 must not appear in the first relation, nor x_1 in the second, and the coefficient of y_1 must be unity in the first relation and that of y_2 unity in the second. Defining

$$\mathbf{A} = \begin{bmatrix} a_{11} & a_{12} \\ a_{21} & a_{22} \end{bmatrix}$$

we then have

$$\mathbf{AB} = \begin{bmatrix} a_{11} + a_{12}\beta_{21} & a_{11}\beta_{12} + a_{12} \\ a_{21} + a_{22}\beta_{21} & a_{21}\beta_{12} + a_{22} \end{bmatrix} \qquad \mathbf{A\Gamma} = \begin{bmatrix} a_{11}\gamma_{11} & a_{12}\gamma_{22} \\ a_{21}\gamma_{11} & a_{22}\gamma_{22} \end{bmatrix}$$

These are the coefficient matrices of the transformed structure, defined, in general, in (9-33) above. Referring to the $\mathbf{A\Gamma}$ matrix, the requirement that x_2 does not appear in the first relation nor x_1 in the second gives the conditions

$$a_{12} = 0 = a_{21}$$

These, in conjunction with the requirements on the coefficients of y_1 and y_2 give

$$a_{11} = 1 = a_{22}$$

Thus the only **A** matrix which will give another structure compatible with the model is the unit matrix; that is, we can proceed directly from the parameters of the reduced form to a *unique* set of structural parameters for the model by formulas (9-44), (9-45), and (9-47). This is an example of *exact identification*, and all the parameters of the model are identified.

Example ii. Now consider the model

$$y_{1t} + \beta_{12}y_{2t} = u_{1t} \tag{9-48}$$
$$\beta_{21}y_{1t} + y_{2t} + \gamma_{21}x_{1t} = u_{2t} \tag{9-49}$$

where the **B** and $\mathbf{\Phi}$ matrices are as defined in Example i but the $\mathbf{\Gamma}$ matrix is now

$$\mathbf{\Gamma} = \begin{bmatrix} 0 \\ \gamma_{21} \end{bmatrix}$$

Premultiplying by an arbitrary **A** of order 2 gives **AB** as in Example i and

$$\mathbf{A\Gamma} = \begin{bmatrix} a_{12}\gamma_{21} \\ a_{22}\gamma_{21} \end{bmatrix}$$

The a priori restrictions on the coefficients of the model then give the conditions

$$\begin{aligned} a_{12}\gamma_{21} &= 0 \qquad \text{therefore } a_{12} = 0 \\ a_{11} + a_{12}\beta_{21} &= 1 \qquad \text{therefore } a_{11} = 1 \\ a_{21}\beta_{12} + a_{22} &= 1 \end{aligned}$$

yielding an A matrix,

$$\mathbf{A} = \begin{bmatrix} 1 & 0 \\ a_{21} & 1 - a_{21}\beta_{12} \end{bmatrix}$$

where a_{21} = an arbitrary element

$a_{22} = 1 - a_{21}\beta_{12}$

There is thus an infinite set of **A** matrices yielding structures compatible with the model, and we have

$$\mathbf{AB} = \begin{bmatrix} 1 & \beta_{12} \\ a_{21}(1 - \beta_{12}\beta_{21}) + \beta_{21} & 1 \end{bmatrix} \quad \text{and} \quad \mathbf{A\Gamma} = \begin{bmatrix} 0 \\ (1 - a_{21}\beta_{12})\gamma_{21} \end{bmatrix}$$

We see that in all these structures the coefficients of the first relation remain unchanged while those of the second vary. We say that the parameters of the first relation are *identified* while those of the second are *unidentified* (or under-identified). To put this same point another way, if we attempt to express the structural parameters in terms of the reduced-form parameters, we find it can be done uniquely for the parameters of the first relation, but not at all for those of the second. From the basic definition in (9-25),

$$-\mathbf{B}^{-1}\mathbf{\Gamma} = \mathbf{\Pi}$$

which gives in this case

$$\frac{-1}{1 - \beta_{12}\beta_{21}} \begin{bmatrix} 1 & -\beta_{12} \\ -\beta_{21} & 1 \end{bmatrix} \begin{bmatrix} 0 \\ \gamma_{21} \end{bmatrix} = \begin{bmatrix} \pi_{11} \\ \pi_{21} \end{bmatrix}$$

that is,

$$\begin{bmatrix} \dfrac{\beta_{12}\gamma_{21}}{\Delta} \\ \dfrac{-\gamma_{21}}{\Delta} \end{bmatrix} = \begin{bmatrix} \pi_{11} \\ \pi_{21} \end{bmatrix} \tag{9-50}$$

where $\Delta = 1 - \beta_{12}\beta_{21}$. From this we obtain directly

$$\beta_{12} = \frac{-\pi_{11}}{\pi_{21}}$$

but there is no means of finding β_{21} and γ_{21}, the parameters of the second relation.

Example iii. Consider

$$y_{1t} + \beta_{12}y_{2t} + \gamma_{11}x_{1t} = u_{1t} \tag{9-51}$$

$$\beta_{21}y_{1t} + y_{2t} + \gamma_{21}x_{1t} = u_{2t} \tag{9-52}$$

where the same exogenous variable appears in both relations. The **AB** matrix is as before, and

$$\mathbf{A\Gamma} = \begin{bmatrix} a_{11}\gamma_{11} + a_{12}\gamma_{21} \\ a_{21}\gamma_{11} + a_{22}\gamma_{21} \end{bmatrix}$$

Since x_1 appears in both relations, the only restrictions on the **A** matrix are those arising from the unit coefficients of y_1 and y_2; that is,

$$\begin{aligned} \alpha_{11} + \alpha_{12}\beta_{21} &= 1 \\ \alpha_{21}\beta_{12} + \alpha_{22} &= 1 \end{aligned}$$

These conditions leave one element in each row of **A** completely arbitrary, and so neither relation remains invariant in different structures. Thus neither relation is identified, and it is impossible to express the structural parameters in terms of the reduced-form parameters, for (9-25) gives

$$\frac{\beta_{12}\gamma_{21} - \gamma_{11}}{\Delta} = \pi_{11}$$
$$\frac{\beta_{21}\gamma_{11} - \gamma_{21}}{\Delta} = \pi_{21}$$

from which none of the four unknown parameters can be obtained.

Example iv

$$y_{1t} + \beta_{12}y_{2t} = u_{1t} \tag{9-53}$$
$$\beta_{21}y_{1t} + y_{2t} + \gamma_{21}x_{1t} + \gamma_{22}x_{2t} = u_{2t} \tag{9-54}$$

The **AΓ** matrix is now

$$\mathbf{A\Gamma} = \begin{bmatrix} \alpha_{12}\gamma_{21} & \alpha_{12}\gamma_{22} \\ \alpha_{22}\gamma_{21} & \alpha_{22}\gamma_{22} \end{bmatrix}$$

Since x_1 and x_2 do not appear in the first relation, we have the condition $\alpha_{12} = 0$. Other restrictions are

$$\alpha_{11} + \alpha_{12}\beta_{21} = 1 \qquad \text{therefore } \alpha_{11} = 1$$
$$\alpha_{21}\beta_{12} + \alpha_{22} = 1$$

The **A** matrix is thus identical with that in Example ii, so that the first relation is identified and the second is not.

If we attempt to express β_{12} in terms of the reduced-form parameters, we have

$$\begin{bmatrix} \dfrac{\beta_{12}\gamma_{21}}{\Delta} & \dfrac{\beta_{12}\gamma_{22}}{\Delta} \\ \dfrac{-\gamma_{21}}{\Delta} & \dfrac{-\gamma_{22}}{\Delta} \end{bmatrix} = \begin{bmatrix} \pi_{11} & \pi_{12} \\ \pi_{21} & \pi_{22} \end{bmatrix} \tag{9-55}$$

so that

$$\beta_{12} = -\frac{\pi_{11}}{\pi_{21}} = -\frac{\pi_{12}}{\pi_{22}} \tag{9-56}$$

In this case the **Π** matrix is seen to be of rank 1 and β_{12} may be expressed in terms of either ratio in (9-56). This is so because, in moving to and fro between structure and reduced form, we have only been performing algebraic manipulations of the system. In *practical* estimation problems, however, we have already seen that a suggested estimation procedure for simultaneous equations, namely, *indirect least squares*, involves obtaining estimates of the reduced-form parameters and from these deriving estimates of the structural parameters. Denoting the estimated reduced-form parameters by

$$\hat{\mathbf{\Pi}} = \begin{bmatrix} \hat{\pi}_{11} & \hat{\pi}_{12} \\ \hat{\pi}_{21} & \hat{\pi}_{22} \end{bmatrix}$$

the application of (9-56) would in general yield two different estimates for β_{12}, according to whether one used the ratio $-\hat{\pi}_{11}/\hat{\pi}_{21}$ or $-\hat{\pi}_{12}/\hat{\pi}_{22}$. These ratios are identical for the *true* reduced-form parameters, but only by accident will they be equal for the *estimated* reduced-form parameters. In other words, the rank of $\hat{\mathbf{\Pi}}$ for this model will in general be 2 while that of $\mathbf{\Pi}$ is 1.

The distinction between Examples ii and iv is that in Example ii the parameter β_{12} is said to be exactly identified while in Example iv it is said to be *overidentified.*

In the examples so far we have paid little attention to the variance-covariance matrices of the structural and reduced-form disturbances. This is because under general assumptions one obtains no help from this quarter in the identification of the coefficients of the variables in the structural relations. However, if we can extend our zero-nonzero restrictions to some of the elements of $\mathbf{\Phi}$, the situation changes.

Example ii*a*. Consider Example ii again:

$$\begin{aligned} y_{1t} + \beta_{12}y_{2t} \qquad\qquad &= u_{1t} \\ \beta_{21}y_{1t} + \quad y_{2t} + \gamma_{21}x_{1t} &= u_{2t} \end{aligned}$$

but now with

$$\mathbf{B} = \begin{bmatrix} 1 & \beta_{12} \\ \beta_{21} & 1 \end{bmatrix} \qquad \mathbf{\Gamma} = \begin{bmatrix} 0 \\ \gamma_{21} \end{bmatrix} \qquad \mathbf{\Phi} = \begin{bmatrix} \sigma_{11} & 0 \\ 0 & \sigma_{22} \end{bmatrix}$$

The contrast with the original specification is that we now postulate the disturbances in the two relations to have zero covariance in the limit $\sigma_{12} = 0$. From the original example β_{12} is identified, and from (9-50) it is expressed in terms of the reduced-form parameters as

$$\beta_{12} = -\frac{\pi_{11}}{\pi_{21}}$$

From the general relation

$$\mathbf{\Phi} = \mathbf{B\Psi B'}$$

between structural and reduced-form variances we have

$$\begin{bmatrix} \sigma_{11} & 0 \\ 0 & \sigma_{22} \end{bmatrix} = \begin{bmatrix} \psi_{11} + 2\psi_{12}\beta_{12} + \psi_{22}\beta_{12}^2 & \psi_{11}\beta_{21} + \psi_{12}(1 + \beta_{12}\beta_{21}) + \psi_{22}\beta_{12} \\ \psi_{11}\beta_{21} + \psi_{12}(1 + \beta_{12}\beta_{21}) + \psi_{22}\beta_{12} & \psi_{11}\beta_{21}^2 + 2\psi_{12}\beta_{21} + \psi_{22} \end{bmatrix}$$

This yields the condition

$$\psi_{11}\beta_{21} + \psi_{12}(1 + \beta_{12}\beta_{21}) + \psi_{22}\beta_{12} = 0$$

Substitution of $-\pi_{11}/\pi_{21}$ for β_{12} in this relation yields β_{21}. Finally, from the second equation in (9-50), γ_{21} can be obtained as

$$\gamma_{21} = -\pi_{21}(1 - \beta_{12}\beta_{21})$$

so that a hitherto unidentified relation becomes identified if it is possible to specify a zero covariance between the disturbance terms. Alternatively, one may show that the conditions specified here imply that the transformation matrix **A** is simply the identity matrix **I**. A similar argument to that used above will also show that the second relation will also be identified if we postulate $\sigma_{22} = k\sigma_{11}$, giving

$$\mathbf{\Phi} = \begin{bmatrix} \sigma_{11} & \sigma_{12} \\ \sigma_{12} & k\sigma_{11} \end{bmatrix}$$

where k is a known constant.

Example iva. If we consider again

$$\begin{aligned} y_{1t} + \beta_{12}y_{2t} \qquad\qquad\qquad\qquad &= u_{1t} \\ \beta_{21}y_{1t} + \quad y_{2t} + \gamma_{21}x_{1t} + \gamma_{22}x_{2t} &= u_{2t} \end{aligned}$$

with the additional assumption that

$$\mathbf{\Phi} = \begin{bmatrix} \sigma_{11} & 0 \\ 0 & \sigma_{22} \end{bmatrix}$$

then β_{12} is identified as before and β_{21} can be obtained as in Example ii*a*. Finally, from (9-55), γ_{21} and γ_{22} can each be expressed in terms of reduced-form parameters, so once again the second relation is identified.

On the basis of the ideas developed in these examples, a general treatment of the identification problem can easily be obtained. Let us make no a priori restrictions on the variance-covariance matrix for the structural disturbances $\mathbf{\Phi}$. Suppose we are then interested in the identifiability of the first relation in the system. This relation may be written

$$\boldsymbol{\beta}_1\mathbf{y}_t + \boldsymbol{\gamma}_1\mathbf{x}_t = u_{1t} \tag{9-57}$$

where $\boldsymbol{\beta}_1$ indicates the first row of **B** and $\boldsymbol{\gamma}_1$ the first row of $\mathbf{\Gamma}$. Premultiplying the reduced form (9-24) by $\boldsymbol{\beta}_1$ gives

$$\boldsymbol{\beta}_1\mathbf{y}_t = \boldsymbol{\beta}_1\mathbf{\Pi}\mathbf{x}_t + \boldsymbol{\beta}_1\mathbf{v}_t \tag{9-58}$$

Now $\quad \boldsymbol{\beta}_1\mathbf{v}_t = \boldsymbol{\beta}_1\mathbf{B}^{-1}\mathbf{u}_t$

$$= [\beta_{11} \quad \cdots \quad \beta_{1G}]\,\frac{1}{|\mathbf{B}|}\begin{bmatrix} b_{11} & b_{21} & \cdots & b_{G1} \\ b_{12} & b_{22} & \cdots & b_{G2} \\ \cdot & & & \cdot \\ \cdot & & & \cdot \\ \cdot & & & \cdot \\ b_{1G} & b_{2G} & \cdots & b_{GG} \end{bmatrix}\begin{bmatrix} u_{1t} \\ u_{2t} \\ \cdot \\ \cdot \\ \cdot \\ u_{Gt} \end{bmatrix}$$

where b_{ij} indicates the co-factor of β_{ij}. Thus, using the result from Chap. 3 that expansions in terms of alien co-factors vanish identically, we have

$$\begin{aligned} \boldsymbol{\beta}_1\mathbf{v}_t &= [1 \quad 0 \quad \cdots \quad 0]\{u_{1t} \quad \cdots \quad u_{Gt}\} \\ &= u_{1t} \end{aligned}$$

The coefficients of $\mathbf{x}_t$ in (9-57) and (9-58) must be identical. Thus

$$-\boldsymbol{\gamma}_1 = \boldsymbol{\beta}_1 \boldsymbol{\Pi} \tag{9-59}$$

Let us assume that the a priori restrictions on the coefficients of the first relation specify that G^Δ is the number of endogenous variables and K^* the number of predetermined variables which appear in the relation with nonzero coefficients, while $G^{\Delta\Delta} = G - G^\Delta$ and $K^{**} = K - K^*$ are the numbers of variables in each class excluded from that relation. Without loss of generality, the numbering of the variables may be arranged to put those with nonzero coefficients at the beginning of each class, so that we may partition the vectors $\boldsymbol{\beta}_1$ and $\boldsymbol{\gamma}_1$ as follows:

$$\begin{aligned} \boldsymbol{\beta}_1 &= [\boldsymbol{\beta}_{1\Delta} \quad \mathbf{0}_{\Delta\Delta}] = [\beta_{11} \quad \cdots \quad \beta_{1G^\Delta} \quad 0_{1,G^\Delta+1} \quad \cdots \quad 0_{1G}] \\ \boldsymbol{\gamma}_1 &= [\boldsymbol{\gamma}_{1*} \quad \mathbf{0}_{**}] = [\gamma_{11} \quad \cdots \quad \gamma_{1K^*} \quad 0_{1,K^*+1} \quad \cdots \quad 0_{1K}] \end{aligned}$$

Partitioning the G rows of $\boldsymbol{\Pi}$ into the first G^Δ and the remaining $G^{\Delta\Delta}$ and partitioning its K columns into the first K^* and the remaining K^{**}, we can then write (9-59) as

$$-[\boldsymbol{\gamma}_{1*} \quad \mathbf{0}_{**}] = [\boldsymbol{\beta}_{1\Delta} \quad \mathbf{0}_{\Delta\Delta}] \begin{bmatrix} \boldsymbol{\Pi}_{\Delta*} & \boldsymbol{\Pi}_{\Delta,**} \\ \boldsymbol{\Pi}_{\Delta\Delta,*} & \boldsymbol{\Pi}_{\Delta\Delta,**} \end{bmatrix}$$

which gives

$$-\boldsymbol{\gamma}_{1*} = \boldsymbol{\beta}_{1\Delta} \boldsymbol{\Pi}_{\Delta*} \tag{9-60}$$

and

$$\mathbf{0}_{**} = \boldsymbol{\beta}_{1\Delta} \boldsymbol{\Pi}_{\Delta,**} \tag{9-61}$$

The parameters of the relation will then be identified if (9-61) can be solved to yield a unique vector $\boldsymbol{\beta}_{1\Delta}$ in terms of the reduced-form parameters $\boldsymbol{\Pi}_{\Delta,**}$, for (9-60) will then yield the vector $\boldsymbol{\gamma}_{1*}$. The discussion of the possibility of identification thus centers on the solution of (9-61).

If the rank of $\boldsymbol{\Pi}_{\Delta,**}$ is G^Δ, then the set of homogeneous equations (9-61) will have only the trivial solution of the zero vector, but this is ruled out since by assumption a structural relation contains at least one endogenous variable. If the rank of $\boldsymbol{\Pi}_{\Delta,**}$ is $G^\Delta - 1$, the ratios of the G^Δ unknown β coefficients may be determined uniquely, and this is all we need since one of the βs, for example, β_{11}, can be arbitrarily set at unity. Thus the relation is identifiable if $\rho(\boldsymbol{\Pi}_{\Delta,**}) = G^\Delta - 1$. Since the matrix has G^Δ rows and K^{**} columns, a necessary condition for its rank to be $G^\Delta - 1$ is that

$$K^{**} \geq G^\Delta - 1 \tag{9-62}$$

This is the *order* condition for identifiability. In words, it means that the number of predetermined variables excluded from the relation must be at least as great as the number of endogenous variables included less one. Adding $G^{\Delta\Delta}$ to both sides of (9-62) gives an alternative form

$$G^{\Delta\Delta} + K^{**} \geq G - 1 \tag{9-63}$$

that is, the *total* number of variables excluded from the relation must be at least as great as the *total* number of endogenous variables in the model less one.

The rank condition for identifiability, which is necessary and sufficient, is

$$\rho(\mathbf{\Pi}_{\Delta,**}) = G^{\Delta} - 1 \tag{9-64}$$

The disadvantage of this condition is that one has to cast the model into reduced form first of all and then examine the rank of a submatrix of reduced-form coefficients. It is simpler and more useful to restate the rank condition in terms of a submatrix of the *structural* coefficients. To do this, denote the whole set of structural coefficients by

$$\mathbf{A} = [\mathbf{B}\ \mathbf{\Gamma}] = \begin{bmatrix} \beta_{1\Delta} & \mathbf{0}_{\Delta\Delta} & \gamma_{1*} & \mathbf{0}_{**} \\ \mathbf{A}_{\Delta} & \mathbf{A}_{\Delta\Delta} & \mathbf{A}_{*} & \mathbf{A}_{**} \end{bmatrix} \tag{9-65}$$

where we partition $\mathbf{A}$ by the first and the remaining $G - 1$ rows and by G^{Δ}, $G^{\Delta\Delta}$, K^*, and K^{**} sets of columns. Premultiplying by $\mathbf{B}^{-1}$,

$$\mathbf{B}^{-1}\mathbf{A} = [\mathbf{I}\ -\mathbf{\Pi}] = \begin{bmatrix} \mathbf{I}_{\Delta,\Delta} & \mathbf{0}_{\Delta,\Delta\Delta} & -\mathbf{\Pi}_{\Delta,*} & -\mathbf{\Pi}_{\Delta,**} \\ \mathbf{0}_{\Delta\Delta,\Delta} & \mathbf{I}_{\Delta\Delta,\Delta\Delta} & -\mathbf{\Pi}_{\Delta\Delta,*} & -\mathbf{\Pi}_{\Delta\Delta,**} \end{bmatrix} \tag{9-66}$$

where both rows and columns of $\mathbf{B}^{-1}$ have been partitioned into two sets of G^{Δ} and $G^{\Delta\Delta}$ and the partitioning of the columns of $\mathbf{A}$ remains as before. It can be seen by comparison of (9-65) and (9-66) that

$$\mathbf{B}^{-1}\bar{\mathbf{A}} = \begin{bmatrix} \mathbf{0}_{\Delta,\Delta\Delta} & -\mathbf{\Pi}_{\Delta,**} \\ \mathbf{I}_{\Delta\Delta,\Delta\Delta} & -\mathbf{\Pi}_{\Delta\Delta,**} \end{bmatrix} \tag{9-67}$$

where

$$\bar{\mathbf{A}} = \begin{bmatrix} \mathbf{0}_{\Delta\Delta} & \mathbf{0}_{**} \\ \mathbf{A}_{\Delta\Delta} & \mathbf{A}_{**} \end{bmatrix} \tag{9-68}$$

Postmultiplying (9-67) by $\bar{\mathbf{\Pi}}$, where

$$\bar{\mathbf{\Pi}} = \begin{bmatrix} \mathbf{I}_{\Delta\Delta,\Delta\Delta} & -\mathbf{\Pi}_{\Delta\Delta,**} \\ \mathbf{0}_{**,\Delta\Delta} & -\mathbf{I}_{**,**} \end{bmatrix}$$

$$\mathbf{B}^{-1}\bar{\mathbf{A}}\bar{\mathbf{\Pi}} = \begin{bmatrix} \mathbf{0}_{\Delta,\Delta\Delta} & \mathbf{\Pi}_{\Delta,**} \\ \mathbf{I}_{\Delta\Delta,\Delta\Delta} & \mathbf{0}_{\Delta\Delta,**} \end{bmatrix} \tag{9-69}$$

Since $\mathbf{B}^{-1}$ and $\bar{\mathbf{\Pi}}$ are nonsingular, $\mathbf{B}^{-1}\bar{\mathbf{A}}\bar{\mathbf{\Pi}}$ and $\bar{\mathbf{A}}$ have equal rank. But from the definition of $\bar{\mathbf{A}}$,

$$\rho(\bar{\mathbf{A}}) = \rho[\mathbf{A}_{\Delta\Delta} \quad \mathbf{A}_{**}]$$

and from an inspection of (9-69),

$$\rho(\mathbf{B}^{-1}\bar{\mathbf{A}}\bar{\mathbf{\Pi}}) = G^{\Delta\Delta} + \rho(\mathbf{\Pi}_{\Delta,**})$$

Hence
$$\rho(\mathbf{\Pi}_{\Delta,**}) = \rho[\mathbf{A}_{\Delta\Delta} \quad \mathbf{A}_{**}] - (G - G^{\Delta}) \tag{9-70}$$

and condition (9-64) may be stated equivalently as

$$\rho[\mathbf{A}_{\Delta\Delta} \quad \mathbf{A}_{**}] = G - 1 \tag{9-71}$$

The matrix appearing in (9-71) is the matrix of coefficients, properly arranged, in the remaining $G - 1$ equations of the endogenous and predetermined variables *excluded* from the first equation. Relation (9-70) also shows that the rank of $\mathbf{\Pi}_{\Delta,**}$ cannot exceed $G^{\Delta} - 1$, for $[\mathbf{A}_{\Delta\Delta} \quad \mathbf{A}_{**}]$ has $G - 1$ rows, so that its rank cannot exceed $G - 1$. Thus even if K^{**} exceeds $G^{\Delta} - 1$ so that $\mathbf{\Pi}_{\Delta,**}$ has G^{Δ} rows and at least G^{Δ} columns, its rank will not exceed $G^{\Delta} - 1$ and a unique set of structural coefficients corresponds to the reduced-form coefficients, as we found in Example iv.

If $K^{**} \geq G^{\Delta} - 1$, the parameters of a relation are identifiable. Our practical estimation procedure may then be influenced by whether $K^{**} = G^{\Delta} - 1$ or $K^{**} > G^{\Delta} - 1$. In the former case $\rho(\hat{\mathbf{\Pi}}_{\Delta,**})$ will, apart from a freakish statistical accident, be equal to $G^{\Delta} - 1$, so that the indirect-least-squares approach is feasible. Replacing the true values in (9-61) by estimated values enables us to solve uniquely for $\hat{\boldsymbol{\beta}}_{1\Delta}$ from

$$\mathbf{0}_{**} = \hat{\boldsymbol{\beta}}_{1\Delta}\hat{\mathbf{\Pi}}_{\Delta,**} \tag{9-72}$$

and then $\hat{\boldsymbol{\gamma}}_{1*}$ is obtained from

$$\hat{\boldsymbol{\gamma}}_{1*} = -\hat{\boldsymbol{\beta}}_{1\Delta}\hat{\mathbf{\Pi}}_{\Delta*} \tag{9-73}$$

If $K^{**} > G^{\Delta} - 1$, then we either have to modify the indirect-least-squares approach to ensure that $\rho(\hat{\mathbf{\Pi}}_{\Delta,**}) = G^{\Delta} - 1$ or else use a method of estimation that does not involve getting back from estimated reduced-form parameters to estimated structural parameters. It is to these various estimation methods that we now turn.

9-3. Estimation Methods

There is now a variety of estimation methods available for use in simultaneous-equation contexts. We shall give an account of them seriatim, leaving for Chap. 10 a comparison of their small-sample properties and some remarks on the choice of estimation method. It is convenient to distinguish between estimation methods which are applicable to a single equation in a model and those which deal with the complete model. It is, of course, possible to estimate all the relations in a model by the application of single-equation methods to each relation in turn. The first four methods to be described are single-equation methods, and the remaining two are complete-system methods. It is assumed in all cases that the relations to be estimated are identified.

Ordinary Least Squares (OLS). One may apply the ordinary-least-squares model of Chap. 4 to a single equation in a model. There are, however, usually two or more endogenous variables in each relation. One may not know which endogenous variable to select as the dependent variable, and no matter which is chosen, the remaining endogenous variable(s) will be correlated with the disturbance term in that relation because of the simultaneous nature of the relations in the model. Thus the least-squares estimators will be biased and they will also be inconsistent. This fact alone will not necessarily rule out the use of ordinary least squares as an estimating method, since the choice of a method in practice has to be made on a balance of the properties of the method and computational simplicity. Moreover, bias is not necessarily the most important property of an estimator, but has to be judged in conjunction with the variance. These matters are taken up in Chap. 10.

Indirect Least Squares (ILS). This method is feasible only when the structural relation is exactly identified. The procedure is to estimate the parameters of the reduced form by the application of ordinary least squares to each reduced-form relation separately and then to derive estimates of the structural parameters from the estimated reduced-form parameters. The latter will be best linear unbiased estimators under assumptions (9-26) to (9-28), but this property does not hold under transformations. For example, as we have seen on page 236, the derived structural estimators are biased. However, if the structural disturbances are normally distributed, then so will be the reduced-form disturbances, and the least-squares estimators of the reduced-form parameters will be maximum-likelihood estimators. Since this property does hold under transformations, the derived structural estimators will be maximum-likelihood estimators.

9-4. Limited-information Single Equation (LISE) or Least-variance Ratio (LVR)

These two methods give the same estimating formula. Consider the first equation of the set $\mathbf{B}\mathbf{y}_t + \mathbf{\Gamma}\mathbf{x}_t = \mathbf{u}_t$, namely,

$$\boldsymbol{\beta}_1\mathbf{y}_t + \boldsymbol{\gamma}_1\mathbf{x}_t = \mathbf{u}_{1t} \qquad t = 1, \ldots, n \tag{9-74}$$

where $\boldsymbol{\beta}_1$ indicates the first row of $\mathbf{B}$, $\boldsymbol{\gamma}_1$ the first row of $\mathbf{\Gamma}$, and $\mathbf{y}_t$ and $\mathbf{x}_t$ are column vectors of G and K elements indicating, respectively, the values of the G endogenous and the K predetermined variables at time t. Using the a priori restrictions on the coefficients of (9-74), we may write it as

$$\beta_{11}y_{1t} + \cdots + \beta_{1G^\Delta}y_{G^\Delta t} + \gamma_{11}x_{1t} + \cdots + \gamma_{1K^*}x_{K^*t} = u_{1t} \qquad t = 1, \ldots, n \tag{9-75}$$

where we assume that the number of predetermined variables excluded from (9-75) is at least as great as the number of endogenous variables included ($K^{**} > G^\Delta - 1$), so that the equation is overidentified. The reduced form of the model $\mathbf{B}\mathbf{y}_t + \mathbf{\Gamma}\mathbf{z}_t = \mathbf{u}_t$ is $\mathbf{y}_t = \mathbf{\Pi}\mathbf{z}_t + \mathbf{v}_t$. Under the assumption of normality and serial independence for the $\mathbf{u}$ vectors, the $\mathbf{v}$ vectors will likewise be normal and serially independent. If we consider the G^Δ endogenous variables which appear in (9-75), we may take the G^Δ equations of the reduced form corresponding to these variables and set up the likelihood function for these G^Δ endogenous variables. This likelihood function will be in terms of the parameters $[\mathbf{\Pi}_{\Delta *} \ \mathbf{\Pi}_{\Delta,**}]$ of the first G^Δ rows of the reduced-form matrix $\mathbf{\Pi}$. Maximizing the likelihood function with respect to these parameters will yield maximum-likelihood estimators $[\hat{\mathbf{\Pi}}_{\Delta *} \ \hat{\mathbf{\Pi}}_{\Delta,**}]$, but since $\hat{\mathbf{\Pi}}_{\Delta,**}$ has at least G^Δ columns in the overidentified case, its rank will normally be G^Δ and so Eq. (9-72),

$$\mathbf{0}_{**} = \hat{\boldsymbol{\beta}}_{1\Delta}\hat{\mathbf{\Pi}}_{\Delta,**}$$

will fail to yield an estimate of the vector $\boldsymbol{\beta}_{1\Delta} = [\beta_{11} \ \cdots \ \beta_{1G^\Delta}]$. The limited-information maximum-likelihood approach is to maximize the likelihood function for the G^Δ endogenous variables, subject to the restriction that $\rho(\hat{\mathbf{\Pi}}_{\Delta,**}) = G^\Delta - 1$. This will determine uniquely the ratios of the G^Δ elements in $\hat{\boldsymbol{\beta}}_{1\Delta}$ from (9-72), and we may then set one of these β coefficients equal to unity. This approach was developed by Anderson and Rubin.[1] It is seen that the application of the method requires one to know, in addition to the specification of the single equation being estimated, merely the predetermined variables appearing in the other equations of the system, for the detailed specification of these other equations is not used in the estimation process, nor is it even assumed to be known. The mathematical development of the limited-information principle is complicated and lengthy, but it may be shown that it reduces in the end to the choice of the elements of $\boldsymbol{\beta}_{1\Delta}$ to maximize[2]

$$L = -\tfrac{1}{2} \log_e \frac{\boldsymbol{\beta}_{1\Delta}\mathbf{W}^*_{\Delta\Delta}\boldsymbol{\beta}'_{1\Delta}}{\boldsymbol{\beta}_{1\Delta}\mathbf{W}_{\Delta\Delta}\boldsymbol{\beta}'_{1\Delta}} \tag{9-76}$$

where $\mathbf{W}^*_{\Delta\Delta}$ and $\mathbf{W}_{\Delta\Delta}$ are certain matrices of residuals. The explanation of $\mathbf{W}^*_{\Delta\Delta}$ and $\mathbf{W}_{\Delta\Delta}$ will at the same time show why the limited-information and the least-variance-ratio approach are identical.

Let us denote the linear combination of endogenous variables which appear in (9-75) by a single symbol, namely,

$$\tilde{y}_t = \beta_{11}y_{1t} + \beta_{12}y_{2t} + \cdots + \beta_{1G^\Delta}y_{G^\Delta t} \qquad t = 1, \ldots, n \tag{9-77}$$

and let us define the following matrices of observations:

$$\mathbf{Y}_\Delta = \begin{bmatrix} y_{11} & \cdots & y_{G^\Delta 1} \\ \cdot & & \cdot \\ \cdot & & \cdot \\ \cdot & & \cdot \\ y_{1n} & \cdots & y_{G^\Delta n} \end{bmatrix} \qquad \mathbf{X}_* = \begin{bmatrix} x_{11} & \cdots & x_{K^*1} \\ \cdot & & \cdot \\ \cdot & & \cdot \\ \cdot & & \cdot \\ x_{1n} & \cdots & x_{K^*n} \end{bmatrix}$$

$$\mathbf{X}_{**} = \begin{bmatrix} x_{K^*+1,1} & \cdots & x_{K1} \\ \cdot & & \cdot \\ \cdot & & \cdot \\ \cdot & & \cdot \\ x_{K^*+1,n} & \cdots & x_{Kn} \end{bmatrix} \tag{9-78}$$

$$\mathbf{X} = [\mathbf{X}_* \quad \mathbf{X}_{**}]$$

[1] T. W. Anderson and Herman Rubin, "Estimation of the Parameters of a Single Equation in a Complete System of Stochastic Equations," *An. Math. Statist.*, vol. 20, pp. 46–63, 1949.

[2] *Ibid.*, and also W. C. Hood and T. C. Koopmans (eds.), *Studies in Econometric Method*, Wiley, New York, 1953, chap. 6. Hood and Koopmans arrive at (9-76) by a different method from the original approach of Anderson and Rubin, who maximized the likelihood function subject to appropriate constraints by using Lagrange multipliers. Hood and Koopmans start with the likelihood function for the *complete* system, and then, by a series of stepwise maximizations, eliminate from the likelihood function all parameters other than those of the equation to be estimated. Finally, even $\boldsymbol{\gamma}_{1*}$ is eliminated from the likelihood function, and the concentrated likelihood function (9-76) is obtained, which is expressed in terms of $\boldsymbol{\beta}_{1\Delta}$.

$\mathbf{Y}_\Delta$ is thus the matrix of observations on the endogenous variables which actually appear in our relation, while $\mathbf{X}_*$ and $\mathbf{X}_{**}$ denote, respectively, the observations on the included and excluded predetermined variables. We may then write

$$\tilde{\mathbf{y}} = \begin{bmatrix} \tilde{y}_1 \\ \tilde{y}_2 \\ \cdot \\ \cdot \\ \cdot \\ \tilde{y}_n \end{bmatrix} = \mathbf{Y}_\Delta \boldsymbol{\beta}'_{1\Delta} \tag{9-79}$$

remembering that $\boldsymbol{\beta}_{1\Delta}$ was initially defined as the row vector $[\beta_{11} \quad \cdot \cdot \cdot \quad \beta_{1G\Delta}]$. The specification of the relation (9-75) is that $\tilde{\mathbf{y}}$ is related to $\mathbf{X}_*$ but not to $\mathbf{X}_{**}$. The least-variance-ratio principle states that the β coefficients in the definition of $\tilde{\mathbf{y}}$ should be so chosen that the ratio of the residual variance when $\tilde{\mathbf{y}}$ is regressed on $\mathbf{X}_*$ to that when $\tilde{\mathbf{y}}$ is regressed on $\mathbf{X}$ is made as small as possible; that is, the addition of the "excluded" predetermined variables $\mathbf{X}_{**}$ should make a minimal improvement in the explained sum of squares in $\tilde{\mathbf{y}}$.

The sum of squares in $\tilde{\mathbf{y}}$ is

$$\tilde{\mathbf{y}}'\tilde{\mathbf{y}} = \boldsymbol{\beta}_{1\Delta}\mathbf{Y}'_\Delta\mathbf{Y}_\Delta\boldsymbol{\beta}'_{1\Delta}$$

If we regress $\tilde{\mathbf{y}}$ on $\mathbf{X}_*$, the vector of estimated coefficients is $(\mathbf{X}'_*\mathbf{X}_*)^{-1}\mathbf{X}'_*\tilde{\mathbf{y}}$ and the explained sum of squares is $\tilde{\mathbf{y}}'\mathbf{X}_*(\mathbf{X}'_*\mathbf{X}_*)^{-1}\mathbf{X}'_*\tilde{\mathbf{y}}$ [using (4-22)]. Hence the residual sum of squares is

$$\boldsymbol{\beta}_{1\Delta}\mathbf{Y}'_\Delta\mathbf{Y}_\Delta\boldsymbol{\beta}'_{1\Delta} - \boldsymbol{\beta}_{1\Delta}\mathbf{Y}'_\Delta\mathbf{X}_*(\mathbf{X}'_*\mathbf{X}_*)^{-1}\mathbf{X}'_*\mathbf{Y}_\Delta\boldsymbol{\beta}'_{1\Delta} = \boldsymbol{\beta}_{1\Delta}\mathbf{W}^*_{\Delta\Delta}\boldsymbol{\beta}'_{1\Delta}$$

where

$$\mathbf{W}^*_{\Delta\Delta} = \mathbf{Y}'_\Delta\mathbf{Y}_\Delta - \mathbf{Y}'_\Delta\mathbf{X}_*(\mathbf{X}'_*\mathbf{X}_*)^{-1}\mathbf{X}'_*\mathbf{Y}_\Delta \tag{9-80}$$

Similarly, the residual sum of squares when $\tilde{\mathbf{y}}$ is regressed on all the predetermined variables $\mathbf{X}$ is

$$\boldsymbol{\beta}_{1\Delta}\mathbf{W}_{\Delta\Delta}\boldsymbol{\beta}'_{1\Delta}$$

where

$$\mathbf{W}_{\Delta\Delta} = \mathbf{Y}'_\Delta\mathbf{Y}_\Delta - \mathbf{Y}'_\Delta\mathbf{X}(\mathbf{X}'\mathbf{X})^{-1}\mathbf{X}'\mathbf{Y}_\Delta \tag{9-81}$$

The least-variance-ratio principle then indicates the choice of $\boldsymbol{\beta}_{1\Delta}$ to minimize the ratio

$$l = \frac{\boldsymbol{\beta}_{1\Delta}\mathbf{W}^*_{\Delta\Delta}\boldsymbol{\beta}'_{1\Delta}}{\boldsymbol{\beta}_{1\Delta}\mathbf{W}_{\Delta\Delta}\boldsymbol{\beta}'_{1\Delta}} \tag{9-82}$$

Comparison of (9-82) and (9-76) shows that when l in (9-82) is minimized, the likelihood L of (9-76) is maximized. Hence limited information and least-variance ratio give identical results.

Differentiating l partially with respect to β_{1i} ($i = 1, \ldots, G^{\Delta}$) and equating to zero gives

$$\mathbf{w}_i^* \boldsymbol{\beta}_{1\Delta}' - l\mathbf{w}_i \boldsymbol{\beta}_{1\Delta}' = 0 \qquad i = 1, \ldots, G^{\Delta} \tag{9-83}$$

where $\mathbf{w}_i^*$ and $\mathbf{w}_i$ denote the ith rows in $\mathbf{W}_{\Delta\Delta}^*$ and $\mathbf{W}_{\Delta\Delta}$. This set of equations may be written

$$(\mathbf{W}_{\Delta\Delta}^* - l\mathbf{W}_{\Delta\Delta})\boldsymbol{\beta}_{1\Delta}' = \mathbf{0} \tag{9-84}$$

which has a nontrivial solution for $\boldsymbol{\beta}_{1\Delta}$ only if the determinantal equation

$$|\mathbf{W}_{\Delta\Delta}^* - l\mathbf{W}_{\Delta\Delta}| = 0 \tag{9-85}$$

is satisfied. It is seen from the definitions of the $\mathbf{W}$ matrices in (9-80) and (9-81) that all their elements are functions of the sample observations. Hence (9-85) gives a polynomial in l, which must be solved for the smallest root $\hat{l}$. This smallest root is substituted back in (9-84) and $\hat{\boldsymbol{\beta}}_{1\Delta}$ obtained from

$$(\mathbf{W}_{\Delta\Delta}^* - \hat{l}\mathbf{W}_{\Delta\Delta})\hat{\boldsymbol{\beta}}_{1\Delta}' = \mathbf{0} \tag{9-86}$$

Finally, the parameters of the predetermined variables in the relation are obtained by regressing the composite variable $\tilde{\mathbf{y}}$ on the predetermined variables $\mathbf{X}_*$ which appear in the relation. As we have seen, the column vector of coefficients in this regression is

$$(\mathbf{X}_*'\mathbf{X}_*)^{-1}\mathbf{X}_*'\tilde{\mathbf{y}}$$

Noting that in (9-75) both endogenous and predetermined variables appear on the same side of the relation and using the definition (9-79), we may then compute the estimated *row* vector of coefficients for the predetermined variables as

$$\hat{\boldsymbol{\gamma}}_{1*} = -\hat{\boldsymbol{\beta}}_{1\Delta}\mathbf{Y}_{\Delta}'\mathbf{X}_*(\mathbf{X}_*'\mathbf{X}_*)^{-1} \tag{9-87}$$

This is exactly what one would obtain if one used Eq. (9-73), namely,

$$\hat{\boldsymbol{\gamma}}_{1*} = -\hat{\boldsymbol{\beta}}_{1\Delta}\hat{\boldsymbol{\Pi}}_{\Delta*}$$

and computed the elements of $\hat{\boldsymbol{\Pi}}_{\Delta*}$ by the straightforward application of least squares for each of the G^{Δ} endogenous variables on the group of K^* predetermined variables in the relation.

Limited-information estimates for the parameters of (9-75) may thus be computed as follows:

1. Set out the observation matrices $\mathbf{Y}_{\Delta}$, $\mathbf{X}_*$, and $\mathbf{X}$ as defined in (9-78).

2. Compute the matrices $\mathbf{W}^*_{\Delta\Delta}$ and $\mathbf{W}_{\Delta\Delta}$ as defined in (9-80) and (9-81).
3. Find the smallest root $\hat{l}$ of the equation

$$|\mathbf{W}^*_{\Delta\Delta} - \hat{l}\mathbf{W}_{\Delta\Delta}| = 0$$

4. Thence determine $\hat{\boldsymbol{\beta}}_{1\Delta}$ from

$$(\mathbf{W}^*_{\Delta\Delta} - \hat{l}\mathbf{W}_{\Delta\Delta})\hat{\boldsymbol{\beta}}'_{1\Delta} = \mathbf{0}$$

and $\hat{\boldsymbol{\gamma}}_{1*}$ from

$$\hat{\boldsymbol{\gamma}}_{1*} = -\hat{\boldsymbol{\beta}}_{1\Delta}\mathbf{Y}'_{\Delta}\mathbf{X}_*(\mathbf{X}'_*\mathbf{X}_*)^{-1}$$

9-5. Two-stage Least Squares

Consider again Eq. (9-75), normalize it by setting $\beta_{11} = 1$, and rewrite as

$$y_{1t} = -\beta_{12}y_{2t} - \cdots - \beta_{1G^\Delta}y_{G^\Delta t} - \gamma_{11}x_{1t} - \cdots \cdots - \gamma_{1K^*}x_{K^*t} + u_{1t} \qquad t = 1, \ldots, n \tag{9-88}$$

This set of equations may in turn be written in matrix form as

$$\mathbf{y}_1 = -\mathbf{Y}_2\boldsymbol{\beta}'_2 - \mathbf{X}_*\boldsymbol{\gamma}'_{1*} + \mathbf{u}_1 \tag{9-89}$$

where

$$\mathbf{y}_1 = \begin{bmatrix} y_{11} \\ \cdot \\ \cdot \\ \cdot \\ y_{1n} \end{bmatrix} \qquad \mathbf{Y}_2 = \begin{bmatrix} y_{21} & \cdots & y_{G^\Delta 1} \\ \cdot & & \cdot \\ \cdot & & \cdot \\ \cdot & & \cdot \\ y_{2n} & \cdots & y_{G^\Delta n} \end{bmatrix} \qquad \boldsymbol{\beta}'_2 = \begin{bmatrix} \beta_{12} \\ \cdot \\ \cdot \\ \cdot \\ \beta_{1G^\Delta} \end{bmatrix}$$

$$\mathbf{X}_* = \begin{bmatrix} x_{11} & \cdots & x_{K^*1} \\ \cdot & & \cdot \\ \cdot & & \cdot \\ \cdot & & \cdot \\ x_{1n} & \cdots & x_{K^*n} \end{bmatrix} \qquad \boldsymbol{\gamma}'_{1*} = \begin{bmatrix} \gamma_{11} \\ \cdot \\ \cdot \\ \cdot \\ \gamma_{1K^*} \end{bmatrix} \tag{9-90}$$

As we have seen, $\mathbf{u}_1$ will in general be correlated with the explanatory variables $\mathbf{Y}_2$. The basic idea in two-stage least squares is to replace $\mathbf{Y}_2$ in (9-89) by an estimated matrix $\hat{\mathbf{Y}}_2$ based on the least-squares regressions of the variables in $\mathbf{Y}_2$ on *all* the predetermined variables in the model and then to apply least squares again to $\mathbf{y}_1$, $\hat{\mathbf{Y}}_2$, and $\mathbf{X}_*$. There is thus a basic similarity between limited information and two-stage least squares in that both methods make use of all the predetermined variables in the model in order to estimate the parameters of a single relation, but do not require a detailed specification of the other relations in the model.

Regressing $\mathbf{y}_2$ on $\mathbf{X}$ gives $\hat{\mathbf{y}}_2 = \mathbf{X}(\mathbf{X}'\mathbf{X})^{-1}\mathbf{X}'\mathbf{y}_2$. Similarly, regressing $\mathbf{y}_3$ on $\mathbf{X}$ gives $\hat{\mathbf{y}}_3 = \mathbf{X}(\mathbf{X}'\mathbf{X})^{-1}\mathbf{X}'\mathbf{y}_3$. Hence

$$\begin{aligned}\hat{\mathbf{Y}}_2 &= [\hat{\mathbf{y}}_2 \quad \hat{\mathbf{y}}_3 \quad \cdots \quad \hat{\mathbf{y}}_{G^\Delta}] \\ &= \mathbf{X}(\mathbf{X}'\mathbf{X})^{-1}\mathbf{X}'\mathbf{Y}_2 \end{aligned} \tag{9-91}$$

or

$$\mathbf{Y}_2 = \mathbf{X}(\mathbf{X}'\mathbf{X})^{-1}\mathbf{X}'\mathbf{Y}_2 + \mathbf{V} \tag{9-92}$$

where $\mathbf{V}$ denotes the matrix of reduced-form residuals for the $G^\Delta - 1$ endogenous variables appearing on the right-hand side of (9-89). We can now rewrite (9-89) as

$$\mathbf{y}_1 = -(\mathbf{Y}_2 - \mathbf{V})\boldsymbol{\beta}_2' - \mathbf{X}_*\boldsymbol{\gamma}_{1*}' + (\mathbf{u} - \mathbf{V}\boldsymbol{\beta}_2') \tag{9-93}$$

or

$$\mathbf{y}_1 = -[(\mathbf{Y}_2 - \mathbf{V}) \quad \mathbf{X}_*]\begin{bmatrix}\boldsymbol{\beta}_2' \\ \boldsymbol{\gamma}_{1*}'\end{bmatrix} + (\mathbf{u} - \mathbf{V}\boldsymbol{\beta}_2') \tag{9-94}$$

Applying least squares to this relation gives

$$\begin{bmatrix}\hat{\boldsymbol{\beta}}_2' \\ \hat{\boldsymbol{\gamma}}_{1*}'\end{bmatrix} = -(\mathbf{A}'\mathbf{A})^{-1}\mathbf{A}'\mathbf{y}_1 \tag{9-95}$$

where

$$\mathbf{A} = [(\mathbf{Y}_2 - \mathbf{V}) \quad \mathbf{X}_*] \tag{9-96}$$

Now

$$(\mathbf{Y}_2 - \mathbf{V})'(\mathbf{Y}_2 - \mathbf{V}) = \mathbf{Y}_2'\mathbf{Y}_2 - \mathbf{V}'\mathbf{Y}_2 - \mathbf{Y}_2'\mathbf{V} + \mathbf{V}'\mathbf{V}$$

and

$$\begin{aligned}\mathbf{V}'\mathbf{Y}_2 &= \mathbf{V}'(\hat{\mathbf{Y}}_2 + \mathbf{V}) \qquad \text{using (9-91) and (9-92)} \\ &= \mathbf{V}'\mathbf{V}\end{aligned}$$

since it is a property of the least-squares fit that the residual is uncorrelated with the regression values; that is, $\mathbf{V}'\hat{\mathbf{Y}}_2 = \mathbf{0}$. Similarly,

$$\mathbf{Y}_2'\mathbf{V} = \mathbf{V}'\mathbf{V}$$

Hence

$$(\mathbf{Y}_2 - \mathbf{V})'(\mathbf{Y}_2 - \mathbf{V}) = \mathbf{Y}_2'\mathbf{Y}_2 - \mathbf{V}'\mathbf{V}$$

Moreover,

$$\begin{aligned}\mathbf{X}'\mathbf{V} &= \mathbf{X}'[\mathbf{Y}_2 - \mathbf{X}(\mathbf{X}'\mathbf{X})^{-1}\mathbf{X}'\mathbf{Y}_2] \\ &= \mathbf{0}\end{aligned}$$

which illustrates the property of the least-squares fit that the residual is uncorrelated with the explanatory values. Thus $\mathbf{X}_*'\mathbf{V}$, which is a submatrix of $\mathbf{X}'\mathbf{V}$, must also be equal to the zero matrix. Using these results, the two-stage least-squares estimator of (9-95) may be written

$$\begin{bmatrix}\hat{\boldsymbol{\beta}}_2' \\ \hat{\boldsymbol{\gamma}}_{1*}'\end{bmatrix} = -\begin{bmatrix}\mathbf{Y}_2'\mathbf{Y}_2 - \mathbf{V}'\mathbf{V} & \mathbf{Y}_2'\mathbf{X}_* \\ \mathbf{X}_*'\mathbf{Y}_2 & \mathbf{X}_*'\mathbf{X}_*\end{bmatrix}^{-1}\begin{bmatrix}\mathbf{Y}_2' - \mathbf{V}' \\ \mathbf{X}_*'\end{bmatrix}\mathbf{y}_1 \tag{9-97}$$

The condition that the inverse matrix in (9-97) exists is the condition (9-62) for identifiability, namely, $K^{**} \geq G^\Delta - 1$. $\mathbf{A} = [(\mathbf{Y}_2 - \mathbf{V}) \quad \mathbf{X}_*]$ is a matrix of order n by $G^\Delta - 1 + K^*$.

Hence $\mathbf{A}'\mathbf{A}$ is a square symmetric matrix of order $G^{\Delta} - 1 + K^*$ and $\rho(\mathbf{A}'\mathbf{A}) = \rho(\mathbf{A})$. Now

$$\mathbf{A} = [(\mathbf{Y}_2 - \mathbf{V}) \quad \mathbf{X}_*] = \mathbf{X}\begin{bmatrix} (\mathbf{X}'\mathbf{X})^{-1}\mathbf{X}'\mathbf{Y}_2 & \begin{matrix} \mathbf{I} \\ \mathbf{0} \end{matrix} \end{bmatrix} \qquad \text{using (9-92)}$$

where $\mathbf{I}$ is the unit matrix of order K^* and $\mathbf{0}$ is a zero matrix of order K^{**} by K^*. Thus the rank of $\mathbf{A}$ cannot be larger than the rank of $\mathbf{X}$, which is K. If the rank of $\mathbf{A}$ is less than $G^{\Delta} - 1 + K^*$, then $\mathbf{A}'\mathbf{A}$ is singular. This will happen if

$$K < G^{\Delta} - 1 + K^*$$

that is, if

$$K^{**} < G^{\Delta} - 1$$

in which case the relationship (9-88) is unidentifiable.

9-6. k-class Estimators

Theil has developed the k class of estimators from (9-97) by defining[1]

$$\begin{bmatrix} \hat{\boldsymbol{\beta}}_2' \\ \hat{\boldsymbol{\gamma}}_{1*}' \end{bmatrix}_k = -\begin{bmatrix} \mathbf{Y}_2'\mathbf{Y}_2 - k\mathbf{V}'\mathbf{V} & \mathbf{Y}_2'\mathbf{X}_* \\ \mathbf{X}_*'\mathbf{Y}_2 & \mathbf{X}_*'\mathbf{X}_* \end{bmatrix}^{-1} \begin{bmatrix} \mathbf{Y}_2' - k\mathbf{V}' \\ \mathbf{X}_*' \end{bmatrix} \mathbf{y}_1 \qquad (9\text{-}98)$$

Three of the estimators we have met so far are members of the k class. Ordinary least squares corresponds to $k = 0$, for then (9-98) reduces to the straightforward application of least squares to (9-88), with $[\mathbf{Y}_2 \quad \mathbf{X}_*]$ as the matrix of observations on the explanatory variables. Two-stage least squares corresponds to $k = 1$, and limited information corresponds to $k = \hat{l}$, where $\hat{l}$ is defined in (9-85). This last result may be proved as follows.

The limited-information estimators are partially defined in (9-86), namely,

$$(\mathbf{W}_{\Delta\Delta}^* - \hat{l}\mathbf{W}_{\Delta\Delta})\hat{\boldsymbol{\beta}}_{1\Delta}' = \mathbf{0}$$

In k-class estimation we have normalized $\boldsymbol{\beta}_{1\Delta}$ by setting the first element, the coefficient of y_{1t}, equal to unity; that is,

$$\boldsymbol{\beta}_{1\Delta} = [1 \quad \boldsymbol{\beta}_2]$$

where $\boldsymbol{\beta}_2$ is the row vector of coefficients of the remaining endogenous variables in the relation (9-88). We can thus dispense with

[1] See H. Theil, *Economic Forecasts and Policy*, 2d ed., North-Holland Publishing Company, Amsterdam, 1961, chap. 6.

the first equation in the set (9-86). To rewrite the remaining equations in the set, notice first of all from the definitions of $\mathbf{W}^*_{\Delta\Delta}$ and $\mathbf{W}_{\Delta\Delta}$ in (9-80) and (9-81) that we can write

$$\mathbf{W}^*_{\Delta\Delta} = \mathbf{Y}'_\Delta\mathbf{B}_*\mathbf{Y}_\Delta = \begin{bmatrix} \mathbf{y}'_1\mathbf{B}_*\mathbf{Y}_\Delta \\ \mathbf{Y}'_2\mathbf{B}_*\mathbf{Y}_\Delta \end{bmatrix} \tag{9-99}$$

where
$$\mathbf{B}_* = \mathbf{I} - \mathbf{X}_*(\mathbf{X}'_*\mathbf{X}_*)^{-1}\mathbf{X}'_* \tag{9-100}$$

and
$$\mathbf{Y}_\Delta = [\mathbf{y}_1 \quad \mathbf{Y}_2] \tag{9-101}$$

Similarly,
$$\mathbf{W}_{\Delta\Delta} = \mathbf{Y}'_\Delta\mathbf{B}\mathbf{Y}_\Delta = \begin{bmatrix} \mathbf{y}'_1\mathbf{B}\mathbf{Y}_\Delta \\ \mathbf{Y}'_2\mathbf{B}\mathbf{Y}_\Delta \end{bmatrix} \tag{9-102}$$

where
$$\mathbf{B} = \mathbf{I} - \mathbf{X}(\mathbf{X}'\mathbf{X})^{-1}\mathbf{X}' \tag{9-103}$$

Taking all equations in (9-86) other than the first thus gives

$$(\mathbf{Y}'_2\mathbf{B}_*\mathbf{Y}_\Delta - l\mathbf{Y}'_2\mathbf{B}\mathbf{Y}_\Delta)\hat{\boldsymbol{\beta}}'_{1\Delta} = \mathbf{0} \tag{9-104}$$

If we rewrite the k-class estimators as

$$\begin{bmatrix} \mathbf{Y}'_2\mathbf{Y}_2 - k\mathbf{V}'\mathbf{V} & \mathbf{Y}'_2\mathbf{X}_* \\ \mathbf{X}'_*\mathbf{Y}_2 & \mathbf{X}'_*\mathbf{X}_* \end{bmatrix} \begin{bmatrix} \hat{\boldsymbol{\beta}}'_2 \\ \hat{\boldsymbol{\gamma}}'_{1*} \end{bmatrix}_k = - \begin{bmatrix} \mathbf{Y}'_2 - k\mathbf{V}' \\ \mathbf{X}'_* \end{bmatrix} \mathbf{y}_1 \tag{9-105}$$

we may multiply out the left-hand side and equate the top element on each side to give

$$(\mathbf{Y}'_2\mathbf{Y}_2 - k\mathbf{V}'\mathbf{V})(\hat{\boldsymbol{\beta}}'_2)_k + \mathbf{Y}'_2\mathbf{X}_*(\hat{\boldsymbol{\gamma}}'_{1*})_k = -(\mathbf{Y}'_2 - k\mathbf{V}')\mathbf{y}_1 \tag{9-106}$$

It is easily shown from (9-92) that

$$\mathbf{V}'\mathbf{V} = \mathbf{Y}'_2\mathbf{B}\mathbf{Y}_2$$

for $\mathbf{B}$ is symmetric and idempotent. In the same way

$$\mathbf{V}'\mathbf{y}_1 = \mathbf{Y}'_2\mathbf{B}\mathbf{y}_1$$

Substitution in (9-106) gives

$$(\mathbf{Y}'_2\mathbf{Y}_2 - k\mathbf{Y}'_2\mathbf{B}\mathbf{Y}_2)(\hat{\boldsymbol{\beta}}'_2)_k + \mathbf{Y}'_2\mathbf{y}_1 - k\mathbf{Y}'_2\mathbf{B}\mathbf{y}_1 + \mathbf{Y}'_2\mathbf{X}_*(\hat{\boldsymbol{\gamma}}'_{1*})_k = \mathbf{0} \tag{9-107}$$

Equating the second elements in (9-105) and solving for $(\hat{\boldsymbol{\gamma}}'_{1*})_k$ gives

$$(\hat{\boldsymbol{\gamma}}'_{1*})_k = -(\mathbf{X}'_*\mathbf{X}_*)^{-1}[\mathbf{X}'_*\mathbf{Y}_2(\hat{\boldsymbol{\beta}}'_2)_k + \mathbf{X}'_*\mathbf{y}_1] \tag{9-108}$$

Substitution in (9-107) then gives

$$(\mathbf{Y}'_2\mathbf{B}_*\mathbf{Y}_2 - k\mathbf{Y}'_2\mathbf{B}\mathbf{Y}_2)(\hat{\boldsymbol{\beta}}'_2)_k + (\mathbf{Y}'_2\mathbf{B}_*\mathbf{y}_1 - k\mathbf{Y}'_2\mathbf{B}\mathbf{y}_1) = \mathbf{0} \tag{9-109}$$

which may be written

$$(\mathbf{Y}'_2\mathbf{B}_*\mathbf{Y}_\Delta - k\mathbf{Y}'_2\mathbf{B}\mathbf{Y}_\Delta)(\hat{\boldsymbol{\beta}}'_{1\Delta})_k = \mathbf{0} \tag{9-110}$$

This is identical with the limited-information estimator (9-104) when k is set equal to $\hat{l}$.

Finally, if we look at the other part of the limited-information estimator given in (9-87), namely,

$$\hat{\gamma}'_{1*} = -(\mathbf{X}'_*\mathbf{X}_*)^{-1}\mathbf{X}'_*\mathbf{Y}_\Delta\hat{\beta}'_{1\Delta}$$

this may be seen to be identical with (9-108) above, which is derived from the k-class estimator. Thus the limited-information estimator is a member of the k class, with $k = \hat{l}$.

This result also provides an alternative way of looking at the meaning of two-stage least squares. If we return to (9-82), where the variance ratio $l = \beta_{1\Delta}\mathbf{W}^*_{\Delta\Delta}\beta'_{1\Delta}/\beta_{1\Delta}\mathbf{W}_{\Delta\Delta}\beta'_{1\Delta}$ is defined, and now define the quantity

$$\varphi = \beta_{1\Delta}\mathbf{W}^*_{\Delta\Delta}\beta'_{1\Delta} - \beta_{1\Delta}\mathbf{W}_{\Delta\Delta}\beta'_{1\Delta}$$

then it can be shown that two-stage least squares is the estimator of $\beta_{1\Delta}$, which minimizes φ. Differentiating φ with respect to $\beta_{1\Delta}$ and setting the result equal to zero gives the set of equations

$$(\mathbf{W}^*_{\Delta\Delta} - \mathbf{W}_{\Delta\Delta})\mathbf{b}'_{1\Delta} = \mathbf{0}$$

Since the first element in $\beta_{1\Delta}$ is set equal to unity, we may use the development from (9-99) to (9-104) above and write this set of equations, with the first one omitted, as

$$(\mathbf{Y}'_2\mathbf{B}_*\mathbf{Y}_\Delta - \mathbf{Y}'_2\mathbf{B}\mathbf{Y}_\Delta)\mathbf{b}'_{1\Delta} = 0$$

But this is exactly what we get when we take (9-110) for k-class estimators and set k equal to unity. Thus two-stage least-squares estimators are found by minimizing the *difference* between the residual sums of squares $\beta_{1\Delta}\mathbf{W}^*_{\Delta\Delta}\beta'_{1\Delta}$ and $\beta_{1\Delta}\mathbf{W}_{\Delta\Delta}\beta'_{1\Delta}$ and limited-information estimators by minimizing the *ratio* of the first to the second.

A choice between members of the k class of estimators depends upon their properties and on computational considerations. The condition for consistency of k-class estimators[1] is that $\underset{n\to\infty}{\text{plim}}\, k = 1$. Thus ordinary least squares is inconsistent, as we have already seen, for $k = 0$. Two-stage least squares is consistent, since $k = 1$, and so also is limited-information maximum likelihood, for $\underset{n\to\infty}{\text{plim}}\, \hat{l} = 1$. The exact small-sample distribution of k-class estimators has not

[1] *Ibid.*, p. 232.

yet been obtained, but some results are available on asymptotic variances. If $\underset{n\to\infty}{\text{plim}} \sqrt{n}\,(k-1) = 0$ and if we define the sampling errors in k-class estimators to be

$$\mathbf{e}_k = \begin{bmatrix} \hat{\boldsymbol{\beta}}_2' \\ \hat{\boldsymbol{\gamma}}_{1*}' \end{bmatrix}_k - \begin{bmatrix} \boldsymbol{\beta}_2' \\ \boldsymbol{\gamma}_{1*}' \end{bmatrix}$$

the asymptotic variance-covariance matrix for the estimators is given by[1]

$$\lim_{n\to\infty} E(n\mathbf{e}_k\mathbf{e}_k') = \sigma^2 \lim_{n\to\infty} n \begin{bmatrix} \mathbf{Y}_2'\mathbf{Y}_2 - \mathbf{V}'\mathbf{V} & \mathbf{Y}_2'\mathbf{X}_* \\ \mathbf{X}_*'\mathbf{Y}_2 & \mathbf{X}_*'\mathbf{X}_* \end{bmatrix}^{-1} \tag{9-111}$$

where σ^2 is the variance of the disturbance term in the equation being estimated. An estimate of σ^2 may be obtained by dividing the sample sum of squared residuals by the number of degrees of freedom upon which it is based, in the usual way, and the probability limit of the matrix on the right may be estimated by the matrix itself. This, of course, is only an approximation to the asymptotic covariance, and beyond knowing that the approximation will improve with increasing sample size, we do not know how yoor it may be for finite sample sizes. Since plim $\hat{l} = 1$, two-stage least squares and limited information have the same asymptotic variance-covariance matrix (9-111). Some work by Nagar on the matrix of second-order sampling moments for k-class estimators suggests that if one is concerned to find a k-class estimator with as small a variance as possible around the true value, the indications are in favor of a k value less than unity, unless there is a large number of predetermined variables *excluded* from the equation in question.[2] This suggests that in small samples two-stage least squares (with $k = 1$) may have an advantage over limited information (with $\hat{l} > 1$), and it is interesting to examine the sampling experiments reported in Chap. 10 with this expectation in mind.

9-7. Tests of Identifying Restrictions

As we have seen, the identifiability of the coefficients in a particular relation depends first of all upon the number of variables excluded from that relation. This a priori exclusion of variables is

[1] *Ibid.*

[2] See A. L. Nagar, "The Bias and Moment Matrix of the General k-class Estimators of the Parameters in Simultaneous Equations," *Econometrica*, vol. 27, pp. 575–595, 1959.

itself subject to uncertainty, and it is desirable to have, if possible, a test of the hypothesized conditions for identifiability. As far as the necessary condition for identifiability (namely, the number of variables excluded) is concerned, the asymptotic distribution of a test statistic is given in Hood and Koopmans.[1] Experimental results suggest that this distribution may not be very closely approximated in finite sample sizes, and Basmann has suggested the following critical region for testing the identifiability hypothesis in finite sample sizes.[2] Refer again to the variance ratio defined in (9-82), namely,

$$l = \frac{\boldsymbol{\beta}_{1\Delta} \mathbf{W}^*_{\Delta\Delta} \boldsymbol{\beta}'_{1\Delta}}{\boldsymbol{\beta}_{1\Delta} \mathbf{W}_{\Delta\Delta} \boldsymbol{\beta}'_{1\Delta}}$$

and define

$$\varphi = l - 1$$

If we substitute the limited-information estimate for $\boldsymbol{\beta}_{1\Delta}$ in (9-82), we obtain the value $\hat{l}$ for the variance ratio. Likewise, if we replace $\boldsymbol{\beta}_{1\Delta}$ in (9-82) by its two-stage least-squares estimate, we shall obtain another value for the variance ratio, say, $\hat{\hat{l}}$. The two corresponding values of φ are denoted $\hat{\varphi}$ and $\hat{\hat{\varphi}}$. Basmann's suggested critical region for testing the necessary condition for identifiability is

$$\frac{n - K}{K^{**} - G^{\Delta} + 1} \hat{\varphi} \geq F_{\epsilon}$$

$$\frac{n - K}{K^{**} - G^{\Delta} + 1} \hat{\hat{\varphi}} \geq F_{\epsilon}$$

where F_{ϵ} indicates the appropriate upper tail of an F distribution with $(K^{**} - G^{\Delta} + 1, n - K)$ degrees of freedom.

9-8. Full-information Maximum Likelihood (FIML)

Consider the complete model

$$\mathbf{By}_t + \mathbf{\Gamma x}_t = \mathbf{u}_t$$

as specified in (9-23) above. On the assumption that the $\mathbf{u}$ vectors are serially independent, the likelihood function for the endogenous variables, conditional upon the values of $\mathbf{x}$, is shown in (9-32) to be

$$L = p(\mathbf{y}_1 \cdots \mathbf{y}_n | \mathbf{x}_1 \cdots \mathbf{x}_n) = |\det \mathbf{B}|^n p(\mathbf{u}_1) p(\mathbf{u}_2) \cdots p(\mathbf{u}_n)$$

[1] Hood and Koopmans, *op. cit.*, pp. 178–183.

[2] R. L. Basmann, "On Finite Sample Distributions of Generalized Classical Linear Identifiability Test Statistics," *J. Am. Statist. Assoc.*, vol. 55, pp. 650–659, 1960.

If we assume $\mathbf{u}_t$ to have a multiarivate normal distribution $N(\mathbf{0}, \mathbf{\Phi})$, where $\mathbf{\Phi} = E(\mathbf{u}_t\mathbf{u}_t')$ is a $G \times G$ symmetric matrix of the variances and covariances of the u_{it}, as in (9-27), then the log of the likelihood is

$$L^* = \log L = K + n \log |\det \mathbf{B}| + \det - \frac{n}{2} \log \det \mathbf{\Phi} - \frac{1}{2} \sum_{t=1}^{n} \mathbf{u}_t'\mathbf{\Phi}^{-1}\mathbf{u}_t \quad \text{(9-112)}$$

Maximizing L^* with respect to the elements of $\mathbf{B}$, $\mathbf{\Gamma}$, and $\mathbf{\Phi}$ leads to very difficult estimating equations for two reasons. First, equations such as $\partial L^*/\partial \beta_{ij} = 0$ give

$$\frac{n}{|\det \mathbf{B}|} \frac{\partial |\det \mathbf{B}|}{\partial \beta_{ij}} - \frac{1}{2} \frac{\partial S}{\partial \beta_{ij}} = 0$$

where $S = \Sigma_{t=1}^{n} \mathbf{u}_t'\mathbf{\Phi}^{-1}\mathbf{u}_t$. Det $\mathbf{B}$ is a function of the coefficients of the endogenous variables in all the equations in the model, and the result is very awkward nonlinear equations in the unknown coefficients. Second, the partial derivatives of quadratic forms $\mathbf{u}_t'\mathbf{\Phi}\mathbf{u}_t$ will also be nonlinear.

A special case of full-information maximum likelihood occurs when these difficulties both disappear. The first one disappears for *recursive* systems. An example of a recursive system is

$$\begin{aligned}
y_{1t} \qquad\qquad\qquad &+ \sum_{j=1}^{3} \gamma_{1j}x_{jt} = u_{1t} \\
\beta_{21}y_{1t} + y_{2t} \qquad\quad &+ \sum_{j=1}^{3} \gamma_{2j}x_{jt} = u_{2t} \\
\beta_{31}y_{1t} + \beta_{32}y_{2t} + y_{3t} &+ \sum_{j=1}^{3} \gamma_{3j}x_{jt} = u_{3t}
\end{aligned}$$

The $\mathbf{B}$ matrix is now triangular, and det $\mathbf{B}$ is unity. Recursive systems are particularly associated with Wold, who has argued that this stepwise chain of causation is a valid representation of economic mechanisms.[1] If in addition the $\mathbf{\Phi}$ matrix is diagonal, that is,

[1] See H. Wold and L. Jureen, *Demand Analysis*, Wiley, New York, 1953. R. Bentzel and B. Hansen, "On Recursiveness and Interdependency in Economic Models," *Rev. Economic Studies*, vol. 22, pp. 153–168, 1954–1955, have argued that even if a recursive structure is appropriate for some appropriately specified time period, the enforced use of data relating to longer time periods induces a simultaneous interdependency.

the contemporaneous disturbances in the G structural relations are not correlated, then the second source of nonlinearities in the estimating equations is removed, and full-information maximum likelihood is identical with ordinary least squares applied to each equation in turn.

Computational procedures for full-information methods in the nonrecursive case are explained by Chernoff and Divinsky.[1]

9-9. Three-stage Least Squares

Another simultaneous method of estimation has recently been proposed by Zellner and Theil.[2] The authors introduce the method by rewriting the two-stage least-squares estimator in a slightly different form. Consider the single equation

$$\mathbf{y}_1 = \mathbf{Y}_2\boldsymbol{\beta}_2' + \mathbf{X}_*\boldsymbol{\gamma}_{1*}' + \mathbf{u}_1 \tag{9-113}$$

where the only difference from (9-89) is that we have omitted the negative signs on the right-hand side. Rewrite (9-113) as

$$\mathbf{y}_1 = \mathbf{Z}_1\boldsymbol{\delta}_1 + \mathbf{u}_1 \tag{9-114}$$

where $$\mathbf{Z}_1 = [\mathbf{Y}_2 \quad \mathbf{X}_*] \qquad \text{and} \qquad \boldsymbol{\delta}_1 = \begin{bmatrix} \boldsymbol{\beta}_2' \\ \boldsymbol{\gamma}_{1*}' \end{bmatrix} \tag{9-115}$$

If we premultiply (9-114) by $\mathbf{X}'$, where $\mathbf{X} = [\mathbf{X}_* \quad \mathbf{X}_{**}]$ is the $n \times K$ matrix of observations on all the predetermined variables in the system, we have

$$\mathbf{X}'\mathbf{y}_1 = \mathbf{X}'\mathbf{Z}_1\boldsymbol{\delta}_1 + \mathbf{X}'\mathbf{u}_1 \tag{9-116}$$

This is a system of K equations in $G^\Delta - 1 + K^*$ unknowns, namely, the components of $\boldsymbol{\delta}_1$. If the relation (9-114) is exactly identified, $K^{**} = G^\Delta - 1$ and the number of unknown parameters is exactly equal to the number of equations. This suggests estimating $\boldsymbol{\delta}_1$ by replacing the disturbance vector $\mathbf{X}'\mathbf{u}_1$ in (9-116) by its expected value, which is the zero vector, thus obtaining the estimator

$$\hat{\boldsymbol{\delta}}_1 = (\mathbf{X}'\mathbf{Z}_1)^{-1}\mathbf{X}'\mathbf{y}_1 \tag{9-117}$$

This, in fact, is the indirect-least-squares estimator.[3]

In the overidentified case, $K^{**} > G^\Delta - 1$, and the number of equations in (9-116) exceeds the number of unknowns, which is the

[1] See Hood and Koopmans, *op. cit.*, chap. 10.

[2] Arnold Zellner and H. Theil, "Three-stage Least Squares: Simultaneous Estimation of Simultaneous Equations," *Econometria*, vol. 30, pp. 54–78, 1962.

[3] See Exercise 9-2.

usual least-squares situation. However, (9-116) is not suitable for the application of ordinary least squares. If we assume the predetermined variables to consist solely of exogenous variables, then the variance-covariance matrix of the disturbance vector $\mathbf{X'u_1}$ is

$$\text{var}\,(\mathbf{X'u_1}) = E(\mathbf{X'u_1u_1'X}) = \sigma_{11}(\mathbf{X'X}) \tag{9-118}$$

where we are assuming $E(\mathbf{u_1u_1'}) = \sigma_{11}\mathbf{I}$, σ_{11} being the constant variance of u_{1t}, the serial covariances being zero. The form of (9-118) suggests applying the generalized-least-squares approach of Chap. 7 to the estimation of the parameters of (9-116). The estimator will then be

$$\hat{\boldsymbol{\delta}}_1 = [\mathbf{Z_1'X(X'X)^{-1}X'Z_1}]^{-1}\mathbf{Z_1'X(X'X)^{-1}X'y_1} \tag{9-119}$$

This is the two-stage least-squares estimator already developed in (9-97).[1]

The essential idea in three-stage least squares is to write *each* equation in the model in the form (9-116) and then to apply generalized least squares to the whole set of relations to estimate all parameters simultaneously. Setting out all equations in the form (9-116) gives

$$\begin{bmatrix} \mathbf{X'y_1} \\ \mathbf{X'y_2} \\ \cdot \\ \cdot \\ \cdot \\ \mathbf{X'y}_G \end{bmatrix} = \begin{bmatrix} \mathbf{X'Z_1} & \mathbf{0} & \cdots & \mathbf{0} \\ \mathbf{0} & \mathbf{X'Z_2} & \cdots & \mathbf{0} \\ \cdot & & & \cdot \\ \cdot & & & \cdot \\ \cdot & & & \cdot \\ \mathbf{0} & \mathbf{0} & \cdots & \mathbf{X'Z}_G \end{bmatrix} \begin{bmatrix} \boldsymbol{\delta}_1 \\ \boldsymbol{\delta}_2 \\ \cdot \\ \cdot \\ \cdot \\ \boldsymbol{\delta}_G \end{bmatrix} + \begin{bmatrix} \mathbf{X'u_1} \\ \mathbf{X'u_2} \\ \cdot \\ \cdot \\ \cdot \\ \mathbf{X'u}_G \end{bmatrix} \tag{9-120}$$

or

$$\mathbf{A} = \mathbf{B}\boldsymbol{\delta} + \mathbf{v} \tag{9-121}$$

which is a system of KG equations in the elements of the vector $\boldsymbol{\delta}$, where $\boldsymbol{\delta}$ represents the column vector of all the unknown parameters of the right-hand side of (9-120). The variance-covariance matrix for the disturbance term in (9-120) is

$$\mathbf{V} = \text{var}\begin{bmatrix} \mathbf{X_1'u_1} \\ \cdot \\ \cdot \\ \cdot \\ \mathbf{X'u}_G \end{bmatrix} = \begin{bmatrix} \sigma_{11}\mathbf{X'X} & \sigma_{12}\mathbf{X'X} & \cdots & \sigma_{1G}\mathbf{X'X} \\ \sigma_{21}\mathbf{X'X} & \sigma_{22}\mathbf{X'X} & \cdots & \sigma_{2G}\mathbf{X'X} \\ \cdot & & & \cdot \\ \cdot & & & \cdot \\ \cdot & & & \cdot \\ \sigma_{G1}\mathbf{X'X} & \sigma_{G2}\mathbf{X'X} & \cdots & \sigma_{GG}\mathbf{X'X} \end{bmatrix} \tag{9-122}$$

[1] See Exercise 9-3.

where

$$\boldsymbol{\sigma}_{ij} = E(\mathbf{u}_i\mathbf{u}_j') = \begin{bmatrix} E(u_{i1}u_{j1}) & E(u_{i1}u_{j2}) & \cdots & E(u_{i1}u_{jn}) \\ \cdot & & & \cdot \\ \cdot & & & \cdot \\ \cdot & & & \cdot \\ E(u_{in}u_{j1}) & E(u_{in}u_{j2}) & \cdots & E(u_{in}u_{jn}) \end{bmatrix} = \sigma_{ij}\mathbf{I}$$

so that σ_{ij} denotes the contemporaneous covariance of the disturbances in the ith and jth structural equations, but by assumption all serial covariances between the two disturbances are zero. Applying generalized least squares to (9-121) then gives

$$\hat{\boldsymbol{\delta}} = (\mathbf{B}'\mathbf{V}^{-1}\mathbf{B})^{-1}\mathbf{B}'\mathbf{V}^{-1}\mathbf{A} \tag{9-123}$$

where the **A** vector and the **B** matrix are defined by the comparison between (9-120) and (9-121). These involve moments of the observed variables only. The **V** matrix, however, involves the unknown disturbance covariances σ_{ij}. The authors recommend that these be replaced by their two-stage least-squares estimates S_{ij}. The variance-covariance matrix for $\hat{\boldsymbol{\delta}}$ is given by

$$\text{var}\,(\hat{\boldsymbol{\delta}}) = \begin{bmatrix} S^{11}\mathbf{Z}_1'\mathbf{X}(\mathbf{X}'\mathbf{X})^{-1}\mathbf{X}'\mathbf{Z}_1 & \cdots & S^{1G}\mathbf{Z}_1'\mathbf{X}(\mathbf{X}'\mathbf{X})^{-1}\mathbf{X}'\mathbf{Z}_G \\ \cdot & & \cdot \\ \cdot & & \cdot \\ \cdot & & \cdot \\ S^{G1}\mathbf{Z}_G'\mathbf{X}(\mathbf{X}'\mathbf{X})^{-1}\mathbf{X}'\mathbf{Z}_1 & \cdots & S^{GG}\mathbf{Z}_G'\mathbf{X}(\mathbf{X}'\mathbf{X})^{-1}\mathbf{X}'\mathbf{Z}_G \end{bmatrix} \tag{9-124}$$

where

$$[S^{ij}] = [S_{ij}]^{-1} \tag{9-125}$$

The authors show that three-stage least squares may be expected to be more efficient than two-stage least squares. As with full-information maximum likelihood, this result depends upon the correct specification of the complete model. There are indications that full-information estimators are very sensitive to specification error and likely to be seriously affected by its presence; it is not yet known if three-stage least squares is equally liable to be affected by specification error.

Example. The following example is not meant to be economically realistic nor is it meant to be an illustration of an efficient computational approach. It is intended as a simple small-scale example of the computation of limited-information and two-stage least-squares estimates for an overidentified equation. The computations are laid out to follow the development of the formulas in the text and are capable of being followed by any student on a desk calculator. More realistic and complex calculations should ideally be done with one of the many programs now available for electronic computers.

Let us postulate a simple national-income model:

$$C_t = \alpha_1 + \alpha_2 Y_t + u_{1t} \tag{9-126}$$
$$I_t = \beta_1 + \beta_2 Y_t + \beta_3 I_{t-1} + u_{2t} \tag{9-127}$$
$$Y_t = C_t + I_t + Z_t \tag{9-128}$$

where C_t = consumption expenditure in time period t
Y_t = gross domestic product in time period t
I_t = gross fixed capital formation in time period t
Z_t = exogenous factor in time period t (namely, gross investment in stocks + government expenditure on goods and services + gross public investment + exports − imports)

The model contains three current endogenous variables, C_t, I_t, and Y_t, and three predetermined variables, namely, I_{t-1}, Z_t, and a variable which is always unity to take care of the constant term in the first two relations.

Data on the variables in the model for the United Kingdom economy 1948–1958 are presented in Table 9-2.

TABLE 9-2. UNITED KINGDOM NATIONAL-INCOME DATA
(£000 in 1954 prices)

Year	Y_t	C_t	I_t	Z_t
1948	13,895	10,706	1,024	2,165
1949	14,377	10,940	1,078	2,359
1950	14,843	11,250	1,123	2,470
1951	15,307	11,089	1,052	3,166
1952	15,360	11,023	980	3,357
1953	15,951	11,474	1,073	3,404
1954	16,680	12,023	1,281	3,376
1955	17,237	12,443	1,474	3,320
1956	17,547	12,548	1,591	3,408
1957	17,788	12,802	1,668	3,318
1958	17,699	13,096	1,709	2,894

SOURCE: 1959 Blue Book on National Income and Expenditure, H. M. Stationery Office, London.

Let us estimate the parameters of the consumption relation (9-126) by both limited-information and two-stage least-squares methods. The equation is overidentified, since two predetermined variables, I_{t-1} and Z_t, do not appear ($K^{**} = 2$) and two current endogenous variables do, so that $G^{\Delta} = 2$ and $K^{**} > G^{\Delta} - 1$. Rewrite the equation as

$$y_{1t} + \beta_{12} y_{2t} + \gamma_{11} x_{1t} = u_{1t} \tag{9-129}$$

where $y_{1t} = 0.0001 C_t \qquad y_{2t} = 0.0001 Y_t$ (9-130)

and $\beta_{12} = -\alpha_2 \qquad \text{and} \qquad \gamma_{11} = 0.0001\alpha_1$ (9-131)

The purpose of the transformations in (9-130) is to express all variables in comparable magnitude for the calculations to minimize the effects of rounding errors. Referring now to (9-78), the basic data matrices for use in the limited-information calculations are:

$$\mathbf{Y}_\Delta = \begin{array}{cc} y_1 & y_2 \\ \end{array} \begin{bmatrix} 1.09 & 1.44 \\ 1.12 & 1.48 \\ 1.11 & 1.53 \\ 1.10 & 1.54 \\ 1.15 & 1.59 \\ 1.20 & 1.67 \\ 1.24 & 1.72 \\ 1.25 & 1.75 \\ 1.28 & 1.78 \\ 1.31 & 1.77 \end{bmatrix} \qquad \mathbf{X}_* = \begin{bmatrix} 1 \\ 1 \\ 1 \\ 1 \\ 1 \\ 1 \\ 1 \\ 1 \\ 1 \\ 1 \end{bmatrix} \qquad \mathbf{X}_{**} = \begin{array}{cc} x_2 & x_3 \end{array} \begin{bmatrix} 1.02 & 2.36 \\ 1.08 & 2.47 \\ 1.12 & 3.17 \\ 1.05 & 3.36 \\ 0.98 & 3.40 \\ 1.07 & 3.38 \\ 1.28 & 3.32 \\ 1.47 & 3.41 \\ 1.59 & 3.32 \\ 1.67 & 2.89 \end{bmatrix}$$

where $x_{2t} = 0.001I_{t-1}$ and $x_{3t} = 0.001Z_t$. Because of the one-period lag in the investment function, we have to start C_t, Y_t, and Z_t at 1949. We have also expressed all figures correct to just two decimal places in order to keep the illustrative calculations simple.

We proceed first to the calculation of $\mathbf{W}^*_{\Delta\Delta}$ as defined in (9-80). The steps are

$$\mathbf{Y}'_\Delta\mathbf{Y}_\Delta = \begin{bmatrix} 14.1017 & 19.3694 \\ 19.3694 & 26.6157 \end{bmatrix}$$

$$\mathbf{Y}'_\Delta\mathbf{X}_* = \begin{bmatrix} 11.85 \\ 16.27 \end{bmatrix} \qquad \mathbf{X}'_*\mathbf{X}_* = 10$$

$$\mathbf{Y}'_\Delta\mathbf{X}_*(\mathbf{X}'_*\mathbf{X}_*)^{-1}\mathbf{X}'_*\mathbf{Y}_\Delta = \begin{bmatrix} 14.04225 & 19.27995 \\ 19.27995 & 26.47129 \end{bmatrix}$$

and so

$$\mathbf{W}^*_{\Delta\Delta} = \begin{bmatrix} 0.05945 & 0.08945 \\ 0.08945 & 0.14441 \end{bmatrix}$$

Next we calculate $\mathbf{W}_{\Delta\Delta}$ as defined in (9-81). The main steps are

$$\mathbf{Y}'_\Delta\mathbf{X} = \begin{bmatrix} 11.85 & 14.7782 & 36.9343 \\ 16.27 & 20.3031 & 50.8319 \end{bmatrix}$$

$$\mathbf{X}'\mathbf{X} = \begin{bmatrix} 10 & 12.33 & 31.08 \\ 12.33 & 15.7853 & 38.4692 \\ 31.08 & 38.4692 & 98.0184 \end{bmatrix}$$

with

$$(\mathbf{X}'\mathbf{X})^{-1} = \begin{bmatrix} 8.355{,}789{,}77 & -1.605{,}427{,}86 & -2.019{,}400{,}65 \\ -1.605{,}427{,}86 & 1.763{,}372{,}32 & -0.183{,}014{,}87 \\ -2.019{,}400{,}65 & -0.183{,}014{,}87 & 0.722{,}348{,}13 \end{bmatrix}$$

and so

$$\mathbf{Y}'_\Delta\mathbf{X}(\mathbf{X}'\mathbf{X})^{-1}\mathbf{X}'\mathbf{Y}_\Delta = \begin{bmatrix} 14.093{,}012{,}05 & 19.358{,}588{,}84 \\ 19.358{,}588{,}84 & 26.601{,}881{,}61 \end{bmatrix}$$

Hence

$$\mathbf{W}_{\Delta\Delta} = \begin{bmatrix} 0.008{,}687{,}95 & 0.010{,}811{,}16 \\ 0.010{,}811{,}16 & 0.013{,}818{,}39 \end{bmatrix}$$

The determinantal equation (9-85) now gives

$$31{,}723l^2 - 1{,}420{,}136l + 5{,}838{,}720 = 0$$

or

$$l^2 - 44.766{,}757l + 184.053{,}161 = 0$$

which has a smaller root of

$$\hat{l} = 4.579{,}938$$

On the substitution of this root in (9-86),

$$(\mathbf{W}^*_{\Delta\Delta} - \hat{l}\mathbf{W}_{\Delta\Delta})\hat{\boldsymbol{\beta}}'_{1\Delta} = \mathbf{0}$$

we obtain

$$\begin{bmatrix} 0.019{,}659{,}73 & 0.039{,}935{,}56 \\ 0.039{,}935{,}56 & 0.081{,}122{,}63 \end{bmatrix} \begin{bmatrix} 1 \\ \beta_{12} \end{bmatrix} = \begin{bmatrix} 0 \\ 0 \end{bmatrix}$$

which gives $\hat{\beta}_{12} = -0.492{,}286$

Finally, substituting this in (9-87) gives

$$\begin{aligned} \hat{\gamma}_{11} &= -\hat{\boldsymbol{\beta}}_{1\Delta}\mathbf{Y}'_{\Delta}\mathbf{X}_*(\mathbf{X}'_*\mathbf{X}_*)^{-1} \\ &= [1 \quad -0.492{,}286]\begin{bmatrix} 1.185 \\ 1.627 \end{bmatrix} \\ &= -0.3841 \end{aligned}$$

From (9-131) we can then write

$$\hat{\alpha}_2 = 0.4923 \qquad \text{and} \qquad \hat{\alpha}_1 = 3{,}841$$

so that the estimated consumption relation becomes

$$C_t = 3{,}841 + 0.4923Y_t \tag{9-132}$$

where the variables are expressed in units of £1,000.

Turning now to the two-stage least-squares estimates, the basic data matrices are the same as before except that the $\mathbf{Y}_\Delta$ matrix is partitioned into two separate column vectors $\mathbf{y}_1$ and $\mathbf{Y}_2$ in accordance with the layout in (9-90).

From (9-92),

$$\begin{aligned} (\mathbf{Y}_2 - \mathbf{V})' &= \mathbf{Y}'_2\mathbf{X}(\mathbf{X}'\mathbf{X})^{-1}\mathbf{X}' \\ &= [16.27 \quad 20.3031 \quad 50.8319](\mathbf{X}'\mathbf{X})^{-1}\mathbf{X}' \end{aligned}$$

for $\mathbf{Y}'_2\mathbf{X}$ is the second row in $\mathbf{Y}'_\Delta\mathbf{X}$ above. Multiplying out gives a row vector with 10 elements, and from this we may obtain

$$\begin{aligned} (\mathbf{Y}_2 - \mathbf{V})'(\mathbf{Y}_2 - \mathbf{V}) &= 26.601{,}515 \\ (\mathbf{Y}_2 - \mathbf{V})'\mathbf{y}_1 &= 19.358{,}460 \\ \mathbf{X}'_*\mathbf{Y}_2 &= 16.27 \\ \mathbf{X}'_*\mathbf{y}_1 &= 11.85 \end{aligned}$$

Substituting these quantities in (9-95) gives

$$\begin{aligned} \begin{bmatrix} \hat{\beta}_{12} \\ \hat{\gamma}_{11} \end{bmatrix} &= -\begin{bmatrix} 26.601{,}515 & 16.27 \\ 16.27 & 10 \end{bmatrix}^{-1} \begin{bmatrix} 19.358{,}460 \\ 11.85 \end{bmatrix} \\ &= \begin{bmatrix} -0.6029 \\ -0.2041 \end{bmatrix} \end{aligned}$$

giving as the estimated consumption relation

$$C_t = 2{,}041 + 0.6029Y_t \tag{9-133}$$

An indication of sampling errors may be obtained from the asymptotic formula (9-111) by substituting estimates obtained from the sample observations. This gives

$$\text{est }(\mathbf{e}_k\mathbf{e}_k') = \sigma^2\begin{bmatrix}\mathbf{Y}_2'\mathbf{Y}_2 - \mathbf{V}'\mathbf{V} & \mathbf{Y}_2'\mathbf{X}_* \\ \mathbf{X}_*'\mathbf{Y}_2 & \mathbf{X}_*'\mathbf{X}_*\end{bmatrix}^{-1}$$

The matrix to be inverted has already been obtained in the calculation of the two-stage least-squares (TSLS) estimates as

$$\begin{bmatrix}26.601{,}515 & 16.27 \\ 16.27 & 10\end{bmatrix}$$

The variance of the disturbance term σ^2 may be estimated by computing the residual sum of squares from the fitted relation and dividing by $n - 2$. For the LISE estimates this procedure yields $\hat{\sigma}^2 = 0.0007$, and for TSLS estimates $\hat{\sigma}^2 = 0.0005$, and the variance-covariance matrices are thus

$$\begin{bmatrix}0.0054 & -0.0087 \\ -0.0087 & 0.0143\end{bmatrix} \quad \text{for LISE}$$

and

$$\begin{bmatrix}0.0038 & -0.0062 \\ -0.0062 & 0.0102\end{bmatrix} \quad \text{for TSLS}$$

References

The seminal article on simultaneous-equation problems is

1. T. Haavelmo: "The Statistical Implications of a System of Simultaneous Equations," *Econometrica*, vol. 11, pp. 1–12, 1943.

His early ideas were further developed in

2. T. Haavelmo: "The Probability Approach in Econometrics," *Econometrica*, vol. 12, supplement, July, 1944, 118 pp.

The first major attack on simultaneous-equation estimation problems is described in

3. T. C. Koopmans (ed.): *Statistical Inference in Dynamic Economic Models*, Wiley, New York, 1950.

A simpler presentation, with emphasis on limited-information estimates, is given in

4. W. C. Hood and T. C. Koopmans (eds.): *Studies in Econometric Method*, Wiley, New York, 1953.

5. L. R. Klein: *A Textbook of Econometrics*, Harper & Row, New York, 1953,

gives an excellent account of the construction of simultaneous-equation models and associated estimation techniques. It also contains an excellent treatment of cross-section analysis.

A valuable reference work on many aspects of multivariate analysis and on time-series analysis is

6. G. Tintner: *Econometrics*, Wiley, New York, 1952.

For more recent work on two-stage least-squares and associated techniques, the basic references are

7. H. Theil: *Economic Forecasts and Policy*, 2d ed., North-Holland Publishing Company, Amsterdam, 1961, pp. 204–240, 326–357.
8. R. L. Basmann: "A Generalized Classical Method of Linear Estimation of Coefficients in a Structural Equation," *Econometrica*, vol. 25, pp. 77–83, 1957.
9. R. L. Basmann: "On the Asymptotic Distribution of Generalized Linear Estimators," *Econometrica*, vol. 28, pp. 97–107, 1960.
10. R. L. Basmann: "The Computation of Generalized Classical Estimates of Coefficients in a Structural Equation," *Econometrica*, vol. 27, pp. 72–81, 1959.
11. A. Zellner and H. Theil: "Three-stage Least Squares: Simultaneous Estimation of Simultaneous Relations," *Econometrica*, vol. 30, 1962, pp. 54–78.

Two mathematical derivations of the *small-sample* properties of these estimators are contained in

12. R. L. Basmann: "A Note on the Exact Finite Sample Frequency Functions of Generalized Classical Linear Estimators in Two Leading Overidentified Cases," *J. Am. Statist. Assoc.*, vol. 56, pp. 619–636, 1961.
13. A. L. Nagar: "The Bias and Moment Matrix of the General k-class Estimators of the Parameters in Simultaneous Equations," *Econometrica*, vol. 27, pp. 575–595, 1959.

For specific work on identification problems see

14. R. L. Basmann: "On Finite Sample Distributions of Generalized Classical Linear Identifiability Test Statistics," *J. Am. Statist. Assoc.*, vol. 55, pp. 650–659, 1960.
15. F. M. Fisher: "Generalization of the Rank and Order Conditions for Identifiability," *Econometrica*, vol. 27, pp. 431–447, 1959.
16. F. M. Fisher: "On the Cost of Approximate Specification in Simultaneous Equation Estimation," *Econometrica*, vol. 29, pp. 139–170, 1961.

An attempt to provide a multiple-equation version of R^2, that is, a single statistic to express the proportion of the variance of the jointly determined variables that has been explained by the predetermined variables, is given in

17. J. W. Hooper: "Simultaneous Equations and Canonical Correlation Theory," *Econometrica*, vol. 27, pp. 245–256, 1959.

Estimation of reduced forms for simultaneous-equation systems may prove impossible if the number of predetermined variables exceeds the number of observations. A way out is suggested in

18. T. Kloek and L. B. M. Mennes: "Simultaneous Equation Estimation Based on Principal Components of Predetermined Variables," *Econometrica*, vol. 28, pp. 45–61, 1960.

An important article describing methods of incorporating *a priori* or *statistical* knowledge about certain parameters into the estimation process, whether for single- or multiple-equation systems, is

19. H. Theil and A. S. Goldberger: "On Pure and Mixed Statistical Estimation in Economics," *Intern. Econ. Rev.*, vol. 2, pp. 65–78, 1961.

Two attempts to deal jointly with simultaneous-equation problems and autocorrelated disturbances are

20. J. D. Sargan: "The Maximum Likelihood Estimation of Economic Relationships with Autoregressive Residuals," *Econometrica*, vol. 29, pp. 414–426, 1961.

and

21. A. Zellner: "Econometric Estimation with Temporally Dependent Disturbance Terms," *Intern. Econ. Rev.*, vol. 2, pp. 164–178, 1961.

Exercises

9-1. Examine the identifiability of the parameters in the model

$$\begin{aligned} y_{1t} + \beta_{12}y_{2t} &= u_{1t} \\ \beta_{21}y_{1t} + y_{2t} + \gamma_{21}x_{1t} &= u_{2t} \end{aligned}$$

under the assumption that the variance-covariance matrix of the disturbances is

$$\mathbf{\Phi} = \begin{bmatrix} \sigma_{11} & \sigma_{12} \\ \sigma_{12} & k\sigma_{11} \end{bmatrix}$$

where k is a known constant.

9-2. Prove the assertion that the estimator defined in (9-117) is the indirect-least-squares estimator in the exactly identified case.

9-3. Prove the assertion that the estimator defined in (9-119) is the two-stage least-squares estimator.

9-4. For the data in Table 9-1, estimate the parameters of the model

$$\begin{aligned} C_t &= \alpha_1 + \alpha_2 Y_t + \alpha_3 C_{t-1} + u_{1t} \\ I_t &= \beta_1 + \beta_2 Y_t + \beta_3 I_{t-1} + u_{2t} \\ Y_t &= C_t + I_t + Z_t \end{aligned}$$

by limited-information and two-stage least-squares methods.

10

Simultaneous-equation Problems: II

10-1. Monte Carlo Studies

Ordinary least squares is seen to give biased and inconsistent estimators when applied to relationships with current endogenous variables on the right-hand side. The other estimators developed for simultaneous-equation systems will also, in general, be biased, but they have the desirable large-sample property of consistency. On the assumption of normal and serially independent disturbance terms limited-information estimators will have the maximum-likelihood properties of asymptotic normality and efficiency (that is, minimum variance with respect to the class of estimators using the same a priori information). Two-stage least-squares estimators are likewise consistent and possess the same limiting distribution as limited-information single-equation estimators.

Asymptotic properties, however, are cold comfort for econometricians typically working with small samples of data. For the practical choice of estimation method the small-sample properties of the various estimators are of crucial importance. Do two estimators with identical asymptotic properties have identical small-sample properties or not? Would a ranking of estimators by the desirability of their asymptotic properties coincide with a ranking on the basis of their small-sample properties? For reasons of mathematical intractability there are as yet few general results on the small-sample properties of simultaneous-equation estimators.[1] An alternative source of information is provided by Monte Carlo studies. The essence of the Monte Carlo approach is to postulate

[1] See, however, Refs. 12 and 13 at the end of Chap. 9.

a model, and then to concentrate on one or more structures within the model by assigning specific numerical values to the parameters, including the elements of the variance-covariance matrix of the disturbances. For any such structure repeated samples of disturbances are drawn from the hypothesized disturbance distribution by using appropriate tables of random numbers. The sample size is usually chosen in the range 15 to 40, to reflect the small sample sizes with which econometricians typically have to work, at least in time-series analysis. In addition, arbitrary values are specified for the exogenous variables, and these are sometimes held constant from sample to sample and sometimes not. The exogenous variables are combined with the disturbance values for each sample to generate values for the endogenous variables. The estimating methods under study are then applied to each sample set of endogenous and exogenous values. This process is replicated a large number of times (typically 50, 100, or 200), and the resultant frequency distributions of estimates are studied in conjunction with the true values of the parameters in order to conjecture the small-sample properties of the estimators.

In studying individual parameters three important criteria are usually distinguished. These are bias, variance, and mean-square error. Bias is the discrepancy between the mean of the sampling distribution of estimates and the true value. If θ denotes the true value of the parameter and $\bar{\hat{\theta}}$ the mean of the sampling distribution of estimates,

$$\text{Bias} = \bar{\hat{\theta}} - \theta \tag{10-1}$$

Variance is simply the variance of the estimates around their mean; that is,

$$\text{var} = \frac{\sum_{i=1}^{N} (\hat{\theta}_i - \bar{\hat{\theta}})^2}{N} \tag{10-2}$$

where N is the total number of replications. Mean-square error is the variance of the estimates around the true value of the parameter being estimated; that is,

$$\text{MSE} = \frac{\sum_{i=1}^{N} (\hat{\theta}_i - \theta)^2}{N} \tag{10-3}$$

and it is easy to see that the mean square error is equal to the variance plus the square of the bias; that is,

$$\frac{\sum_{i=1}^{N} (\hat{\theta}_i - \theta)^2}{N} = \frac{\sum_{i=1}^{N} (\hat{\theta}_i - \bar{\hat{\theta}})^2}{N} + (\bar{\hat{\theta}} - \theta)^2 \qquad (10\text{-}4)$$

The rationale of the mean-square-error criterion is that estimates near the true value are "good," those far away are "bad," irrespective of the direction of the discrepancy, and so all discrepancies are squared and averaged. It is clear from (10-4) that a biased estimate may thus show a smaller mean square error than an unbiased one if it more than compensates for its bias by having a smaller variance. Criteria (10-2) and (10-3) are sometimes expressed in square-root form as the standard deviation and root-mean-square error, respectively.

Basmann has recently pointed out that it is meaningless to seek information about the bias and/or the mean square deviation of an estimator if that estimator does not possess finite first or second moments.[1] It is still, of course, meaningful to compare the frequency distributions of estimates yielded by different methods, and comparisons between *sample* mean square deviations for different estimators still provide some useful summary information on the dispersion of the estimates even though the appropriate moments may not exist for one or more of the estimators. It would be most useful if Monte Carlo studies always presented full frequency distributions of estimates, but this is not the case for those already published.

In assessing various estimators the relevant criteria depend on the purposes for which one wants an econometric model. It is possible to distinguish at least three separate interests. First, one may be concerned with the structural parameters and regard precise knowledge of their numerical values as a desirable end, for these are the basic parameters of economic theory. Second, interest may center upon the parameters of the reduced form, for the coefficients of the exogenous variables in the reduced-form equations are short-term multiplier values showing the estimated effect of changes in

[1] R. L. Basmann, "A Note on the Exact Finite Sample Frequency Functions of Generalized Classical Linear Estimators in Two Leading Over-identified Cases," *J. Am. Statist. Assoc.*, vol. 56, pp. 619–636, 1961.

exogenous variables on the various endogenous variables.[1] Third, one may be concerned with the overall properties of the system and in particular with the forecasting precision that can be achieved by using the reduced form to predict values of the endogenous variables for given values of the predetermined variables.[2] For individual parameters, whether of the structure or the reduced form, bias, variance, and root mean square are relevant to the assessment of different estimators; for forecasting performance the conditional accuracy of the forecast for given predetermined variables is the prime consideration. In surveying the Monte Carlo studies we shall look for information on all three points, but as we shall see, not all studies provide information on all points. In looking at structural equations we shall be concerned with four estimators, namely, ordinary least squares (OLS), two-stage least squares (TSLS), limited-information single equation (LISE), and full-information maximum likelihood (FIML). This excludes estimation by the use of instrumental variables and two special k-class estimators proposed by Nagar.[3] Once the structural parameters have been estimated by any one of the above methods, straightforward algebraic solution of the equations for the current endogenous variables will give the corresponding reduced-form coefficients. It is also possible to estimate the reduced-form coefficients by the direct application of least squares to each reduced-form relation. We shall call this method least squares with no restrictions (LSNR), so that we have five different methods to compare for reduced-form coefficients.

The Summers study was based on the following model:[4]

$$\begin{aligned} y_{1t} + \beta_{12}y_{2t} + \gamma_{11}z_{1t} + \gamma_{12}z_{2t} \qquad\qquad\qquad\qquad\quad + \gamma_{10} &= u_{1t} \\ y_{1t} + \beta_{22}y_{2t} \qquad\qquad\quad + \gamma_{23}z_{3t} + \gamma_{24}z_{4t} + \gamma_{20} &= u_{2t} \end{aligned} \tag{10-5}$$

with the disturbances u_1, u_2 having a bivariate normal distribution.

[1] See, in particular, A. S. Goldberger, *Impact Multipliers and the Dynamic Properties of the Klein-Goldberger Model*, North-Holland Publishing Company, Amsterdam, 1959.

[2] See L. R. Klein, "The Efficiency of Estimation in Econometric Models," pp. 216–232 in *Essays in Economics and Econometrics*, The University of North Carolina Press, Chapel Hill, N.C., 1960.

[3] A. L. Nagar, "A Monte Carlo Study of Alternative Simultaneous Equation Estimators," *Econometrica*, vol. 28, pp. 573–590, 1960.

[4] R. Summers, "A Capital-intensive Approach to the Small Sample Properties of Various Simultaneous Equation Estimators," unpublished paper, 1962. I am very grateful to Professor Summers for permission to quote from his paper.

In addition to the eight β and γ parameters in (10-5), one has to specify the parameters of the variance-covariance matrix of the u's, the number of observations T in each sample, and the number of replications N, that is, the number of different samples drawn from the specified population for each set of parameter values. Table 10-1 shows the six different parameter sets (experiments) chosen by Summers.

TABLE 10-1. PARAMETER COMBINATIONS USED IN SAMPLING EXPERIMENTS

Experiments	β_{12}	γ_{11}	γ_{12}	γ_{10}	β_{22}	γ_{23}	γ_{24}	γ_{20}	σ_{11}	σ_{12}	σ_{22}	T	N
1A and 1B	−0.7	0.8	0.7	−149.5	0.4	0.6	−0.4	−149.6	400	200	400	20	50
2A and 2B	−0.7	0.8	0.7	−149.5	0.4	0.6	−0.4	−149.6	400	200	400	40	50
3A and 3B	−0.1	0.8	0.7	−149.5	0.4	0.6	−0.4	−149.6	400	200	400	20	50
4A and 4B	−1.3	0.8	0.7	−149.5	0.4	0.6	−0.4	−149.6	400	200	400	20	50
5A and 5B†	−0.7	0.8	0.7	−149.5	0.4	0.6	−0.4	−149.6	400	200	400	20	50
6A and 6B‡	−0.7	0.8	0.7	−149.5	0.4	0.6	−0.4	−149.6	400	200	400	20	50

† In experiments 5A and 5B, $\gamma_{21} = +0.5$ instead of zero as assumed in all experiments except experiments 6A and 6B.

‡ In experiments 6A and 6B, $\gamma_{21} = -0.5$ instead of zero as assumed in all experiments except experiments 5A and 5B.

The difference between the A and B experiments lies in the degree of intercorrelation between the exogenous variables, the z's. In experiment B they are fairly highly correlated, while in experiment A they are approximately uncorrelated. Each z series is positively autocorrelated since it was selected to represent real economic data. Notice also the presence of specification error in experiments 5 and 6. In these two experiments the z_1 variable was present in the second equation with a nonzero coefficient, but in the estimation procedures it was assumed that the structure specified in (10-5) was correct and that γ_{21} was zero.

Turning first to look at the results obtained for structural coefficients by the various estimating methods employed, one must emphasize that it is impossible to do full justice in the summary tables below to the wealth of information presented in Summers' detailed tables. Summers employed four different methods of estimating the structural parameters, namely:

Limited-information single-equation (LISE)
Two-stage least-squares (TSLS)
Ordinary least-squares (OLS)
Full-information maximum-likelihood (FIML)

In any given experiment 50 replications of an estimating method yield 50 estimates of each structural parameter. For each parameter these 50 values yield estimates of bias, standard deviation (SD), and root-mean-square error (RMSE), as described earlier. If we pool experiments 1A to 4A, in which there is no specification error, and remember that there are eight parameters (βs and γs) in each experiment, we have 32 parameters in all, each of which is estimated by four methods. For any criterion such as root-mean-square deviation, one may simply note which estimator gives the smallest abso-

TABLE 10-2. FREQUENCIES OF BEST RESULTS FOR STRUCTURAL PARAMETERS, EXPERIMENTS 1A TO 4A†

Estimator	Frequencies		
	Bias	SD	RMSE
LISE	12½	0	2½
TSLS	5	½	6½
OLS	1	20	7½
FIML	13½	11½	15½
Total	32	32	32

† Compiled from detailed tables in R. Summers, "A Capital-intensive Approach to the Small Sample Properties of Various Simultaneous Equation Estimators," unpublished paper, 1962. Fractions arise when two or more estimators tie for lowest value of a criterion.

lute value for that parameter. Table 10-2 contains frequency distributions showing the number of times out of a possible 32 that each estimator produced the lowest value for a given criterion.

As an illustration of the information contained in Table 10-2 we see that for only 1 parameter out of the 32 considered does OLS show the least bias among the four estimating methods and for only 5 did TSLS show the least bias. The next column of the table confirms in rather striking fashion the minimum-variance property of OLS, but it is, of course, minimum variance around a biased mean. The final column on RMSE is the most important and displays the overall superiority of FIML as judged by this criterion. It is rather remarkable, however, how the minimum-variance property of OLS has helped to offset the bias and give a frequency on RMSE which is marginally better than TSLS and well ahead of LISE.

Another way of looking at the relative performance of these four estimators is to concentrate upon a single criterion such as RMSE and assign the rankings 1, 2, 3, 4 to the estimators in ascending value of RMSE for each of the 32 parameters. The results of this computation are shown in Table 10-3. Low values imply good

TABLE 10-3. STRUCTURAL PARAMETERS, RANKINGS BY RMSE, EXPERIMENTS 1A TO 4A†

Estimator	LISE	TSLS	OLS	FIML
Total ranks	83.5	75.0	107.5	54.0

† Compiled from Summers' detailed tables.

TABLE 10-4. FREQUENCIES OF BEST RESULTS FOR STRUCTURAL PARAMETERS, EXPERIMENTS 5A AND 6A†

Estimator	Frequencies		
	Bias	SD	RMSE
LISE	5	0	4⅚
TSLS	5	0	3⅚
OLS	5	14	5
FIML	1	2	2⅓
Total	16	16	16

† Compiled from Summers' detailed tables.

TABLE 10-5. STRUCTURAL PARAMETERS, RANKINGS BY RMSE, EXPERIMENTS 5A AND 6A†

Estimator	LISE	TSLS	OLS	FIML
Total ranks	36	32	38	54

† Compiled from Summers' detailed tables.

estimates. Table 10-3 takes into account the total performance of a parameter, and not just the number of times it turns out best of all. On this basis FIML comes out at the top of the poll, with TSLS in second place, LISE in third, and OLS a poor fourth.

Tables 10-4 and 10-5 present similar information for experiments 5A and 6A, in each of which a specification error is made in the second equation. The main contrast with the results of experiments 1A to 4A is that on these criteria FIML no longer appears as the best estimator; in fact it now has the worst performance of the four, with the lowest frequencies on bias and RMSE and the greatest total on ranks. On the rank criterion TSLS comes out best, with LISE next and OLS marginally behind that. Summers' B set of experiments gave a lot of computational trouble initially because the intercorrelation of the z's produced an observation matrix with a determinantal value very near zero, so that rounding errors assumed an undue importance in the lengthy series of calculations. Summary tables like those above do not, however, yield a strikingly different picture. In experiments 1B to 4B, FIML has the lowest value of RMSE for 16 parameters out of 32, followed by OLS with 10, TSLS with 6, and LISE with zero. On the rankings, TSLS is as good as FIML, with 63 and 63.5, respectively; OLS is next, with 85; and LISE last, with 108.5. In experiments 5B and 6B, with specification error, TSLS and OLS are much better on both criteria than LISE and FIML.

The criteria underlying the above tables are essentially concerned with the "nearness" to the true value of the estimates yielded by a particular estimator. Clearly, in many applications it is important to choose an estimator that will maximize the chance of obtaining an estimate within some prescribed interval about the true value. It is also very important to be able to apply standard procedures of statistical inference, that is, to test hypotheses about structural parameters and to compute confidence intervals. This is conventionally done by computing an estimate of the standard error of some parameter estimate and then working with a Studentized ratio.

$$r = \frac{\text{parameter estimate} - \text{parameter value}}{\text{estimated standard error}}$$

It is thus vital to check whether such a procedure is valid for each of the estimators being compared. Summers has done this by applying the Kolmogoroff-Smirnov test to the sample distributions of Studentized structural-coefficient estimates to test for normality. Specifically, the hypothesis under test is

$$H_0: f(r) \text{ is } N(0,1)$$

His main results are shown in Table 10-6.

Summers' own conclusions about Table 10-6 are as follows:

In the experiments where there was no specification error, the null hypothesis was accepted in almost every case for LISE and TSLS. In the experiments containing a specification error, the results for LISE and TSLS were only slightly less favorable. OLS did not fare so well, however. In almost no case could one have made a sensible judgement about β_{ij} or γ_{ij} on the basis of an OLS estimate.[1]

TABLE 10-6. NORMALITY TESTS OF STRUCTURAL-COEFFICIENT ESTIMATES, 0.95 SIGNIFICANCE LEVEL†

Percentage of acceptances of H_0 in:	LISE		TSLS		OLS	
	Eq. I	Eq. II	Eq. I	Eq. II	Eq. I	Eq. II
A experiments	100.0	79.2	100.0	83.3	37.5	45.8
B experiments	100.0	85.0	90.0	85.0	0	30.0

† Summers' table 3.

Summers also presents a valuable set of results on reduced-form coefficients. In the notation of Chap. 9, the basic relationship between structural and reduced-form coefficients is

$$\mathbf{\Pi} = -\mathbf{B}^{-1}\mathbf{\Gamma}$$

Any set of estimates of structural parameters yields a set of estimated reduced-form parameters by substitution in this relation. In addition, one may estimate reduced-form parameters by the direct application of least squares to the equations of the reduced form. This method is described as least squares with no restrictions (LSNR) since no attention is paid in the estimation process to a priori restrictions on the structural relations. This gives five methods of estimating reduced-form coefficients.

Tables 10-7 and 10-8 present a summary of the reduced-form results for experiments 1A to 4A.

For these experiments free from specification error FIML shows up as the best method, with TSLS as second best and LISE as third.

Similar tables for experiments 5A and 6A change this ranking, however. The direct application of least squares to the reduced-form equations now appears best on the RMSE criterion in both tables, with TSLS as second best. Similar computations for the B experiments put FIML as best, with TSLS as second best.

[1] *Ibid.*, p. 25.

TABLE 10-7. FREQUENCIES OF BEST RESULTS FOR REDUCED-FORM COEFFICIENTS, EXPERIMENTS 1A TO 4A†

Estimator	Frequencies		
	Bias	SD	RMSE
LISE	$4\frac{1}{2}$	$2\frac{7}{12}$	$3\frac{1}{12}$
TSLS	9	$4\frac{1}{12}$	$5\frac{7}{12}$
OLS	3	$15\frac{3}{4}$	$5\frac{1}{2}$
FIML	$8\frac{1}{2}$	$15\frac{1}{12}$	$21\frac{7}{12}$
LSNR	15	$2\frac{1}{2}$	$4\frac{1}{4}$
Total	40	40	40

† Compiled from Summers' detailed tables.

TABLE 10-8. REDUCED-FORM COEFFICIENTS, RANKINGS BY RMSE, EXPERIMENTS 1A TO 4A†

Estimator	LISE	TSLS	OLS	FIML	LSNR
Total ranks	116	106.5	159	65.5	153

† Compiled from Summers' detailed tables.

TABLE 10-9. FREQUENCIES OF BEST RESULTS FOR REDUCED-FORM COEFFICIENTS, EXPERIMENTS 5A AND 6A†

Estimator	Frequencies		
	Bias	SD	RMSE
LISE	3	$1\frac{1}{2}$	0
TSLS	2	$3\frac{1}{2}$	2
OLS	0	$7\frac{1}{3}$	$3\frac{1}{2}$
FIML	2	$4\frac{1}{3}$	4
LSNR	13	$3\frac{1}{3}$	$10\frac{1}{2}$
Total	20	20	20

† Compiled from Summers' detailed tables.

TABLE 10-10. REDUCED-FORM COEFFICIENTS, RANKINGS BY RMSE, EXPERIMENTS 5A AND 6A†

Estimator	LISE	TSLS	OLS	FIML	LSNR
Total ranks	65	59	68	63.5	44.5

† Compiled from Summers' detailed tables.

Summers' third basic contribution in this paper is to study the relative predictive powers of the various estimators. This is done by computing the expected values of the endogenous variables y_1 and y_2 for specified values of the z's. The estimators are then compared on a pairwise basis by counting for each endogenous variable for specified groups of experiments the proportion of times one method gave estimates closer to the true value than the other. If the methods were equally efficient in prediction, the expected value of this proportion would be $\frac{1}{2}$. Observed proportions were then tested for significant differences from the expected value of $\frac{1}{2}$. Summers' main conclusion is as follows:

In almost every individual contest, OLS was revealed inferior to its opponent. The aggregate statistics for the various groups in every case reveal FIML, LISE, TSLS, and LSNR to be superior to OLS. The significant differences for the other pairwise comparisons are not as striking, however.[1]

Leaving OLS on one side, Summers concludes that the ranking of the four remaining methods must be extremely tentative.

In the misspecification experiments TSLS is distinctly inferior to the other three methods when the predetermined variables are not highly intercorrelated; it performs much better, relatively, when they are. This may only be a consequence of an inability to perceive the inferiority of TSLS because of lack of power. On balance, it seems appropriate to rank TSLS low. Surprisingly, FIML appears somewhat better than the others. It was expected that FIML would be thrown off the scent more than the others by the misspecification. Surely for large enough values of γ_{21} this would happen. Also surprisingly, LSNR did not distinguish itself in these experiments. It appears that when dealing with a small sample, exploiting the *a priori* information about the model through the use of FIML or LISE will more than compensate for slight errors in specifying the model. LSNR is not misled by the incorrect constraint on the π's, but at the same time it does not make use of the correct ones; on balance, in competing with LISE and FIML it is the loser for the compromise when the degree of inaccuracy of the constraint is not too great.

The differences between the methods in the first four experiments were quite small. One would be rash to conclude more than that LSNR is relatively weak. FIML's performance is again surprising. On the basis of its optimum large-sample properties, one would have expected it to stand out much more in comparison with the other methods. In the region of the parameter space covered by the first four experiments, it appears that as far as conditional predictions are concerned, economy in computa-

[1] *Ibid.*, p. 27.

tion can safely supplant statistical efficiency as a basis for choosing between FIML, LISE, TSLS and LSNR.[1]

Basmann's study was based on the following structure:[2]

$$\begin{aligned}
-y_{1t} - 2y_{2t} + 1.5y_{3t} + 3x_{1t} \qquad\qquad\qquad\qquad\qquad - 0.6x_{5t} + 10 &= \epsilon_{1t} \\
1.5y_{1t} - y_{2t} \qquad + 0.5x_{1t} + 1.5x_{2t} + 2.0x_{3t} - 2.5x_{4t} \qquad + 12 &= \epsilon_{2t} \\
0.1y_{1t} - 4y_{2t} - y_{3t} + 1.6x_{1t} - 3.5x_{2t} \qquad + 1.2x_{4t} + 0.4x_{5t} - 5 &= \epsilon_{3t}
\end{aligned} \tag{10-6}$$

Normal disturbances were used with a sample size of 16 and 200 replications. For the parameters of the first equation in (10-6) the results shown in Table 10-11 were obtained. OLS estimates have

TABLE 10-11. SUMMARY OF BASMANN'S RESULTS†

		Parameter				
	True value	β_{12} −2.00	β_{13} 1.50	γ_{11} 3.00	γ_{15} −0.60	γ_{16} 10.00
Bias	OLS	1.11	−0.37	−0.67	0.01	−20.69
	TSLS	0.06	−0.03	−0.05	−0.05	5.28
	LISE	−0.69	0.16	0.53	−0.03	−14.00
Standard deviation	OLS	1.01	0.23	1.04	0.68	150.27
	TSLS	1.56	0.37	1.45	0.79	173.96
	LISE	4.17	1.04	3.87	1.32	318.77
Mean square deviation	OLS	2.24	0.19	1.53	0.46	23,007.90
	TSLS	2.44	0.14	2.11	0.63	30,288.84
	LISE	17.89	1.11	15.25	1.74	101,809.74

† R. L. Basmann, "An Experimental Investigation of Some Small Sample Properties of GCL Estimators of Structural Equations: Some Preliminary Results," General Electric Company, Handford Laboratories, Richland, Wash., 1958, tables 5.2.1, 5.2.2, and 5.2.3.

the worst bias, but on the mean square deviation they are marginally better than TSLS in four cases out of five, and both are substantially better than LISE. The two striking contrasts with Summers' results are, first, the very good performance of OLS and, second, the very substantial margin by which the TSLS results are better than LISE, with respect to both bias and variance.

[1] *Ibid.*, pp. 31–32.

[2] R. L. Basmann, "An Experimental Investigation of Some Small Sample Properties of GCL Estimators of Structural Equations: Some Preliminary Results," General Electric Company, Handford Laboratories, Richland, Wash., November, 1958, mimeographed.

Wagner's study used a three-equation model,

$$\begin{aligned} y_1 - \beta_1 y_2 \qquad\qquad\qquad & - \gamma_1 = u_1 \\ - \beta_2 y_2 + y_3 - \gamma_2 z_1 \qquad & - \gamma_3 = u_2 \\ y_1 - \quad y_2 + y_3 \qquad + z_2 \quad & \quad = 0 \end{aligned} \tag{10-7}$$

with independently and identically normally distributed disturbances, sample size of 20 and 100 replications.[1] The exogenous variable z_2 was taken to represent a trend variable, and z_1 was y_2 lagged one time period. The first equation was estimated for each of two models, which differ only in the variance-covariance matrix of the disturbances. The results are shown in Table 10-12. As

TABLE 10-12. SUMMARY OF WAGNER'S RESULTS†

	True value	Model I		Model II	
		β_1 0.5000	γ_1 0.2500	β_1 0.5000	γ_1 0.2500
Bias	OLS	0.0137	−0.3006	0.0087	−0.1845
	LISE	0.0045	0.1201	0.0049	−0.0940
Standard deviation	OLS	0.0107	0.3120	0.0453	1.2542
	LISE	0.0174	0.4610	0.0460	1.2641
Root-mean-square error	OLS	0.0174	0.4333	0.0462	1.2677
	LISE	0.0179	0.4764	0.0463	1.2676

† Based on H. Wagner, "A Monte Carlo Study of Estimates of Simultaneous Linear Structural Equations," *Econometrica*, vol. 26, pp. 117–133, tables V and VI, 1958.

expected, OLS shows a greater bias but a smaller variance than LISE. Contrary to the results of Summers' studies, OLS here shows as good a mean square deviation as LISE. This may be due to the specification of relatively small values for the disturbance variances in model I; the smaller the disturbances, the smaller will be the difference, in general, between different estimates. In model II the variances are much greater than in model I, but a very high negative covariance is also specified.

Nagar's study employed the same basic model as Wagner's,[2] except that he omitted the constant terms in (10-7). He calcu-

[1] H. Wagner, "A Monte Carlo Study of Estimates of Simultaneous Linear Structural Equations," *Econometrica*, vol. 26, pp. 117–133, 1958.

[2] Nagar, *loc. cit.*

lated TSLS estimates, as well as two other k-class estimators. For the first equation in (10-7) OLS has a greater bias than TSLS, but their mean square errors are approximately the same.[1] Nagar also computed the coefficients of the second equation in (10-7). For each parameter OLS has a greater mean square variance than TSLS in model I and a smaller variance in model II, which suggests that in this model the high negative covariance between the disturbances favors OLS against TSLS and LISE.

The Neiswanger-Yancey study presents a very interesting analysis of the effects of specification errors connected with the presence of time trends.[2] All the models studied so far have specification error as far as OLS is concerned, in the sense that the conditions required for the valid application of OLS are not fulfilled, but with the exception of experiments 5 and 6 in the Summers' study, the assumptions made have been appropriate for the simultaneous-equation estimators. One interesting feature of the Neiswanger-Yancey study is the comparison of OLS and LISE estimators in conditions where specification error applies to both.

Two basic models are employed: model I is

$$\begin{aligned} y_{1t} &= \beta_{12}y_{2t} + \gamma_{11}z_{1t} + \gamma_{12}z_{2t} + \gamma_{10} + u_{1t} \\ y_{2t} &= \beta_{22}y_{2t} + \gamma_{23}z_{3t} + \gamma_{24}z_{4t} + \gamma_{20} + u_{2t} \end{aligned} \tag{10-8}$$

Model II differs from model I only in the insertion of time as an exogenous variable in each relation. Sample sizes of 25 are used with 120 replications. Two sets of data are employed. In the first set A, the exogenous variables z and the disturbances u are random normal deviates; there is intercorrelation among the z's and a small positive correlation between u_1 and u_2, but all covariances between z's and u's are zero. In the second set of data B, a time trend is added to all the z's and u's of the first set, and this of course imparts time trends to y_1 and y_2. It also gives fairly substantial positive correlations between the z's and the u's, thus violating the basic assumption in simultaneous-equation estimation that the disturbances are uncorrelated with the exogenous variables. A specification error exists in applying OLS to both data sets A and B, and a specification error exists for LISE with data set B

[1] *Ibid.*, table I.

[2] W. A. Neiswanger and T. A. Yancey, "Parameter Estimates and Autonomous Growth," *J. Am. Statist. Assoc.*, vol. 54, pp. 389–402, 1959.

but not with data set A. Table 10-13 shows the results of applying model I to data set A.

This is the conventional situation where OLS involves a specification error and LISE does not. As in all the previous studies, OLS shows a substantial bias compared with LISE, but has a smaller variance around its sample mean. On the root-mean-square criterion LISE is superior to OLS, though the discrepancy is very slight for the coefficients of the exogenous variables. A

TABLE 10-13. PARAMETER ESTIMATES FOR MODEL I WITH DATA SET A†

	True value	Parameter					
		β_{12}	β_{22}	γ_{11}	γ_{12}	γ_{23}	γ_{24}
		−0.40	0.60	0.10	0.45	0.25	0.80
Bias	OLS	0.1444	−0.1015	0.0335	−0.0572	0.0238	−0.1488
	LISE	−0.0264	−0.0080	−0.0007	0.0064	−0.0032	0.0091
Standard deviation	OLS	0.1049	0.0804	0.0568	0.0645	0.0834	0.2932
	LISE	0.1281	0.0918	0.0671	0.0747	0.0870	0.3201
Root-mean-square error	OLS	0.1783	0.1295	0.0695	0.0823	0.0864	0.3288
	LISE	0.1308	0.0922	0.0677	0.0750	0.0870	0.3202
$\lvert\hat{\theta} - \theta\rvert > 2$ SE	OLS	46	33	12	24	8	10
	LISE	7	9	5	5	5	3

† Adapted from W. A. Neiswanger and T. A. Yancey, "Parameter Estimates and Autonomous Growth," *J. Am. Statist. Assoc.*, vol. 54, pp. 389–402, table 397, 1959.

valuable feature of this study is shown in the last two rows of the table. These figures show the number of cases out of the possible 120 in which the estimate $\hat{\theta}$ differs from the true value θ by more than 2 standard errors. This is where the greater bias of OLS is a serious disadvantage, for even where root-mean-square errors are not very different, the OLS procedure appears to involve a greater risk of incorrect inferences, a result which was also obtained in the Summers study.

Turning now to the data set B, where all variables contain trends and the disturbances and exogenous variables are correlated, the main results are shown in Table 10-14. LISE estimates now no longer display a uniformly smaller bias than OLS, and for two parameters their root-mean-square deviation exceeds the OLS figure. The balance between the two techniques is now more even, and in both cases there is a high probability of incorrect inferences, especially in relation to the coefficients of the endogenous variables.

Neiswanger and Yancey next include time as an exogenous variable in each structural equation in order to see to what extent this will diminish the effects of the specification error on the estimates. The results are remarkably similar to those reported in Table 10-13 for trend-free data.[1] LISE biases are once again much smaller than

TABLE 10-14. PARAMETER ESTIMATES FOR MODEL I WITH DATA SET B†

	True value	Parameter					
		β_{12} -0.40	β_{22} 0.60	γ_{11} 0.10	γ_{12} 0.45	γ_{23} 0.25	γ_{24} 0.80
Bias	OLS	0.3838	0.3520	0.0685	0.1081	0.1872	−0.1525
	LISE	0.0937	0.3943	−0.0003	0.2486	0.1503	−0.0209
Standard deviation	OLS	0.1765	0.1145	0.0994	0.0939	0.2061	0.7439
	LISE	0.2444	0.1346	0.1080	0.1184	0.2141	0.7751
Root-mean-square deviation	OLS	0.4224	0.3703	0.1207	0.1433	0.2784	0.7593
	LISE	0.2618	0.4166	0.1080	0.2753	0.2616	0.7752
$\lvert\hat{\theta} - \theta\rvert > 2$ SE	OLS	62	101	7	13	32	10
	LISE	14	101	3	47	21	8

† Adapted from W. A. Neiswanger and T. A. Yancey, "Parameter Estimates and Autonomous Growth," *J. Am. Statist. Assoc.*, vol. 54, pp. 389–402, table 395b, 1959.

OLS biases, their mean square deviations are marginally better, and the proportion of incorrect inferences lower. The authors thus recommend the inclusion of time as a substitute for excluded variables which might impart a trend to disturbance terms and thus set up correlations between disturbances and exogenous variables. They also show that the inclusion of time when it is not needed has apparently no deleterious effect on the estimates yielded by either method, and the estimated coefficient of time will in general be small relative to its standard error.[2]

Ladd's study was designed primarily to observe the effect of superposing errors of measurement on the variables in a simultaneous-equation system.[3] He used the same model as Neiswanger and

[1] *Ibid.*, table 396.
[2] *Ibid.*, pp. 398–399.
[3] G. W. Ladd, "Effects of Shocks and Errors in Estimation: An Empirical Comparison," *J. Farm Economics*, vol. 38, pp. 485–495, 1956.

Yancey in (10-8) above and then superposed measurement errors. The sample size was 30, and there were 30 replications. OLS and LISE estimators were compared. Ladd concluded that the observation errors imparted little bias to either estimator but that it did increase the standard errors. A comparison of the two estimators yielded the familiar conclusions of a greater bias but a smaller standard deviation for OLS. Mean square errors were not calculated. Klein has used Ladd's estimates to compute reduced-form parameters.[1] He has also estimated the reduced-form coefficients directly by least squares (LSNR). He found that for the comparison between OLS and LISE, the bias of the former was greater in all 8 cases and its standard deviation was greater in 6 cases out of 8, so that its mean square deviation must be greater in *at least* 6 cases out of the 8. LISE and LSNR showed rather similar biases, but the former had a smaller standard deviation for all 8 parameters.[2]

In addition to the Summers analysis, only one further study of relative forecasting efficiency appears to have been completed so far. This is a study by Foote and Waugh on the relative merits of least squares and limited information for forecasting purposes.[3] The model used was a four-equation one, namely,

$$\begin{aligned} Y_1 &= -0.1Y_4 + Z_1 + u_1 \\ Y_2 &= -(Y_4 - Z_2) + u_2 \\ Y_3 &= -4Y_4 + Z_3 + u_3 \\ Y_1 + Y_2 + Y_3 &= Z_4 \end{aligned} \tag{10-9}$$

The variable Y_4 represents the price of a commodity, and Y_1, Y_2, and Y_3 represent separate utilizations of the commodity. Each utilization is taken as a function of price and some exogenous factor Z_1, Z_2, or Z_3. Z_4 represents the fixed supply of the commodity, and the price is set so as to clear the market in each period. This is reflected in the fourth equation of the set (10-9). The disturbances are constructed to be intercorrelated.

[1] L. R. Klein, "The Efficiency of Estimation in Econometric Models," pp. 216–232 in *Essays in Economics and Econometrics*, The University of North Carolina Press, Chapel Hill, N.C., 1960.

[2] *Ibid.*, pp. 231–233.

[3] R. J. Foote, *Analytical Tools for Studying Demand and Price Structures*, U.S. Department of Agriculture, Agriculture Handbook 146, 1958, pp. 128–142. A brief abstract of this study appears in *Econometrica*, vol. 26, pp. 607–608, 1958.

The authors first conducted a forecasting experiment in which the values of Y_1, Y_2, and Y_3 were forecast on the assumption that the value of Y_4 was known for the forecast period as well as the values of the exogenous Z variables. This seems a rather suspicious procedure, and so we report here only the results of a second and more straightforward experiment in which all Y values are forecast solely on the basis of reduced-form coefficients and the values of the exogenous variables. Two sets of reduced-form coefficients were used, namely, those obtained by applying least squares directly to each of the four reduced-form equations (LSNR) and those derived algebraically from the limited-information estimates of the structural parameters of (10-9). In the computation of these estimates a single set of 100 sample observations was used.

For the forecasting experiment 25 values of Z were drawn (*a*) from the same range as the 100 initial observations used in estimating the parameters, and then another 25 (*b*) from twice the range. Within (*a*) a further set of Z values were drawn which were kept fixed over the 25 observations. The above procedure was repeated a second time, thus giving six separate experiments with 25 values of each Y to be predicted in each experiment. Defining d_{it},

$$d_{it} = Y_{it} - \hat{Y}_{it} \qquad i = 1, \ldots, 4; t = 1, \ldots, 25$$

where Y_{it} is the actual, and $\hat{Y}_{it}$ the predicted, value of Y_i in period t. The authors define the mean-square error for Y_i as

$$S_{di}^2 = \sum_{t=1}^{25} \frac{d_{it}^2}{24} \qquad i = 1, \ldots, 4$$

The values of this statistic for the six experiments are shown in Table 10-15. The figures in the first eight rows of this table, for Z values drawn from the initial range, show LISE superior to LSNR in 12 cases out of 16, but the margin of superiority is usually small and in most cases is less than 10 per cent. The last four rows of the table show LISE superior in 5 cases out of 8. In 2 of the cases the margin is substantial, being well over 50 per cent; on the other hand, in 2 cases the least-squares margin of superiority is equally substantial.

This study does not show any striking difference between the forecasting efficiency of LISE and LSNR. The comparison, however, has been made for only a single set of coefficients of each type applied to six different sets of values for the disturbances and the exogenous variables. Much more work needs to be done in this field. It would, in particular, be important to study relative forecasting efficiencies in a situation where estimates were computed afresh for repeated samples of fairly small size and each set of estimates used in prediction.

TABLE 10-15. MEAN SQUARE ERRORS FOR FORECASTS BY LSNR AND LISE†

When the Z's are drawn over:	Sample			
	First		Second	
	LSNR	LISE	LSNR	LISE
(*a*) The initial range, and they vary:				
Y_1	4.4	3.8	4.6	3.9
Y_2	18.1	18.9	23.2	25.9
Y_3	38.4	36.6	46.0	45.7
Y_4	47.4	44.0	55.3	54.2
and are fixed:				
Y_1	4.8	4.3	5.3	4.8
Y_2	24.4	22.6	21.0	23.3
Y_3	48.9	44.3	43.8	45.7
Y_4	53.0	48.6	57.1	57.0
(*b*) Twice the initial range:				
Y_1	5.5	5.8	5.3	5.2
Y_2	26.7	22.9	25.2	50.9
Y_3	55.1	29.1	50.6	70.5
Y_4	58.0	33.0	59.0	53.1

† R. J. Foote, *Analytical Tools for Studying Demand and Price Structures*, U.S. Department of Agriculture, Agricultural Handbook 146, 1958, p. 137.

10-2. Conclusion

These sampling studies all cast some light on the choice of estimators for structural parameters, less light on the choice of estimators for reduced-form parameters, and very little on relative forecasting efficiency. On structural parameters the evidence would appear to be that FIML is the best method. Its disadvantages, however, are still very serious; the computational burden is very heavy, and the optimal properties of the estimator depend heavily upon the correctness of the a priori specification of the model. This latter fact alone, given our present ignorance and uncertainty about specification, is probably sufficient to rule out FIML as a practical tool. Concentrating then on single-equation estimators and leaving on one side the special case of indirect least squares for exactly identified relations, the best choice among the remaining methods would appear to be TSLS first, LISE second, and OLS third, but this is by no means a hard and fast ruling. On the mean-square-deviation criterion the Summers study shows TSLS superior to LISE and both of them superior to OLS. However, when specification error appears in experiments 5 and 6, all three methods do just about as well, with perhaps LISE a slight margin behind the TSLS and OLS a little way farther behind in third place. The type of specification error considered by Neiswanger and Yancey also appears to eliminate the superiority of LISE over OLS, and even the smaller bias feature of LISE does not hold. The Basmann study shows TSLS superior to LISE by a much more pronounced margin than Summers', but OLS also appears much better than LISE and just as good as TSLS on the mean-square-deviation criterion. When the specification is correct and OLS appears just as good as TSLS or LISE on the mean-square-deviation criterion, either of the latter estimators is still preferable to OLS because of the greater bias of OLS and the associated greater probability of incorrect inferences.

On reduced-form parameters we have direct evidence only from Summers' and from Klein's calculations with Ladd's data. It appears that the direct application of least squares to the reduced-form equations (LSNR) is not to be recommended. On the mean-square-deviation criterion the Summers study shows TSLS superior to LISE and the latter ahead of OLS. Klein's figures, based on a much smaller number of replications than Summers', show LISE superior to OLS. Although there is not so much evidence here, what there is does not suggest a conflict between estimators for structural and reduced-form parameters.

There are, however, many unresolved issues. One is the question of forecasting efficiency. Another general one is raised by the possible joint presence of simultaneous-equation problems and some of the complications such as errors in variables, autocorrelation, and heteroscedasticity, which we have considered in relation to single-equation models. It is important to emphasize that all the theoretical and empirical work that we have reported in Chaps. 9 and 10 is based on the assumption of serially independent disturbances. We have thus no evidence on which to base a choice between, say, applying a simultaneous-equation method to a model involving serially correlated disturbances or some modification of ordinary least squares on the lines of Chap. 7 to each relation of some simultaneous model. Both will be incorrect, but in some cases one will be more incorrect than the other, and vice versa. However, as the references in the last five chapters will have shown, much work is now under way in all these areas and we may look forward to a continuing increase in the statistical tools at our disposal and a more precise delineation of the conditions in which each should ideally be applied.

References

The basic Monte Carlo studies referred to in this chapter are

1. R. Summers: "A Capital-intensive Approach to the Small Sample Properties of Various Simultaneous Equation Estimators," unpublished paper, 1962.
2. R. L. Basmann: "An Experimental Investigation of Some Small Sample Properties of GCL Estimators of Structural Equations: Some Preliminary Results," General Electric Company, Handford Laboratories, Richland, Wash., November, 1958, mimeographed.
3. H. Wagner: "A Monte Carlo Study of Estimates of Simultaneous Linear Structural Equations," *Econometrica*, vol. 26, pp. 117–133, 1958.
4. A. L. Nagar: "A Monte Carlo Study of Alternative Simultaneous Equation Estimators," *Econometrica*, vol. 28, pp. 573–590, 1960.
5. W. A. Neiswanger and T. A. Yancey: "Parameter Estimates and Autonomous Growth," *J. Am. Statist. Assoc.*, vol. 54, pp. 389–402, 1959.
6. G. W. Ladd: "Effects of Shocks and Errors in Estimation: An Empirical Comparison," *J. Farm Economics*, vol. 38, pp. 485–495, 1956.

See also

7. L. R. Klein: "The Efficiency of Estimation in Econometric Models," pp. 216–232 in *Essays in Economics and Econometrics*, The University of North Carolina Press, Chapel Hill, N.C., 1960.
8. "A Symposium on Simultaneous Equation Estimation," *Econometrica*, vol. 28, pp. 835–871, 1960.

Index